CAREERXROADS

career (cross) roads

Gerry Crispin & Mark Mehler

MMC Group
Kendall Park, NJ

MMC Group
P.O. Box 253
Kendall Park, NJ 08824
908-821-6652
mmc@careerxroads.com
http://www.careerxroads.com

REGISTER

Send us your e-mail address (and any new sites, changes, or comments- when you can). We promise to e-mail you **FREE** updates to keep your copy of CAREERXROADS fresh. Tell your colleagues. Help your friends. To register, Fax, mail or, send an e-mail to: mmc@careerxroads.com. Type: "Register" in the body of the e-mail message. We agree to ONLY send you our updates. We will not share, sell or otherwise abuse your e-mail address.

If you prefer, stop by
http://www.careerXroads.com
(we archive all updates here)

Name:_____Company:_____

e-mail:_____

-Optional-
-Address-:_____

_____ZIP: _____

Phone:_____Fax:_____

My interest in **CAREERXROADS** (please check one)

jobseeker_____   recruiter_____

other
(please specify_____)

Thank you for purchasing CAREERXROADS. We are interested in hearing what you think and we're always interested in any new sites or types of sites you would like reviewed. Send e-mail to: mmc@careerxroads.com

Gerry Crispin & Mark Mehler

More praise from recruiters and job seekers for CAREERXROADS:

"I just received my copy of CXR and could not be more pleased."
   - Allyson Adamusik, Bristol-Myers Squibb

"Wow, this is excellent. I'm interested in subscribing to your mailing list."
   - Michael Bratter

"Allow me to say how incredibly useful your and Gerry's book has and continues to be both for me and my colleages.
   - Gabriel Anthony, The Executive Source

"Thought you would like to get some good news today. I recommended a web site from your book, CXR and my client had excellent results. The site is Asia-Net and the client received more than 50 qualified resumes. Thank you for writing such a useful and informative reference book for us."
   - Kim in Tampa

"We met at the SF HR Intranet conference earlier this year. Your generousity ...which allowed me to share with other HR people at ___ has paid off tremendously for our HR department - and even helped with an OFCCP audit we had! Many thanks again for such a wonderful tool."
   - Gail Dresner

"Thank you for presenting an interesting and informative program on using the internet for recruiting. I certainly share your excitement with using the internet to reduce the cost of recruiting and have started my own journey with the tools you've given me. "
   - Joanne Byron, Olin Corporation

"I received your directory. What a fantastic book. I am going to share it with the powers that be at MCI. I can't believe you both put this together on top of working full time. CONGRATULATIONS, this is quite an accomplishment and I want to thank you both for your efforts ."
   - Joan Papp, Staffing Specialist-MCI

" I have purchased a copy of your CXR book and think it is GREAT! I am consulting for _____ and am proposing they purchase a copy for each of their regional offices. "
   - Cindy Irvine, Internet Consultant

Where Talent and Opportunity Connect on the Internet

"The book has become a valuable resource in our Internet Reference collection. Congratulations on providing others with such a useful and well organized tool."
- Christopher Carbone. Acquisitions Librarian-South Brunswick, NJ

"Looking for a good independent guide to web recruiting sites? Look for CXR, a unique directory that never goes out of date."
- Ward Christman, JobNet

"CXR provides detailed reviews and ratings of more than 475 job, resume and career mgmt. sites on the WWW. CXR saves hours of surfing from site to site by pinpointing the best places to look for opportunities by region, area of specialty, college, diversity and more."
- James a. Cox, Editor-In-Chief, THE MIDWEST BOOK REVIEW

"I got your book and I find it extremely useful. Great idea to have downloadable new versions of it... My clients love it and I think you have a winner."
- Basil Rouskas, Basil Rouskas Associates

"As a recruiter in the search business and a former technical recruiter at ___. I wanted to share my thoughts of what a wonderful source this is for anyone who is in the business of recruiting, or anyone who is just looking for employment. In essence it serves a huge purpose to many, many people, both inside and outside the HR industry. As technology continues to grow and as recruiting becomes a larger and more complicated process for those of us in the industry, this lends a quick, easy read solution to our recruiting needs. It is a great tool that all recruiters should have."
- Christine T. DeCarlo, The Executive Source

"I have been giving out your website info to everyone who calls in and has internet access."
- Kathy, Netshare, Inc.

"I was listening to this Senior go on and on about this great book he was using to find job leads for his first job and, suddenly, when he mentioned the Internet, I asked: 'Is it CAREERXROADS?'. He replied, 'Yes, but how did you know?'. "
- Jaime Beth Crispin, Junior, SUNY-New Paltz

Acknowledgements

For our third edition, there are many individuals who helped us along the way

Our spouses, Diane and Beth, who wonder sometimes whether we've taken leave of our senses. Without them we would not have had any reason to do this or anything else for the last twenty odd years.

Our children Jaime Beth, Gerry and Dara. Its amazing what they've put up with.

Mark's daughter, Lauren, "researcher par excellance", who spent endless hours pulling up new web sites for us to review.

Gerry's mom. This "young" 84 year old took our last edition down to the local bookstore, walked in and simply said, "This is my son's book. How many do you want to buy." He bought six.

Marc Liebeskind, who created the template that allowed our ACT! database, to be printed out in minutes, formatted and camera ready. Without his help we would still be in the middle of the alphabet.

The members of the Princeton Human Resource Network Group both new and old, who share a commitment to one another's success. And to Dick Stone, the groups founder, a true professional who finally discovered the net this year.

Jim Taylor, "super recruiter", who convinced his spouse that we had something here...and to Teresa Taylor, newly employed with the IEEE, who knew what to do.

Ira Sprotzer, the Rider University professor, who first supported incorporating our workshop with an internet computer lab and to Mike Goodman, Cornell University's NYSSILR NY Campus Director who brought the workshop to the HR community.

Our HR cybersupporters and cyberfriends. We literally spoke with hundreds of web designers, web owners and web heads about what they are doing or trying to do. We've participated on several lists- HRNet especially and have developed e-mail pen pal relationships with many more. We thank them all for sharing. We are particularly indebted to the insights of the authors who participated in this edition: Tracey Claybrooke, Nancy Heimbaugh, Bob Levenstein, Will Matlack, Amy Naples, Margaret Riley, Scott Sandberg and John Sullivan.

We look forward to your comments about CAREERXROADS....where talent and opportunity connect on the Internet.

Gerry Crispin & Mark Mehler
mmc@careerxroads.com
http://www.careexroads.com

About the Authors

Gerry Crispin and Mark Mehler have each been involved in the employment field for their entire careers. Nationally recognized experts, they have pooled their knowledge of the hiring process and emerging technology to chart the developing strategies & tactics of job seekers and company recruiters.

CAREERXROADS is partly the result of Gerry's and Mark's volunteer involvement as contributors to a networking group of human resource professionals seeking new employment. Over the last six years, the group's meetings-every third Saturday morning-are where job leads are shared and where increasingly information gleaned from the Internet is included. As the speed, access and accuracy of technology improved these job seeker's chance of success, Mark and Gerry began incorporating the ideas in their respective day jobs and joined forces to share what they've learned about the World Wide Web. **They conduct HR and Staffing Clinics to provide hands-on experience for practitioners and consult with major corporations on using the web as a recruiting tool.**

Gerry Crispin has been active in the human resource profession for more than 25 years and counts his certification as a Senior Professional in Human Resources (SPHR) among his most satisfying accomplishments. An engineering graduate from Stevens Institute of Technology, he began his career in human resources with Johnson & Johnson's largest consumer products company after completing a graduate degree in Organizational Behavior. Gerry's responsibilities have included career services, human resource management, organizational change and staffing during his career as a practitioner. Today, as vice president of Shaker Advertising Agency, Inc., one of the nation's largest independent advertising firms specializing in recruitment advertising, he creates and places help-wanted advertisements and consults with clients on their staffing strategies. A volunteer leader with the Society for Human Resource Management, Gerry chairs their national committee on employment and speaks frequently on the emerging technology topics.

Mark Mehler is a highly successful consultant to major corporations on high volume recruiting strategies and systems. With over 20 years of human resource experience, Mark founded the MMC Group in 1992 and focused his fledgling company's efforts on staffing process improvements by applying emerging technology solutions to set new standards for performance and cost savings. Prior to his work with clients such as Johnson & Johnson, Martin Marietta and G.E., Mark held human resource management positions with Cookson America, Millipore Corporation and Beatrice Companies. Mark received his B.S. in Economics from Fairleigh Dickinson University.

Table of Contents

READ ME FIRST

Authors' Notes

"Late nights and longer weekends" sounds more like the theme song for a country singer's romantic lament than two human resource professionals facing web burnout from reviewing hundreds of new sites devoted to employment.

As predicted in our first two editions, the steady trickle of cyberspace job leads has indeed become a flood. Job seekers are using the web in very large numbers to seek employment....and leaving a trail for recruiters to follow. With little to guide them but common sense and a strong desire to get an edge, applicants relentlessly "drill", "scroll" and "click through" layers of "content" to find the freshest "leads", then "cut & paste", "attach & send " or simply "point & click" in the hopes that they will be "searched & selected".

Keeping track of the sites that make a difference has been partly a business necessity, partly curiosity about what will come next and partly amazement over how fast staffing strategies, techniques and procedures are changing- even as we write. The speed with which emerging technologies like the Internet are being incorporated into every aspect of the employment function gives new meaning to the phrase "get out ahead of the curve". Instead of triggering an image of a rapidly rising business graph, the picture this phrase is more likely to conjure up these days is one of being strapped to the front hood of a fast car that has suddenly encountered an unexpected curve in the road. Picture, if you can, trying to make observations from this vantage point and immediately extrapolating the data gathered to describe the road ahead. It is both exhilarating ...and risky to say the least.

NEW in 1998

For fans of the earlier editions of CAREERXROADS, you'll see some major changes to our 1998 directory:

• EVERY site in our previous editions has been reviewed...once again.

• Hundreds of new sites have been added to the 1998 edition.

• The 500 "best" sites reviewed here actually include some not-so-great-still-under-construction-we-don't-get-it "works in progress". No surprise there and our notes should reflect that "we call 'em like we see 'em".

• Why 500? It was a nice place to stop. Actually, we could have called it the "best 1000" but, there would have been many more questionable sites included. We could not have reviewed 1500 sites without including companies, search engines, temp firms, placement agencies, or a few extra virtual-resume shops willing to write a winning resume for $9.99...and do your horoscope at no extra cost. We think we left most of the fly by night spacecadets out but we also had to leave out some great companies worth benchmarking, a few outstanding staffing firms with gazillions of openings and, other private organizations to keep this directory's size reasonable and it's mission focused. By including sites like Student Center with its links to 35,000 corporations to help job seekers get to their targeted companies we reduced 17,500 pages in this directory. Ok, so maybe we wouldn't have done that. Just pay attention to the articles, check out our cross-references beginning on page 340, or send us an e-mail and we'll see that you get where you want to go.

• Nearly 50% of the job sites that were active in the beginning of 1997 are gone. Really! Gone! We think there should be a Web Staffing Hall of Fame for some of these ill fated but otherwise fabulous, well intentioned efforts like the "Virtual HeadBook", "Unemployed DJ's" and "Career Paradise". We hope you'll find replacements here with a longer shelf life among "FuneralNet", "Hollywood Web", and "Hard@Work". If you have a tendency to take things too seriously- surf to these sites when you need to chill out (and with FuneralNet, try not to take that literally).

• 385 of the sites reviewed here will let you post and see jobs for free or, for a fee.

• 278 of the sites reviewed here will let you post or see resumes for free or, for a fee

• 33 sites claim Career Management is their reason to be (and almost all of the rest offer at least a few suggestions and tips).

• 34 sites are devoted to helping the college grad find his or her way in the world.

• The Recruiter's "Toolkit" and Job Seeker's "Kitbag" are sites that help find, organize, track or communicate information. We have included a few sites of these in the 1998 edition and plan to review many more in the future. More importantly are the articles written by some of the 'Net's pioneers, students and denizens. Their comments, insights and observations are well worth your time

• DIVERSITY, SPECIALTY, GEOGRAPHIC and other cross reference lists are significantly enhanced from last year's edition.

Trends to Watch
Here are our observations from the "intersection" where talent and opportunity connect on the net:

• **The cost to post jobs is going down.** Various successful business models are developing that do not rely on charging for each opening. Examples that don't fit this "$s for jobs" model, like HeadHunter, Asia-Net and Yahoo, are the tip of an iceberg. Some are expanding rapidly and giving the pioneers who don't adapt (and that's anyone with more than 3 years in cyberspace) conniptions.

• **"Multiple Points of Entry" won't last another year... without full disclosure.** Imagine that you are looking for a job in an out of the way site and suddenly, after clicking on their jobs button, you find yourself "entering" one of four or five of the largest job databases. Lately, "career hubs"- like Career Mosaic, The MonsterBoard, E•Span and others have increased their efforts to provide multiple points of entry through associations, publications, community organizations and bulletin boards. These large, successful, multi-service career sites depend on high-volume traffic and by offering their career model to smaller specialty niche sites, they increase their traffic and let the niche site appear to provide a service to its membership. Employment opportunities directed to these niche sites are posted to the career hub. While it is convenient to simply "click through" and reach a large job database from wherever you happen to be on the net, job seekers may have already been there and may really want to find a job database focused on their unique interests. As associations and other organizations recognize their "community's" true value, we believe they will be reluctant to have their members "pass through". Eventually, corporations will also come to understand the value of niche sites and look elsewhere to seek talent.

• **Many Intrusive "In Your Face" Techniques will Backfire.** New forms of "Intrusive" advertising are on the rise and being applied to staffing. Flashy banners and links pop up in some of the most unlikely places. They are even showing up while your computer downloads the graphics on the site! Not so much a problem when you are looking for work but, if you are in the middle of discussing a technical fix for a company you enjoy, that flashing job link asking if you want to work for the "world's greatest...", may spark unintended consequences. Expect to see shareware that helps the user screen this clutter out. The real trouble brewing though is the growing ability of recruiters to acquire large lists of targeted e-mail addresses and without permission "spam" these potential candidates. Corporations interested in retention should monitor these uninvited messages to their employees now.

• **Pay for Performance is More than a Possibility.** Most employers are used to paying for a service not for a result. On the internet we know much more than the fact that the job information appears at a particular location. We also know how many people saw "impressions" of it...how many "clicked through" to get additional information or perhaps even filled out a form, registered, etc. Expect to see more insistence by employers on payment for candidates who take action.

• **Print + Online- A Powerful Combo.** Publishers are finally providing their print classifieds on the web as an added value component. 1998 will be the year that publishers will either demonstrate that they've learned to adapt online recruiting in their repetoire or the "Fat Lady" will be singing the end of print classifieds as we know it. How many newspapers, magazines and trade journals can you name that aren't touting their online component? The success of models developed by CareerPath, AdOne, Town Online, Mercury Center, Washington Post and others will determine whether billions of dollars will stay in the same hands or move elsewhere in the next few years. We believe Professional Associations can combine the print and online components better than anyone- look what SHRM's HRNews has accomplished. Paid job advertisements fill 12 pages instead of 2 each month. Neither print nor online strategies alone could have produced this result. We can think of dozens of strategies to strengthen the publisher's position. Unfortunately, in this cyber race for the hearts and minds of tomorrow's job seekers, most publishers are still standing around waiting for the ink to dry while everyone else has already read the story.

• **Technology for its own sake is on the wane.** A few companies are actually on the edge of combining every known emerging technology related to staffing into one coherent package. These elements include: intranet systems for posting internal openings with instant connections to half a dozen websites; optical scanning and applicant tracking software and systems; web-based, private resume databases; PC-to-PC interview networks; interactive voice recognition and web driven assessment tools. (See Dr. John Sullivan's article for explanation to most of these concepts). We may have moved too far too fast and, while this may sound like heresy, many organizations may have already bought more technology than they need. We believe costs will dramatically drop in 1998. Companies will be more informed about purchasing guidelines for all HR systems. Measurement and ROI will be "in" and the trend toward operational solutions that can be outsourced through the net will reach new highs.

• **Online "Community" is more than a concept.** Corporate and 3rd party staffing strategies haven't even begun to determine how this fits in to the equation. Talent Alliance is an example and so is Asia-Net, although exactly why, isn't readily apparent from their website. It's behind the scenes that a growing trend toward "community" is evident. It's on the "Listservs" and in the "chat rooms" and at the "webwatercoolers". It's not being written about with any accuracy because there isn't a concrete metaphor to explain this virtual activity. As PC-to-PC, "chat" and other yet-to-be-thought-of communication strategies develop, job seekers AND corporate hiring authorities will have even more options for finding, connecting, sharing and experiencing each other DIRECTLY. This could give 3rd party "information providers" nightmares. In this "community" the role of the 3rd party as an intermediary will not be what it is today

• **Don't forget the "Law of Unintended Consequences".** We keep our perspective by reminding ourselves that no matter what result we expect, something else is sure to turn up that will have even more of an effect. To help our readers develop their own point of view, we have developed the following three Cyber Rules of Staffing:

Rule #1: When in doubt, point and click.
Lead, follow or get out of the way. Staffing as a human resource function is now recognized all the way to the executive suite for it's time dependent critical contribution to a company's success. In a few short years, the tactical skills necessary to perform this function will be radically different than they are today. Since you can't get experience on the net vicariously, we argue that recruiters and job seekers alike need to aggressively seek their own point of entry and get out there now.

Rule #2: Follow the Job Seeker.
It amazes us how few recruiters follow this advice. We encourage taking your boss on a field trip to a local library, school, community center etc. We challenge the notion that universal access is a long way off. We invite you to pretend you are an applicant and to look for a way into your own company via the net. If you haven't done it, you will be surprised.

Rule #3: Whoever owns the most e-mails, wins.
Seems to us that the wrong question is being asked. The questions we often hear sound like: "How can I find, save and search more resumes, etc. etc.
What if the question were: "How can I instantly inform a large number of folks who are interested and qualified to join my company that I have an opening available right now." We feel the solutions to this second question are more likely to succeed long term.

Finally, remember that CAREERXROADS isn't just a printed book opened to page__ in your hands. It's changing as you read these lines- someone just sent us a new site to review. Another site has moved, it's URL changed and it's new address is being sent to us. A recruiter stuck trying to find optical physics professionals may be sending us a query via e-mail. A job seeker wants to know how to find leads in Peoria, Il. These events won't take place in a book but they are also a part of CAREERXROADS. We are not a book and we're also not a website. We are a community...something we learned from Dale Bowen at Asia-Net who is half our age. We make the commitment to keep you in touch with what is changing on the net. REGISTER your e-mail address and we'll send you updates. We won't sell or give away your e-mail and we won't send you anything without your permission.

Happy Hunting
Gerry & Mark

The RECRUITER'S "TOOLKIT"
& the JOB SEEKER'S "KITBAG"

CAREERXROADS was first envisioned with both the job seeker and recruiter in mind. We felt then and still feel that too many professionals look to find a "yellow brick road"- a straight and narrow path to the one Oz. We realized that the prevalent metaphor was a little too naive so we imagined instead a country crisscrossed with roads, few signs but a whole lot of intersections, cross roads if you will, where both employer and candidates could meet, cross paths so to speak and make a choice or two. We were less concerned about the road map than the "michelin" type guide, that travelers would need on their journey.

Along with the reviews about what readers might find on their journey, we thought some would want to pack along a few helpful tips or advice from those who travel frequently. At the turn of the Century, early automotive enthusiasts called these little handbooks and assorted tire patches- "tookits" and "kitbags". This online version then is self-explanatory. If you can navigate the web and are either looking for people or your next opportunity, here are some insights from colleagues who are doing it for a living- an eclectic group of professionals willing to share their point of view. We hope they will stimulate you, the reader, and help you to make better choices about what to do when you come to an intersection...or have a flat.

(Note: In the reviews throughout the 1998 Directory, you'll find "RT" as a designation for "Recruiters Toolkit" and JSK as a designation for "Job Seekers Kitbag" to indicate that the site may assist in accomplishing a goal rather than provide job leads or candidates directly.)

Dr. John Sullivan of San Francisco State University leads off this section with a look beyond the pressures of today toward a strategy for tomorrow. In **"What the Future Holds"** John describes where he views web technology taking us.

As a consultant who has both feet firmly planted in the Bay Area's corporate staffing organizations and also as a teacher of a new generation of recruiters, **"Tips For the Recuiter's Toolkit"** is another offering from John's observations of the hi-tech world of staffing.

Amy Naples of Bluestone Consulting works in a young, entrepreneurial environment that is always looking for new talent. The usual methods were not working so she turned to the web for additional help. In her article **"Outside the Box: Technical Guru Wanted"** she explains her day-to-day strategy of keeping ahead of the curve and working with her managers to achieve success.

Tracey Claybrooke provides internet recruitment training and consults on staffing with a broad base of clients. In her article **"Choose the Best Sites to Connect with Candidates: Roll the Dice Once Around the Monopoly Board"**, she offers some important suggestions recruiters need to pass "Go".

Scott Sandberg advises on web design. He is a consultant with a difference and combines his creative talents with extensive knowledge about the recruiting and advertising industries. His point that "just putting up a site and having a URL is not enough", comes across loud and clear in **"Establishing Your Presence: Build a Site and Drive Candidates to You"**.

E-Span's Nancy Heimbaugh offers extensive advice for job seekers in **"If You're Fishing for a Job, Use the Net! or How to Use Chat Rooms, Newsgroups and Listservs to Expand Your Network."** What is often one of the most confusing areas of the web, Maureen describes step-by-step. You'll learn where to go and what you will find when you get there.

Bob Levinstein of NationJob raises a very important point for job seekers in **"Resume Roulette"**. Do you really know where your resume goes when you post it to a site? Bob gives the insiders view of what can happen.

"Preparing Your Resume for E-Mail" is back from the 1997 edition by popular demand. It is the most frequently asked question by a job seeker. Will Matlack has written this article that focuses on the basics. Recruiters should be insisting that advice similar to this be followed. Try posting your company's version on your web site.

Margaret Riley the Author of The PLA Guide to Internet Recruiting, The Riley Guide (page 290) contributes: **"Your Next Career Move: Push on Doors Marked Pull"**. This article emphasizes job search strategies on the Internet. Most important is to read between the lines and get a flavor of her "attitude" suggestions for job seekers.

Finally, we thought it appropriate to let John Sullivan get the last word in with **"Tools for the Job Seekers KitBag"**. His practical "real time" advice on what you will need to do to get your next job is excellent food for thought...for all of us.

What the Future Holds

Dr. John Sullivan
Professor of Human Resources and Executive Coach
College of Business, San Francisco State University
e-mail - johns@sfsu.edu

The process of finding a job has changed dramatically in the last few years. Web pages, globalization, electronic resume scanning, 24 hour access to E-mail, and other innovations have forever changed the way we look for jobs. The job search process will continue to change at an even faster rate due to the continuing shift away from physical labor toward knowledge workers. Another contributing factor is the fact that long term employment with one firm is becoming the exception, and as a result there will be a dramatic increase in the number of times in our lifetime that we will be in the job search mode. This means that great job search skills will become a necessity rather than something we will occasionally need!

Some of the shifts in the employment process outlined below are already being tried at some progressive companies. As a job seeker you need to be prepared for these changes if you are to have a competitive advantage in the search process.

New Developments in Employment

• Pre-Qualifying Candidates and "Relationship Recruiting" •
Most "old style" recruiting is done on a hit or miss "Looking/ Opening strategy". It assumes that the best candidate is LOOKING for a job AT EXACTLY THE SAME TIME A COMPANY HAS AN OPENING! I call that "blind coincidence" recruiting. Recruiters (or candidates for that matter) can no longer rely on these lucky coincidences when "looking and opening " to perfectly match their needs if they expect to hire the very best.

A better approach is what I call "Relationship Recruiting". The basic premise is that recruiters are continually building "relationships" with the best potential hires in a given field through "Personal Courting". Recruiters use occasional calls, e-mails, lunches and "Push" E-Letters (periodic E-Mail newsletters sent by the company) to build a relationship BEFORE an opening occurs. This allows most (or all) of the "prequalifying" and assessment of candidates can be done in advance. This shifts the basic approach from a one time "coincidence hire" to a new approach of "I'm ready to leave now but I will wait until your company has an opening" (or even before an opening occurs for a superstar recruit)! As an applicant, you can become a "Relationship Hire" by pre-selecting companies and jobs you want and building relationships with recruiters before you "need" a job. The reduced pressure "because you don't need a job tomorrow" also allows you over-time to provide more examples of your skills and work than in a normal Look\Opening situation. Executive recruiters already use a similar approach and you can use it to stand out from the rest of the "need a job right away" crowd!

• *Remote Hiring (PC Hiring)* •

Traditionally all hiring was done on a face to face basis. Candidates came to the office and interviewed in front of the hiring manager. This can slow the hiring process considerably (trying to coordinate availability of meeting times), increase costs (flying the candidate in) and is often unrealistic in a global corporation.. One company (Hewlett Packard) has already begun introducing relatively simple technology to allow for real time "Video-Conference" Interviews. They are setting up a network of video equipped computers at college campuses to allow for remote interviewing. Other companies can take advantage of this new technology through their own video conferencing set-ups and/ or those at Chain Copy Centers that also have video setups. As another option an applicant might also suggest a telephone interview to the recruiter, when the costs of flying candidates in is prohibitive.

• *Remote Work (From Anywhere)* •

New technology (Fast modems and video equipped PC's) and changing corporate policies will allow many people (especially knowledge workers) to do their work from home, or on the road. This will expand your job choices because you will no longer have to live in the same city as the company. This will allow a candidate to ignore the lack of "local" want ad openings and search the web for openings anywhere in the world. These "remote jobs" might only require you to visit the company headquarters once a year.

• *"Push Cast" Technology (To Automatically Bring Job Openings To You)* •

In the future the process of searching for jobs will shift from the current approach where you must actively look in a multitude of sources (want ads and web pages) for jobs to a new "Automatic" approach. This automatic "push" technology starts when you "pre-register" (or when recruiters pre-select you as a viable candidate) for certain types of jobs just once and job openings are automatically sent (or pushed) to you by a vendor or software package via confidential e-mail. This "reduced effort" approach will make job searching significantly easier because the targeted openings will come automatically to you.

• *Resume / Job Opening "Mining"* •

There are two basic elements in recruiting- finding the candidates and assessing them. The first (finding candidates) which used to be a relatively difficult task for recruiters is becoming increasingly easy as a result of large modern databases, on-line "yellow" pages and Job Posting Web pages.. In the future firms will use data mining techniques that will supply complete lists of 1) qualified candidates to companies, 2) job openings to individuals and 3) do computerized references very much like they now do credit checks. By sorting professional organization membership data, journal mailing lists, on-line "yellow pages and WEB "registration hits" agents will be able to provide candidate profiles instantaneously to subscriber firms, worldwide. Individuals will be able to subscribe to a world wide job opening list for their targeted job.

• *A "Futureview"* •

In a world of rapid and constant change companies must learn to focus on the future (and in some cases to forget the past). Most job seekers tend also to focus on what they have done in the past (Many recruiters do too). Unfortunately most progressive companies are starting to ask different questions like "What WILL you do for me in the FUTURE". We call that a "Futureview". In a similar light, they want to know if you can use newer tools and methods that didn't exist the last time you solved the problem. Actually, even if you have never done the task before it is to your advantage to show the recruiter how you WOULD do it! That will get you more attention then someone who tells how they "did it" using "Jurassic Park" tools that no longer fit the companies current needs. Provide this "Futureview" in your cover letter, as an attachment to your resume or in the interview.

• *Virtual Reality Job Simulations* •

Advanced technology will also allow companies to better assess the capabilities of it's recruits. Computerized simulations (like flight simulators for pilots) allow corporations to put employees in "what If" situations to see how they can perform BEFORE they are actually hired. This will help applicants who perform poorly in interviews but who do well in the actual job.

• *Sharing Job Openings Among Strategic Partners* •

Many major firms, especially in hi-tech, have developed "strategic partnerships" with other firms in their industries (A strategic partnership is where firms cooperate on the development of new products without having to merge). The next step might be a joint internal job posting system where the partners share "selected" job openings. This "cross pollination" between each other's teams would further build the relationship between the two firms. These placements may be temporary assignments, job rotations or even permanent placements in some cases.

Tips for rhe Recruiter's "TOOLKIT"

Dr. John Sullivan
Professor of Human Resources and Executive Coach
College of Business, San Francisco State University
[e-mail - johns@sfsu.edu

This is a list of employment practices recruiters might consider while attempting to move into 21st Century HR.

- Do a survey of all hires and ask them why they accepted the job (and what were their concerns).

- Do a survey of all rejected offers and find out what were the deciding factors in their decision.

- Consider your customers as a recruiting source. Who else respects our firm and might be inclined to want to work for us. You might also involve large corporate customers in the selection process so that you improve the likelihood that new hires will be able to meet your customers needs. It might also build customer loyalty, as they feel some "ownership" of those selected.

- Sign on to a HR Listserver to exchange ideas and ask questions (i.e. HR-NET, D-RECRUIT).

- Develop an E-Letter (a periodic e-mail newsletter) to keep potential candidates interested in your company.

- Begin tracking recruiters / recruitment tools / and sources used in the hiring process. See which produces high performers, long tenure employees, and bad hires.

- Identify key jobs and key managers. Stop treating all jobs as having equal importance.

- Stop looking just at the cost of hire and filling "reqs" and focus more on the Quality of the hire and/ or any potential business gains from a hire.

- Prove that everything you do results in a higher quality hire. Stop assuming old practices still work and "good people trying hard" always produce a quality hire. Drop all employment practices that don't make a significant difference.

- Consider "weekend" hires, consultant to hire, simulations and temp to hire strategies to improve the accuracy of the selection process.

- Increase referral bonus levels and begin giving a larger bonus for high performing hires.

- Develop "prequalifying" systems for internal candidates to increase the number of internal transfers and also to increase retention rates.

- Realize that hiring must be owned and done by MANAGERS. Employment consults and teaches but does not DO hiring.

- Develop JIT hiring systems like "corporate resources" (hiring a superstar even when there is no current opening) to capture superstars who are likely to be on the market for only one week or less.

- Develop "Personal Courting" and relationship building programs with potential recruits so that hiring processes are not just one time "flash" occurrences.

- Realize one of the primary functions of recruitment and hiring is to build and reinforce the corporate image and culture as well as to increase corporate capabilities and productivity. Remember recruiting is marketing and all potential recruits are also potential customers.

- Start forecasting the future (unemployment rates, the pool of qualified candidates, business cycles, the changing needs of your customers etc.) and stop just "reacting to reqs" when they hit your desk.

- Do internal customer satisfaction surveys to see what managers and applicants want "more of and less of".

- Identify how your employment practices differ from your direct competitors. You can't beat the competitor if you all do the same things the same way.

- Drop forever the idea that recruitment and hiring must be face to face. Develop remote recruitment and hiring practices that are superior to face to face ones.

- Begin the process of becoming an Employer of Choice in your industry. Gather information on what is needed and sell it to top management.

- Develop metrics (in conjunction with the CFO) to identify and prove the Business Impacts of a great hire and the costs of a bad hire. Make hiring great employees THE corporate competitive advantage over your competition.

- Develop forecasting tools which "forecast corporate FAT" (excess employees) before an RIF is necessary and identify future retention issues so that you will have to do less recruiting.

- Develop a rotation program where employment specialists spend time each year working in the field and "learning the business".

- Get line managers to "sponsor" and "own" changes and revisions in employment systems.

- Consider creating "feeder channels" for future University hires. For example sponsor "Learn to be a _____ training classes, student clubs, internships, "Professor summer internships" and short term professor / manager swap programs).

- Develop and sponsor internet business chat rooms and listservers to develop relationships with potential applicants.

- Capture reference names given by high performers and consider them as potential hires.

- Track down high-performers that were "voluntary terminations" and attempt to get them to return.

- Track offer "turndowns" and contact them again at periodic intervals.

- Drop or weaken employment "rules" and approvals to decrease your time to hire. Identify things that slow down the hiring process and that you can't prove make a difference (No you don't need a job description in order to hire someone etc.).

- Calculate the average performance rating, bonus pay, awards, promotions and productivity of those hired this year and compare it to last years hires. Smile if you see an improvement!

Outside the Box:
Technical Guru Wanted

by Amy Baron Naples, SPHR
Director of Human Resources
Bluestone Consulting, Inc.
Bluestone Software, Inc.

As a seasoned Human Resources professional, I've spent a great deal of time recruiting for a multitude of positions. In retrospect, I've come to realize that, over time, I had adopted the philosophy "when in Rome...". Frankly, while I had always prided myself on the notion that I was imaginative and extremely resourceful, my approach to the recruiting process had certainly become stale. As the consummate professional, developing a recruitment strategy meant considering several fundamental factors: job elements, budgetary consideration, and what newspaper to use!

I'd been working in a highly technical environment for about six months, happily recruiting as I had always done in the past. Suddenly and without warning, the influx of resumes began diminishing almost as fast as computer technology in the outside world was expanding. Unexpectedly, recruiting qualified people had become quite a formidable task!

I continued plodding along in a conventional manner, but just wasn't achieving the results I was accustomed to in the past. I chalked it up to the time of year; the location of the ad; the weather; the amount of white space, etc. When a company director presented me with the most outlandish advertising copy I'd ever seen, and asked me to get it in the following Sunday's newspaper, I laughed and thought you've got to be kidding! Only a crazy person would answer this type of ad!

C++ Guru Wanted
Way Cool Next Generation
Cross Platform Client/Server
Development Tool Project

Just as I had suspected, we didn't get any responses to our ad. However, believe it or not, that was a good thing! His outrageous request had helped me recognize that in this day and age, the prevailing recruiting methodologies were no longer the most efficient and cost effective approach. Traditional recruiting, even with a bit of creative flair, just didn't cut it in such a competitive market place.

As the Director of Human Resources for a young, rapidly expanding technology company, one of my greatest challenges continues to be the task of recruiting software engineers. Three years ago, after a lot of thought, and minimal returns using the traditional HR recruiting methodology, I knew I had to search for candidates in some pretty unfamiliar and uncomfortable places. Naturally, given my current work environment, the World Wide Web seemed like the most logical place to begin my search.

For those skeptics out there that are thinking, of course she'd find technical people on the Web , be assured that if you've got a non-technical position to fill, you can find what your looking for out in Cyberspace. Whether you are looking for nurses, accountants, human resource professionals, (and the list goes on), that's the place to be!

For those of you who are novices, fear not! If you can point and click , you can recruit on the World Wide Web. When I first ventured on to the Web, foolishly, I was too embarrassed to admit that I didn't have a clue. What other choice did I have but to learn on my own? Now, if you don't know how to surf, you can ask your friends, relatives, or even your children! Undoubtedly, someone in your circle will know what to do.

However, let me caution you---before you embark on your trip through Cyberspace, you need to define your recruiting strategy. There is an infinite number of sites for both recruiters and job seekers, so it pays to narrow your search as much as possible before beginning your quest. If you don't, you will waste an inordinate amount of time visiting sites that are not appropriate to your specific needs. Save yourself precious time by determining how much money, if any, you have in your recruiting budget. Can you afford to pay a fee to post your job vacancies? Are you willing to pay for relocation? What prominent characteristics does your ideal candidate possess? If they hang out in Cyberspace, where do they go? Poll your employees ask them what sites peak their interests. You need to think like they think.

Three years ago, when I first started my quest for the mother lode , it took a while to even find a decent Website. Now they're everywhere. All you really need to know is how to spell resume ! Using YAHOO as a search tool is one of the easiest ways to begin. While there are thousands of other more direct routes to take, this is simple and a great way to learn.

When you locate YAHOO, type in the word resumes . That will bring up a list of hyperlinks to sites where resumes are posted. Generally, these links will list specific categories of skills, such human resources, accounting, or computer skills (the most prevalent), etc. As you get deeper into your search, you find instructions on posting job advertisements and linking your homepage to YAHOO. Clicking one hyperlink will lead you to another, and another, and another.

If you don't want to spend a lot of time surfing, you may want to try a few specific sites. We've had success with sites that charge a fee, and those that do not. For example, Career Mosaic, ESpan, and the On-line Career Center (OCC) are a few of my company's favorite sites. Using the Monster Board over a six month period, netted us approximately 7,000 resumes in the appropriate job categories. Some of our favorite free sites are America's Job Bank, Career Exchange, NJ Jobs, Virtual Resume, and Yahoo Classifieds.

Typically, different companies have different recruiting needs. What works for us may not necessarily work for you. Whereever possible, contact someone at a website's headquarters before you sign a contract or make a commitment of time or money. Ask detailed questions regarding typical costs and demographics. Also find out what types of individuals frequent their sites---both from a recruiting and job seekers perspective.

I'd like to suggest that in your search for candidates, you consider using the Web in several different ways. Naturally, searching various websites is the easiest, and most basic approach, and it is certainly a great place to begin. If you are lucky enough to recruit for a company with a homepage, you can use that to your advantage. Your homepage is an incredible marketing tool. It is absolutely a great way to advertise job vacancies and sell your company. Use your homepage to discuss company culture, benefits, career opportunities, etc. In fact, many sites will allow you to set up a direct link to your homepage. A potential candidate can read your company's ad on the OCC, and in a matter of seconds, hyperlink to your homepage. Of course, as with everything on the Web, some will charge a fee for that service, and some will not.

I'd also like to suggest that you begin your searches early in the day. Create an email template so you can contact potential candidates in a hurry. With email, recruiting in different time zones is no longer an issue. If you see a resume you like, chances are, hundreds of other recruiters have seen it as well. Save yourself time and headaches by emailing them immediately. Time is critical, and playing phone tag with voice-mail will get you no where fast.

There are many advantages to recruiting on the World Wide Web. You have access to more people and a broader selection of applicants. You are no longer limited to your immediate geographical region--your search is worldwide. It's convenient, easy to use, and more often than not, inexpensive. Market research has shown that more than 80% of college students have free access to the Internet, and typically, eight out of ten people use the Internet to look for jobs. It's a great way to reach students, and to save money on printing and re-printing recruitment collateral.

While there are many advantages to using the Web, there are also some caveats. Internet use means sifting through large numbers of resumes, often by a limited staff. Many quality people do not have access to the Net. In my experience recruiting in the technical arena, I've noticed that quite often, highly skilled technical workers do not post their resumes on the Web. The demand for their skills is so high that all they need to do is sit and wait for the telephone to ring! As the numbers of job seekers and recruiters using the Internet continues to grow by leaps and bounds, competing for a potential new hire's attention becomes more and more difficult. Be clear that if you are interested in a resume you've found on line, so are a hundred other recruiters! Speed is essential, and certainly, for most of us, time is often very limited. Furthermore, if you are not willing to pay for relocation, or will only hire United States citizens, you will have to discard many a resume. Remember, when you post a job on the Internet, its there for the whole world to see.

As I've said before, searching for resumes on-line can be quite time consuming. In an effort to reduce the time highly paid professionals spend on-line, it may be cost effective for your company to hire a Sourcing Specialist . This seems to be a growing trend in many companies. The Sourcing Specialist, or Junior Recruiter (call it what you like), is responsible for identifying new sites on line, passing the good ones on to the company recruiter, and tracking results.

As professionals, our desire to succeed and to move our organizations to another plateau is directly related to our willingness and ability to adapt to our internal and external environments. In a world where web technology is no longer viewed as a passing craze , but is considered the norm, passive recruiting will no longer suffice. Web technology is changing the way we communicate and the way we live our lives. People spend their time in front of a computer, surfing the web, rather than sitting in an easy chair reading the paper.

Choose The Best Sites To Connect With Candidates: Roll The Dice Once Around The Monopoly Board

by Tracey Claybrooke
Claybrooke and Associates, Inc.
tracla@aol.com

As children our parents taught us "don't put all of your eggs in one basket", as adults our advisors tell us "diversify your investments". The strategy to winning monopoly is to diversify and take chances. Recruiting on the Internet is no different. The key to successful Internet recruiting is to diversify, change and take chances.

As with Monopoly the game company can provide the player with basic directions, it is the strategy of the player that determines who wins the game. This article will provide you with basic directions and an introduction to Monopoly or Recruitment Strategy.

The way to play this game successfully is to first define what type of talent you are seeking. Defining the type of talent will determine how the game is played. For example, if your mainstay of recruiting is "non-technical, banking professionals" then your strategy will be different from those who are seeking SAP & Oracle Programmers.

The second strategy is to learn what Internet sites are going to provide a constant flow of candidates. More specifically what career sites cater to a broad spectrum of professionals in all different disciplines? These sites may include; OCC, Espan, Monster Board, & Career Mosaic. Remember these sites attract people from around the world. In addition Career Resource Specialists are now accessing this information for their clients and the passive job seeker who wants to explore "What is out there" may happen to come across your companie's opportunity. The reality is, these sites touch a very large audience therefore your results or return on investment is somewhat unpredictable.

The third step is to define "what resume databases are available for the population of people I am trying to seek". There are numerous resume databases on the web. To fight your way through this jungle, use the CareerXRoads, resume reference section to make this search easier. This guide will provide you with a comprehensive listing of websites to review that allow the Internet Recruiter to obtain both free and fee resumes.

The game instructions up to this point provide passive or general access to candidates. These steps are considered the internet "chance" cards. You may win or you may lose. Now we need to consider what is "The Park Place" of our Internet recruitment strategy. This is what we call moving from a general to a more targeted candidate search on the net.

There are a couple of simple ways to engage in a more targeted candidate search on the Internet. First is to refer to the "SPECIALTY" section of CareerXRoads and look for the sites that relate to the type of people you are seeking. These sites may provide you access to resumes, job posting abilities, names, list-servs, publications and other industry related resources. These sites can create a road map for your targeted search. Monopoly and targeted recruitment are similar, once you identify and obtain all of the information or properties, you can now begin to build. The houses you add to "Park Place" makes the property more valuable. The more your research and work these major industry hubs, the more valuable of a recruiting resource they will be to you.

The second part of this strategy is to go to the Newsgroups, identify the discussion groups that relate to the type of people you are seeking and ask the source. In other words, find a specialty newsgroup and post an article that asks the participants "where do you look for jobs in your field?. The answers will provide you access to another "Park Place".

A third way to target your candidate sourcing efforts is to identify professional associations that target the type of people you are seeking. These sites may provide you with the ability to post jobs and retrieve resumes, access to chapters around the world, the ability to post jobs on the specific chapter sites, access into industry related discussion groups, and the ability to link your company website to theirs.

A fourth way of maximizing your monopoly game is to subscribe to industry related list-servs. List-servs are private online discussion groups that are broken down by industry or discipline. You search the types of List-servs by going to www.listz.com. These discussion lists give you names, & email addresses of the people you want to recruit.

Recruiting is no different than Monopoly it is all a game, yet the outcome can be influenced by how you play it. There are no right ways to recruit on the Internet, yet there are ways that you can effectively build a strategic Internet recruitment strategy. The Internet is rapidly changing, therefore your recruiting strategy will continually change. There will always be the staple career properties, it will be the chance cards that will continue to evolve. Invest in this strategy and this strategy will invest in you. Take chances, use your own candidates to guide you, and build on the staple career sites that have developed into a strong entity on the Internet.

Establishing Your Presence:
Build a Site and Drive Candidates to You

by Scott Sandberg
'Freelance Writer and Internet Consultant'
sandberg@interaccess.com

The Internet is already a crowded place. Companies large and small, as well as assorted recruiters, are all vying for the attention of the very same candidates your company hopes to attract. Posting your company's openings at the various career hubs on the Internet is a good start. But to be truly successful, your company needs to build a solid career site of its own.

Once your company establishes a site dedicated to its current job openings, you can start leveraging the true power of the Internet - one to one communication. With your company's own employment presence, you can pull prospective candidates away from the major career hubs - each one crowded with your competition - and onto your own career site. Without the distraction of thousands of other job opportunities, candidates will be better able to focus on the advantages that your company has to offer them.

Establish the Scope of Your Site

Many companies already have their own Web sites that include an area for employment opportunities. If your company is one of them, that's great. However, you still need to evaluate its effectiveness for your recruiting efforts. How much response is it generating? Has it reduced costs? Has it increased efficiency? These are all valid questions to ask when evaluating your company's employment area on the Web.

Of course, if your company has little or no information on the Web regarding careers, it's time to get wired, and start hiring. What follows are some suggestions for how you can build or enhance your company's employment site on the Web and drive qualified candidates to it.

• Post all open positions in as much detail as possible.
This will help cut down on unqualified responses.

• Make the employment section of the site easy to find.
Include a link from the home page. Also, a simple, easy-to-access directory structure such as www.mycompany.com/careers/ will help candidates to access your career site more quickly, without having to go through the home page. If you work with a large national or international organization, allow visitors to access opportunities by location,

as well as department and/or job title. Also, consider including a search engine that allows visitors to plug in key words that return appropriate job openings. Create an online application. This eliminates the "I don't have my resume together" excuse used by many passive job seekers who are still excellent candidates for your positions. If your company employs a resume management system (Resumix, ResTrac, etc.), you may have the option of having all or some resumes/applications uploaded directly to that system. You'll save time and money when you can eliminate scanning or re-keying of information. Be sure to keep the area current. Nothing will be more frustrating for candidates than finding job openings that were posted six months ago. You'll also avoid looking at resumes for positions you've already filled.

• Offer special incentives to your target audience.

For example, if you're recruiting technical professionals, offer them free access to training materials (online or offline) or something else that will make it worth their while to visit your site. Lastly, provide a means of contact, be it e-mail, a fax number or a telephone number. You may find a candidate whom, after speaking to one of your people, or getting a quick response to some questions in an e-mail, suddenly submits a resume for your consideration.

Driving Candidates to Your Site

Once you've got your employment site up and running (and it's been double-checked for spelling and grammatical errors, as well as technical glitches), it's time to let people know that you're out there. While there's a lot you can do toward that end online, don't neglect the traditional means of disseminating information about your company as well.

• Press releases are always a good idea.

Whether you're announcing a brand new corporate site, or simply the HR portion of the existing company site.

• Start getting your company's URL in print.

Put it on your business card, in your recruitment ads, on your brochures, on your letterhead - anywhere you'd put your address and phone number. And don't forget about that e-mail address.

• Notify your employees that you've posted job openings on the Web.

Employee referrals are always a welcome alternative to running an ad.

• Establish links from some of the major career hubs.

Sites such as Career Magazine, the Monster Board, Career Mosaic, OCC, CareerMag, NationJob etc. Experiment and measure results.

• Survey Your Recent Hires.

Find out what professional organizations your employees may be involved in and seek those organizations out on the Web. They may be willing to include a link to your site for a reciprocal link, or they may offer sponsorship opportunities.

• If you have the budget...

...consider placing banner advertisements on non-recruitment oriented sites that will reach the passive job seeker. An ad network, such as DoubleClick, can help you more effectively target those candidates that might qualify for your openings.

...offer free access to training tools, a seminar, or something else of value to professionals who register at your Web site. This can help you to generate a mailing list of candidates in a specific field.

• Lastly, talk it up.

Whenever you are out and about - at industry events, seminars, wherever - let people know about your company's Web site. Word of mouth is always a strong advertising vehicle.

Find the Right People for the Job

When it comes time to finally start writing the HTML, you'll have to decide who's going to do the actual work on your company's home page or recruitment site. If you're company already has a home page up, and the company has been happy with whoever created it, it probably makes sense to use that same company or person. They're already familiar with your company, the structure of your company's home page, and the way your company likes to work.

If, however, you're starting from scratch, or you just need to find another vendor, it pays to do your homework. Rates for Web site development are all over the board, from dirt cheap to outrageously expensive. While it's true that more often than not "you get what you pay for", in the field of Web development, the most expensive company won't always be the one that best suits your needs. So, if you are going outside the company to have your Web site created, talk to a few companies. Take a look at the sites they've created. Then talk to some of their clients. Also, consider taking a look at Advertising Age's Internet publication, Net Marketing at netb2b.com. It can give you an idea of median rates in major markets across the country, as well as a list of developers in major metropolitan areas.

Of course, if you don't have the budget to hire an outside vendor, consider creating your page in-house. Your IS department is a good starting point. However, if you currently don't have the staff to devote to an Internet project within IS, consider doing it yourself. There are plenty of good HTML editors available out there that make publishing a Web page a point and click affair. Some examples are Adobe's Pagemill, and Microsoft's Front Page. Or, download the latest version of Netscape Communicator, which is bundled with a very competent editor. However, once you've finished your Web site, be sure to test it by viewing it through a couple of different browsers. Netscape Navigator and Microsoft's Internet Explorer are the most popular, but you might want to see how your page looks through AOL's browser, as well.

What are you waiting for?

You can start using the Internet to recruit qualified candidates today. Post a job at one of the career hubs. Or, start building that dedicated recruitment site you've been designing in your head. Remember, the Internet is perfect for experimentation. Whatever you do today, you can change with a few quick keystrokes tomorrow. So what are you waiting for? The Internet can be a powerful tool for recruiting. Start using it today.

If You're fishing for a Job, Use a Net!:
How to Use Chat Rooms, Newsgroups and Listservs to Expand Your Network

Nancy Heimbaugh
Contributing writer for E-Span
info@espan.com

If you're seriously fishing for a job and want to land a good one, use the Net! There are lots of teeming ponds to go job-fishing in, and many resources and methods to use.

If you're an Internet veteran, chances are you first got your feet wet in online communication by using chat rooms and/or newsgroups. These were popular long before the recent proliferation of Web sites and online job services. You may think that now chat rooms, newsgroups and listservs (mailing lists) are old-fashioned. Think again, and look again. These three established ways of networking online are constantly evolving. As they capitalize more on the potential of the Internet and the increasing capabilities and knowledge of people who use the Web, they will improve dramatically.

Finding the right job for you and building a rewarding career often requires extensive resources, research and contacts. Chat rooms, newsgroups and listservs can be great sources of ideas, information, inspiration and even job leads.

When you're fishing and you're really hungry, do you just sit idly on the bank and hope a fish jumps into your bucket? No. You get together your equipment and the right bait. Then you look for an area where the fish are biting. If you're really eager to catch fish, you probably have more than one line. And you cast again and again. It's the same with your job search. The more lines you have, the better chance you have of getting bites and reeling in the right employer. Chat rooms, newsgroups and listservs are like well-stocked ponds you can fish in free! So get your equipment together and start testing the waters. To use chat rooms, you need Internet access, a Web browser, a modem and a computer that's fast enough to let you get a word in now and then. To use newsgroups, you need Internet access, a Web browser and a modem. With listservs, if you have e-mail, you're ready.

While the best way learn is through hands-on exploration and experience, following is basic "How To" information to help job seekers capitalize on the opportunities available through chat rooms, newsgroups and listservs.

One important word of advice: make sure you're fishing in the right pond. There are numerous interactive sites on topics ranging from medical problems to parenting....from cooking to golf...from handling your finances to fishing! Many of them will probably catch your interest, but remember --- your goal is to land a job. So try to stay focused. A good rule of thumb is to use the most specific sites that apply to your field.

Netiquette

If you do enjoy fishing, you know that if you muddy up the waters or make a lot of noise, you won't get any bites and you will annoy your fellow fisherman. That's fishing etiquette.

Etiquette for chat rooms, newsgroups and listservs is commonly called netiquette. As a newcomer, you don't want to make waves. Large, established chat rooms and newsgroups frequently have help files, guidelines and FAQ (Frequently Asked Questions) right online. Listservs often provide this information in your welcome letter. Read these carefully so that you seem knowledgeable and make a good impression.

To get comfortable with netiquette and procedures, you may want to test the waters in a chat room, newsgroup or list not related to your career. But be careful --- you can get hooked fast. Communicating about a hobby or interest can familiarize you with the process, but it probably won't help you land a job.

Chat Rooms

They're not just for small talk --- they're for serious job talk. Yes, there are chat rooms where enthusiasts discuss the earliest Star Trek episodes or the latest Melrose Place. But there are numerous chat rooms about industries or careers.

How do you use them? First, it's different depending upon your system and equipment and the specific chat room. Many of the popular chat rooms have help files where you can learn how to talk the talk. There's even a "sign" language --- emoticons. These are keyboard symbols or abbreviations you use to express emotions. You may want to visit the following sites to get a chat room primer:
www.otn.net/chatroom/help.html
www5.zdnet.com/zdwebcat/content/chat (Click on Chat 101)

The next section tells you how to find a chat room on a topic related to your career. When you find one, you simply enter the URL. You'll be asked to enter your name and a picture to join. (The picture is optional.) If you want to contribute anything to the discussion, you will have to specify a name. If you want to just look and listen, you can leave the fields blank. Simply press join to enter the chat room.

How do you find a chat room related to your career?

...On the Web:

Use a search engine such as Yahoo, Infoseek, Excite, or Lycos to search for appropriate chat rooms. Type in keywords such as: jobs or careers, chat or talk, or your particular field. A word of warning: you'll be overwhelmed. During a recent search using Infoseek, using the keywords business and chat resulted in more than 23 million sites. You could make a career out of viewing them! Try typing in your career field first. Then narrow your search by adding the word chat or talk.

Sites you may want to visit include the following:

www.clickit.com/bizwiz/bizwiz.htm

www.aboutwork.com (Lets you search to find someone in your industry and your state)

www.talkcity.com

www.hardatwork.com

...Online Services

Visit online services where chat utilities are often more organized and easier to use.

.CompuServe - Career Management Forum

.AOL - Career Chat in the Career Center

What do you say after you say "Hello?"

Especially if you are not familiar with chat rooms, you may want to monitor the discussion for awhile before you announce your arrival. Just watch the screen to get a feel for the flow of the conversation, learn who's who, and see how to converse. Remember that, even though you're talking through a keyboard, it is conversation --- not a typed oration. It's also informal and fast-paced. Your goal is to make contacts and learn.

Ask for leads and advice. Find out how you can enhance or update your skills, and therefore your employability. Make sure other participants know you're actively seeking new employment. Chatting without getting to the point --- landing a job --- is like dangling your fishing line right above the water. You won't get any nibbles!

Before you say "Goodbye": Remember to bookmark your favorite career chat rooms. That makes it easy to return to the site. Since chat rooms and their participants are ever changing, when you find a relevant site, it pays to go back again and again and to expand your network.

Newsgroups

Also called Usenet, newsgroups are a network of discussion groups. They contain opinions and information on almost any subject. Topics range from rock climbing to rock groups... from sports teams to legal issues. The popular Web browsers such as Navigator and Internet Explorer have built-in newsgroup reading capabilities. All it takes to post messages to and receive messages from newsgroups is e-mail.

There are Web-based services which are let you specify the topic you're interested in and then search for appropriate newsgroups using keywords. Three of the most popular and functional ones are:

Deja News (www.dejanews.com)
tile.net (www.tile.net/news)
Liszt (www.liszt.com/news)
Reference (www.reference.com)

Deja News Newsgroups Hierarchy lists more than 15,000 newsgroups, so you will probably find some topics related to your job field. A good way to begin networking through newsgroups is to post a question or a response to an article. This can begin a dialog which can eventually lead to job information. (However, unlike chat rooms in which you sometimes get instant responses, it can be days before people respond to your posting.) To post a comment, click on the "To: News" button. An e-mail screen will pop up, and you simply type your message.

You can also initiate an article and post it in appropriate newsgroups. To try the direct approach, you might ask for career information. Be sure you're in an appropriate newsgroup. Then make sure your subject line conveys your goal. For example, "Are there careers in history outside the classroom?" This approach can attract mentors who have great connections.

Listservs

A listserv (mailing list) is a group of people who exchange e-mail about a subject of mutual interest. For example, there could be a mailing list about bass fishing where avid bass fishermen exchange fish stories! If you join a mailing list about your career field, you'll get mail on the subject, and you'll meet people and make the all-important job connections. Some mailing lists are public and some are private or restricted to specific groups of people. Every mailing list has a topic or group of topics to which all messages distributed on it are expected to relate. There are more than 66,000 free lists. It's important to note that mailing list are not commercial. Advertising products or services or soliciting business is taboo on most lists. So you should be somewhat subtle in your job search; instead of posting a "Position Wanted" ad, post a request for information on how to enhance your skills or what kind of career opportunities exist in your field.

The following three sites not only let you search for appropriate lists, they also give good information on how to use them, including some common "netiquette" rules. It's a good idea to read the introductory information on one of these sites before searching for and signing up for a list.

...Liszt (www.liszt.com)
This directory has more than 70,000 mailing lists. You can use Liszt

Select to explore 15 categories of lists. The business category has 21 subcategories ranging from accounting to trades.

...Reference
(www.reference.com)
..AOL Mailing List Directory
(http:/ifrit.web.aol.com/mld/production/mld-general.html) This directory contains more than 3200 mailing lists. You do not have to subscribe to AOL to search it.
...The List of Lists
(catalog.com/vivian/interest-group-search.html)
...Publicly Accessible Mailing Lists
(www.neosoft.com/internet/pam/index.html)
...Tile.Net
(www.tile.net/lists) Searches for information in 33 different categories

When you find a list you like, subscribe by sending a request to the list server. (The address usually begins with "listserv," "majordomo," or "listproc.") You'll receive a welcome note from the list maintainer telling you how to post messages, get the FAQ, etc. Then you'll begin receiving messages via e-mail. To respond and enter into the discussion, simply type your message and hit the "reply" button. Your message will be sent to everyone on that particular mailing list.

Another option on many lists is to sign-up for announcements. This is usually as simple as signing on and signing up. For example, tile.net has a page called tile.net/signup. There are more than 50 categories of information to sign up for. There are places to sign up for news specifically for related to many professional fields.

Announcements are usually somewhat formal. They're the e-mail equivalent of newspaper press releases. They are not discussion material to which you reply. However, they can be a terrific source of information. For example, if you looking for a job in sales, it would help you to know that a large company was locating in your area or that an existing company was introducing a new product line, etc.
Be patient and persistent.

Good fishermen learn that some days the fish aren't biting at a favorite fishing hole. They either move on to another site or decide to come back another day.

It's the same with chat rooms, newsgroups or listservs. You'll probably have to cast about on several sites numerous times before you get promising nibbles, and actively cultivate your contacts before you get actual job bites. Chat rooms, newsgroups or listservs are not job services --- they're communication services. Just remember that communication, information and contacts are key to successful networking that can help you land a good job.

Resume Roulette

by Bob Levinstein
Vice President, NationJob, Inc.
erlevinstein@nationjob.com
http://www.nationjob.com
Phone: 800/292-7731 Fax: 515/964-6737

Confidentiality, on the Internet- if you believe the news media (with all their sincere concern for our personal privacy), the firewalls have ears and your fingers should tremble at every keystroke. Personally, I think you can relax. You don't have time to read your own e-mail: is it really likely that some shadowy "They" is poring over every Bill Gates joke you've ever re-forwarded? Even if "they" were, the potential damage from the "discovery" of most e-mail messages is pretty minor. Common sense should prevail.

But what about your resume? Web sites and newsgroups designed to accept such postings abound, and the prospect of getting a fabulous job offer out of the blue appeals to the Lotto player in all of us. (Maybe they're using the web to select the next ambassador to the Fiji Islands!) But what's the downside?

If you already have a job, the fact that you're circulating your resume could hurt you if your employer finds out. Would you assign the next big project to the guy or gal with one foot already out the door? And, unlike your e-mail, which your bosses have no compelling reason to read, there is a legitimate business purpose in looking at resumes on-line.

But with all of the resumes floating around the net, what are the odds that they'll find yours? If they're actually looking, (more on this in a moment) the odds are pretty good for several reasons.

• Key word searching. As your company is likely to be looking for others with skills and experience similar to yours, and that search may bring up your resume.

• Your resume may be in more places than you think. In order to increase the total number of resumes they offer for searching, sites often "cull" resumes from newsgroups and repost them. You may not be able to find all of the places where your resume is listed, much less update or delete it, so it may remain accessible for a very long time.

So what can you do to protect yourself? Some sites offer to block your name and contact information until someone is specifically interested in your resume and you approve the transfer. This seems to be a reasonable solution if you trust the people who manage the site—and as long as your employer can't guess it's you from reading the rest of your resume. (Your employer probably knows your current title, your last job, where you went to school, etc.)

Other services promise to prevent your current employer from accessing your resume at all. I find this solution highly questionable, as computers aren't very good at understanding that the text strings "IBM", "Inter. Bus. Mach.", and "International Business Machines" all represent the same company, much less the names of various subsidiaries.

Fortunately, there is a better way: the intelligent agent or "push technology" model. These services are typically free and simple: enter your e-mail address, then use a series of menus and key words to define exactly what you're looking for in a job. (The better services code jobs in various types of categories: position type, location, salary, etc. for more accurate matching). From then on, any new jobs received by the service that match your quaifications and preferences are automatically e-mailed directly to you. You can then read a detailed position description and decide if you're interested. If so, you apply directly to the company offering the job. (Authors' note: NationJob's intelligent agent- P.J. Scout™ was an early pioneer of this model, and currently serves NationJob's subscribing job seekers. See the directory listing for more info).

The advantages to the job seeker are obvious: your name is never given out to employers unless you decide to contact them, so there's no risk of your resume being sent to your boss. Further, because you decide which positions you're interested in, you won't be contacted about irrelevant openings.

But the advantages to the employer are even greater. Under the resume database model, recruiters have to spend their time searching through resumes, contacting each potential candidate, explaining the position available, finding out if the candidate is interested in working for them, and waiting for an up-to-date resume. Under the intelligent agent model, all of this work is done for them: they simply list a position and qualified, informed candidates contact them.

No statistics exist on what percentage of people posting resumes on the web find—or lose—jobs as a result. That one success story posted at www.HappyResu-Land.com could represent one person in ten or one person in ten thousand; there's no way to tell. So how should you handle your on-line job search?

1. Evaluate your own situation. How likely is it that your current employer will be searching for resumes on-line? How much trouble will

you be in if they find your resume listed?

2. Thoroughly evaluate sites before posting your resume. This is a tough one, as it's easy (and inexpensive) to make web sites appear "established", but there are clues. Are there companies you've heard of listing jobs on the site? Awards/reviews of the site from names you recognize? Can you easily find out who owns/operates the site? What guarantees of privacy do they provide?

Resume posting is only one method of finding a job on-line, and probably not the best. Agents, large general career sites, and industry- or position-specific web sites are all better places to start. They may not have the mystique that a stranger may call and ask you to be Mel Gibson's new masseuse or the head of NBC, but they're a lot more likely to result in some good solid job leads.

Preparing Your Resume for E-Mail

by Will Matlack on behalf of Resumix, Inc.
Independent Public Relations Consultant
San Francisco, CA
wmatlock@msn.com

Because e-mail is immediate and requires no paper, copying, or post-age, it is the least expensive and fastest method of getting your re-sume into play. More companies are implementing technology that allows electronic submission of resumes, and many of these also in-clude resume processing systems. These systems automatically pro-cess your resume to extract your skills, experience, and other qualifi-cations for immediate matching o the requirements of open positions. Companies with these capabilities usually make note of them in their ads or on their World Wide Web sites. Before you e-mail your resume, there are two key things to consider- file type and content.

File Type
If you have a data file of your current resume, submitting it is very easy. You have two very basic options, Copy/Paste or Save As an RTF file. In the first option you need to have both the word processing docu-ment file open and your e-mail program open. Go to you resume docu-ment and perform a "select all" operation from the edit menu. You can also select the entire content of the document by right clicking and dragging your mouse from the top of the document to the end.

After your selection is complete, move your mouse into the e-mail docu-ment and perform a paste operation. In Windows this can be done either by either left clicking and selecting "paste" or holding down the 'Ctrl' key and pressing the 'v' key. All of the text of your resume will be pasted into the e-mail document ready for sending.

The important thing to remember about this method is that you will lose all of the document's formatting during transmission. This is not a major issue for companies using resume processing systems, but if you would like to retain some formatting, you need to save your re-sume in Rich Text Formatting (RTF) first. If you have a lot of formatting on your resume, RTF won't save all of it, but if you review the RTF file before sending it, you can fine tune it to get back a majority of the formatting.

Saving in RTF is only slightly more complicated than the cut and paste process just described. The first step is to open your resume data file then select the "Save As" function in the "file" menu. A dialog box will open up giving you a wide variety of file types for the "Save As" pro-cess. Select the Rich Text Format or the RFT, change the file name to something like "ResumeRTF," then save the file. Changing the file

name will ensure that your original file will remain intact. You can then perform
the copy/paste operation in the same manner as discussed above.

Another option is to send either the original word processing file or the RTF file as an attachment to your e-mail message, but this could add an unnecessary level of complication to the process. Resume processing systems may not be able to access the attachment directly.

Content
The rules for resume content are totally different for resumes that will be submitted to companies using resume processing systems, versus those that process resumes manually. For example, extract meaningful information on skills, experience, and education directly from the e-mailed resume and place them in a comprehensive database. This data is then matched to the requirements of the open positions to produce a list of the most qualified candidates. The system has no limitation on how much information can be extracted from a single resume.

This means that if your resume is being e-mailed to a company with a resume scanning system, you should put down every little bit of information about yourself that you can thing of. Since these systems are specifically used to match skill sets to position requirements, try to list every skill you can think of-the length of your resume simply won't matter. These systems allow you to represent your qualifications more fully than before.

Some companies offer an online program that will step you through the process of building an electronic resume that will be maximized for the processing systems. Look for this program on company World Wide Web sites; it's called Resume Builder.

If your resume is going to a company that has not advertised a resume scanning system, you should prepare its content in a traditional manner for a paper resume. This means editing it for easy visual access to the information it contains and keeping its length no more than two pages if possible. As explained above, you will have limited formatting available, so it is best to save the document as an RTF and make use of the formatting it provides you.

A general rule of thumb is to have two versions of your resume available-one for e-mailing companies with processing capabilities and one for e-mailing to those who will visually process it. If in doubt, you can always send both versions.

Your Next Career Move:
Push on Doors Marked Pull

by Margaret F. Riley, MSLIS
Author, The Riley Guide
www.dbm.com/jobguide
Margaret F. Riley, MSLIS
mfriley@erols.com

Many job seekers view the Internet as the world's largest database of position announcements, a statement that is partially true. It isn't only one database; it's a collection of thousands of them. However, it does include more job listings accessible from one location (your computer) than any other resource known to man, woman, or child. That's the good news. The bad news is they are not neatly arranged in any recognizable order nor is there a directory or catalog to everything out there. So, how do you get to those things that are most important to you, the sites with leads that speak directly to you? Don't wait for the jobs to come to you, go to them using a couple of simple strategies and the right tools for surveying the electronic landscape.

Think of the Internet like a shopping mall. Each site is another retail outlet just waiting for you to come in and browse around, checking out the merchandise in the hope that you will find something which fits you just right. The problem is that all the stores have similar merchandise, it's all pretty much the same, none of it fits right, and there's so much of it that you can't possibly look in every corner. Can you see yourself walking around this mall, pulling open the door for all these different stores and exiting again in frustration? So why do it? Instead of passively pulling open the doors to these stores, try aggressively pushing against them. Walk in and demand attention. They have staff available. Instead of you looking around these megamalls trying to find the right fit, make the staff work for you. Make the Internet work for you as your agent instead of you trying to fit into the way it works.

As you begin your job-shopping trip, it would be good to browse through a catalog of merchandise, taking some time to look at the variety of things offered and reading the descriptions on those that look more interesting. You have a particular thing you are interested in but you want to see how many things you can find which meet your need and how they describe themselves. Turn to one of the Internet's virtual libraries and begin your search by browsing through their collections. These catalogs of Internet merchandise offerings will introduce you to a variety of resources to help you in your search for new employment. Yes, we have lists of potential employers in the industry you are interested in. We also carry directories with information on any topic, whether it's related to a particular industry, occupation, or skill. We can even point you towards many sites and services with job listings targeted for your field, including recruiters who work to find people just like you.

Yahoo (www.yahoo.com), The Galaxy (galaxy.tradewave.com), and LookSmart (www.looksmart.com) can all be used as catalogs for beginning your online journey. You can search them using keywords to find the various resources included, but take the time to browse their shelves and look for things which didn't turn up in your search. These libraries will also help you to find the right words to use in your searches for information as well as alternative terms to use. Because they are controlled and categorized, it is possible to find information and resources related to your areas of interest that you did not know where there. Using these libraries to begin your search will quickly let you know if your wording is correct. If it is, these libraries will immediately return to you a list of possible avenues to explore.

Now that you've done your initial exploration through these major catalogs, you want to take another step. Yes, you saw some interesting merchandise, but you want more detailed information. Instead of just looking at a general store with a few chairs in stock, you want to find a store that specializes in chairs. You know you want one, you even have an idea of the features you want, but now you want to find all of them together so you can really compare and contrast them. Using your virtual library, you begin identifying directories and catalogs which concentrate on only one subject, be it a particular field of study, industry, or profession. In a traditional library, these might be referred to as directories or subject indexes, but online we call them online resource guides. These sites and electronic resources have been designed to concentrate only one idea and to explore that idea as thoroughly as possible, linking in as much information and listing as many resources as possible to hopefully create a complete catalog on this one topic.

Online resource guides come in many forms. The Riley Guide (www.dbm.com/jobguide/) is an online resource guide focusing on work opportunities and career information. It has a particular focus, covers this topic as completely as possible, and is run by people with an established expertise in this area. Another example would be Hoover's Online (www.hoovers.com), a service of the people who publish the well-known and respected Hoover's Business Almanacs. If you want some fast yet accurate information on a major employer or a quick view of some of the major players in a particular industry, then this is a great place to go. Resource guides might be compilations of links and resources on a particular topic or they might be the online version of a print publication, but they will always lead you to more information and resources in any given area. The Argus Clearinghouse (www.clearinghouse.net) is a library of over 600 resource guides in 12 major subject areas. You'll find it easy to search, easy to browse, and a welcome addition to your bookmarks. Through these services you can find even more employers to contact, more industry information for your notes, and many employment resources not yet added to the larger virtual libraries.

As you have been checking out the various catalogs and specialty stores looking at the merchandise which interests you, industry information, potential employers, and even some job announcements, you have been picking up on words, ideas, even products you want to explore further. Maybe you even have some manufacturers (employers) you'd like to explore in even more depth. After all, you don't want to buy a chair (job) from someone who is getting ready to go out of business nor do you want to do business with someone who has a reputation for bad materials, bad production, or bad customer service. You want to target your search for a new chair to the best producer you can find. Now is the time to start digging for the little bits of information that can make or break your search. Now we go to the search engines, those huge indexes of keywords that match us back to the pages where our words or phrases were found.

There are several good search engines you can use in your search for hidden information. AltaVista (www.altavista.digital.com) and HotBot (www.hotbot.com) both claim to index over 50 million pages of Internet information. While Lycos (www.lycos.com), InfoSeek (www.infoseek.com), and Excite (www.excite.com) don't make claims on their content, they probably cover up to ninety percent of the same resources. Which search engine should you use? Whichever one is most comfortable to you. They will all give you pretty much the same information, the difference is how you enter the terms and how you can manipulate the search to present the results you want. One of the advantages of AltaVista and HotBot is the ability to search phrases. This is a step above the simple And / Or / Not capability found in most search engines. It means the words you enter must be found on the indexed page exactly as you have entered them, not one word up here, another down there, and the third waaaaay at the end.

What exactly are we looking for with the search engines? Anything and everything. Take some of the industry terms you found in your search of the libraries and resource guides and search them here to see if you can find more definitions and applications of these words. Search some of the employers you found and see what kind of news reports, press releases, and mentions you find floating around. Search product names to pull up reviews, discussions, and complaints about these and add all of this information to your file for each. If you have an interview scheduled, search the name of the person you are interviewing with to see if you find anything interesting about him or her, like a recent professional award. You never know when something like this can come in handy.

It looks like our shopping trip has turned into a pretty involved process, but to find the best you have to know the manufacturers and their products.

To find the best employment opportunities and the best sites to target our search requires the best research. You are moving general to specific, using the libraries to begin your search and find a path, focusing on select employers and opportunities as you travel down that path using the online resource guides, and finally targeting and selecting the leading candidate through the search engines. Managed in this way your job search is no more difficult than buying a new car. The difference is once you have selected the car or the job, you now have to turn the tables and become the sales person, but that's a different article.

Tools for the Job Seeker's "KITBAG"

Dr. John Sullivan
Professor of Human Resources and Executive Coach
College of Business, San Francisco State University
e-mail - johns@sfsu.edu

As a job seeker you must think and act differently if you are going to gain a competitive advantage over others. You must find the jobs faster and sell yourself better if you are to "beat" other applicants to that great job. You must have a competitive advantage that goes beyond a simple resume and reading the want ads. Gaining a competitive advantage begins with thinking and acting differently- we call that "TOX" (Thinking Outside the boX)! Some of the "tools" listed here are simple tools while others, although they might seem unusual on the surface, are advanced "outside the box recruiter tricks" designed to give you the edge!

Basic Tools

• Using Key Words •

You might not realize it but few resumes submitted to large firms are still read by "people". Computerized scanners search all resumes looking for pre-selected "key words". Typical jobs have between 30 and 100 key words (they are generally skills, problems, management tools, and company or university names). If you don't use these key words you WILL NOT be selected for an interview! The color of the paper, nice prose and neatness won't impress a computer! To find out if they scan in resumes just call the Human Resource department and just ask if they use a scanning system (Resumix and Restrac are common brand names). If you want to know for sure how many key word "hit's" you have and you are incredibly bold ask a "friend" in HR to "run" your resume through their system. It will rank you, compared to other candidates, and tell you the keywords you hit!

• Pre-Test Your Resume •

There are a lot of stereotypes about resumes that no longer hold as a result of new technology. For example "one page only" resume rules go by the wayside when a computer is scanning your resume. There are several ways to pre-test your resume to make sure it gets you an interview. Here are a couple of ways to find out how good yours is.

Circle Test - Have several friends circle all the items in the resume that impress them put an x through all items that they don't like (or are negative), and a ? by all items that confuse them or slow them down. In a great resume the circled items should cover the top 3 problems, the top 5 skills, the minimum years of experience required and your top 5 accomplishments. Keep revising it until all the important items get circled. and all "x ed" and "? ed" items are revised,

Name that job test - Cover your name on your resume and give it to a Human Resource recruiter or a manager in your field. Give them 2 minutes to read it and ask them to "close their eyes" and "name that job" that the resume qualifies for. Then revise your resume and repeat until you have developed the most convincing resume possible for your target job. .

Ranking test - Gather together 4 resumes from friends or coworkers who are in/ or seeking the same job as you are. Ask 3-5 professionals to review the job description. Put the resumes in a stack with the names covered. Have the individuals rank the resumes from most to least qualified. Revise your resume until you consistently come out on top.

A Partnership With The Recruiter - Start your job search with a new "mindset". Stop thinking that you are a bother to the recruiter. The real truth is that YOU are the goal of their search. Recruiters want to find you. So think of it as a partnership- they want to find you as much as you want to be found. Your job in this partnership is to do your homework, find out their exact needs, then tailor the information you put in your resume and present it in your interview so that it provides them with convincing evidence (ammunition) that you meet their needs.

• Ammunition •
Many recruiters want to hire you but they can't "sell you" to their boss because you didn't provide them with the right ammunition (information).
Don't just say you can do the job prove it! Be sure to provide them with examples that show that you have a high level of the competencies and skills they need. Also show that you know the actual problems you will face in the job and that you CAN solve each one. Make a list of all of their job requirements and in simple business language show that you have their required skills and you can solve each of their problems.
A portfolio - If you were an artist, chef or musician you wouldn't try to sell your self solely based on "words". You would include brief scanable summaries or samples of your actual work (a picture, a menu or a tape). Consider providing work summaries or examples with your resume, in an e-mail, through your own web page or bring them to the interview.

• Company WOW's •
"Knowing the target company" is essential if you are to impress the recruiter. Unfortunately, reviewing the Annual report and visiting the Web page is becoming so easy to do that it does not give you a competitive advantage over others who have also read them. The real competitive advantage is knowing the "inside story" and what I call "Com-

pany WOW's! WOW's are brief "facts" that generally only an insider or an expert would know. Put a few of these in your conversation, cover letter or interview and you will definitely stand out. Wow's are generally gotten from people "who like to talk". So call salespeople (and competitors salespeople), the PR department, read their CEO's articles or speeches (call their assistant and ask for copies) or just visit the restaurant across the street at lunch and ask employees about their WOW products, plans or "problems". It's not that hard. If you are a student ask your professor for an assignment to study the company and just ask the receptionist "is there anyone who might mentor a "needy student" or just ask a friend or relative who works there.

Other possible WOW's
Say you own their stock and you follow it (Buy one share)
Tell them you bought their "newest" product and you love it
Go to one of their product presentations and tell them how great it was

• *Trying For An Out Of State Job?* •
Many companies are reluctant to interview "Non-local" candidates because of the travel costs. You might be able to overcome that obstacle by suggesting a telephone interview.

ADVANCED TOOLS

• *I Have The Solution To Your Problem!* •
If you are really bold or if realistically don't meet the job requirements you might try the "Consultants" approach. Ask around or read articles about the company and try to find the biggest problems facing the department or function you want to work in. Be bold and work out your solution to one of the problems (pre-test it on experts). Then send either an outline of your solution or a part of your solution directly to the Department head and/ or the hiring manager. Attach a brief cover page saying this is the solution they are looking for and IF THEY SEE IT WOULD WORK ñ Call you! It must be brief, easily scanable in 2 minutes and it must make them curious enough to want to call you in to see the rest! You might try it at less desirable competitors first to see if the "bait' is good enough to try on your primary target. If you are a student mail them a copy of a solution or idea and ask them to review it for you. As part of a class assignment. You might get an interview if your idea works.

• *Ask for a "Tryout"* •
Managers are always skeptical about words-they want proof. Offer to work an evening or weekend for free to show them how you perform in their operation. It is not uncommon for 1/3 of all hires to come from temporary or contract positions. So "ask for a tryout", just like in sports.

Another option is to act as a free off-site consultant on a problem and help them solve it with the expectation you would be hired at the end of the tryout!

• Get Ahead Of The Competition •

Try to find out about jobs before everyone else. Almost all companies post all jobs internally before they get on the web page. Ask any employee to share the internal posting list or look for possible jobs so you can prepare your "Sales Pitch" and have it on the managers desk before the competitors. You can generally also buy the Sunday paper on Friday night and get a day and a half jump on preparation time over regular readers. If you know a recruiter, they know about an opening when the "req." is filled out, which may be as much as three weeks before the ad appears.

• Don't Go It Alone! •

Instead of searching alone, form a job search network with 4 6 friends. Share what you learn, critique each other and in general give support. A team is more likely to have a "friend" inside the firm that can help you polish and focus your approach.

• Use Technology To Gain A Competitive Advantage •

Today there are numerous "Electronic Bulletin Boards/ Chat rooms" and Listservers (Automatic E-mail discussion groups) that allow you to ask questions about job search tools and that will let you know what the biggest problems and hottest solutions in your specific technical field. They are fast and the best in the field usually participate in them. They allow you to get exposure without having to put on a suit. Recruiters also participate, so the odds are good that you will be noticed if you post a great idea or solution.

• Plot Your Growth Rate •

If you run into a manager that is technically or "visually oriented" try giving them a "Plot" or graph of your career growth. Plot raises, great performance appraisals, new competencies, awards and promotions. Plot it on a graph and visually show your rapid and continuous career growth compared to your peers. By seeing it in a "visual" format you might get the attention of technical managers who are impressed with graphs and creativity.

• Show You Are A "Better" Hire! •

Not all employees are equal,even though they may have the same technical qualifications. Managers look (but don't always find) better employees like these:

Continuous Learners - Employees that develop and learn on their own without the need for training classes and mentors

Low Maintenance - Employees that don't need warnings, discipline or that take up management time.

Agile - Workers that can do multi-tasks simultaneously and that add to "bench strength" and fill in for other jobs in a pinch

Bar Raisers - People who continually expect and get more from themselves and those around them

TOX Thinkers - Those who think differently (outside the box) and can get others to do the same

CAREERXROADS
The 1998 Directory to the 500 Best Job, Resume amd Career Management Sites on the World Wide Web

How to use this Directory

There are no standards that dictate what a WWW job or resume site should look like, what information it should contain, how it should be organized, how the quality of that information might be measured, what means should be used to search it, deliver it or even what services might be provided.

Our organization of this Directory and our comments throughout CAREERXROADS are framed from the job seekers point of view:

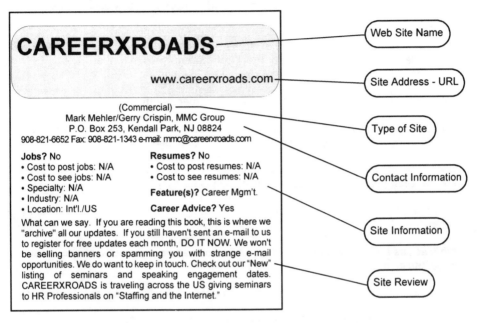

• How can I reach this site via the WWW **(URL)**? How can I reach the owners **(Contact Information)**?

• Is this site committed to providing opportunity **(JOBS)**, advice **(CAREER ADVICE)**, the means to communicate their skills and interests **(RESUME)** to others.

• How expensive **(COST)** is it to see the openings that are posted here or to submit my resume? Do employers have any restrictions or expenses associated with postings or searching for my resume?

• Are most of the jobs posted at this site organized with any critical emphasis such as the educational degree or skill requirements **(SPECIALTY)**, industry or economic sector of the economy **(Industry)**, the geographic emphasis **(LOCATION)**.

• **(COMMENTS)** Is the site easy to use? Is the information limited, extensive? How much does it cost? What else can job seekers, or employers, do to connect here?

Note to Site Owners:

We adjusted spacing to ensure your site is listed in a natural alphabetical sequence.

The 1998 Directory is organized into two distinct sections:

An *Alpha Listing* and a *Cross Reference Listing* highlight each site's features, services or areas of emphasis.

The Cross Reference Listings (See Table of Contents for page numbers) include:

• *Career Management* - Sites which emphasize information about careers, job search and counseling.

• *College* - Sites that focus primarily or exclusively on the entry level job seeker. Some sites with multiple level services have strong enough college presence that they have been included as well.

• *Diversity* - Sites that contain gender or minority career information.

• *Industry and Specialty* - Sites or specific pages on a site that only emphasize a single academic discipline, industry focus or some special emphasis

• *Jobs* - The majority of sites in this directory contain jobs. We have specifically indexed those that allow you to post your company openings for a fee or for free.

• *Location* - Sites that focus exclusively on providing services for a specific country or region of the US.

• *Publications* - The newspapers, trade publications and magazines that offer classified help wanted advertising on-line.

• *Push* - Sites that send employment related information directly to the desktop via e-mail.

• *Resumes* - Sites that post for a fee or for free.

Rating System:

We selected what we considered the **"Best of the Best"** job, resume and/or career management sites for 1998 based on several criteria. We looked at the ease of access; value of the content, navigation, business model, real world marketing strategy and general chutzpah. For 1998 we reviewed over 1,000 sites, included 500+ in this directory and designated 37 as the "Best of the Best." We included some because of what we think they will do and others we don't even like but clearly can't ignore their impact. In the end, each company and each person should judge their own best sites by the results they achieve. Expect many changes to this list in the coming months. We have designated this icon as our symbol for these sites.

100 Careers in Cyberspace

www.globalvillager.com/villager.wsc

(Commercial)
Global Communications Services, Inc.
3130 Rt. 10 West, Denville, NJ 07834
201-989-0501 Fax: 201-943-8137 e-mail: arild@pcstar.com

Jobs? Yes
• Cost to post jobs: Fee
• Cost to see jobs: Free
• Specialty: IT/Web
• Industry: All
• Location: US

Resumes? No
• Cost to post resumes: N/A
• Cost to see resumes: N/A

Feature(s)? N/A

Career Advice? Yes

100 Careers... provides direct contact information for positions and lists openings that are confidential (you have to go through the site to get to the company). Cost to post is $20 per month for 2 months, or you could look at a package for high volume. Site's search engine works well but we have not seen any changes in this site since our last review.

100 Careers in Wall Street

www.globalvillager.com/villager/csc.html

(Commercial)
Global Communications Services, Inc.
3130 Rt. 10 West, Denville, NJ 07834
201-989-0501 Fax: 201-328-9216 e-mail: arild@pcstar.com

Jobs? Yes
• Cost to post jobs: Fee
• Cost to see jobs: Free
• Specialty: Finance/Business
• Industry: Finance
• Location: US/EC/NY/NYC

Resumes? No
• Cost to post resumes: Fee
• Cost to see resumes: Free

Feature(s)? N/A

Career Advice? No

Like it's sister site (100 Careers In Cyberspace), 100 Careers in Wall Street has 70+ jobs posted and provides the job seeker with direct contact information to the employer. A search engine makes it easier to hone in on the best opportunities and, for recruiters, there are over 250 potential candidates in the site's database. The posting price for a job is $40 for two months. Candidate information has either direct contact or, in some cases, is coded for confidentiality. The job seeker is charged $15 to post a resume.

4Work

(Commercial)
Jim Burkholder, Access Influential Inc.
5650 Greenwood Plaza Blvd., Suite 250, Greenwood Village, CO 80111
800-789-0145 Fax: 303-741-9702 e-mail: recruit@4work.com

Jobs? Yes
- Cost to post jobs: Fee
- Cost to see jobs: Free
- Specialty: All
- Industry: All
- Location: US

Resumes? Yes
- Cost to post resumes: Free
- Cost to see resumes: Fee

Feature(s)? Push to Applicant, Search by State

Career Advice? Yes

4Work is a premier design. A solid search form enables the job seeker to enter the location where they wish to work (State) and the skills they posses. 4Work will then match and "push" jobs to them. For employers, the cost is $30 per month to post a job. Volunteer opportunities and internships are posted for free. Site also contains a human resource directory which houses links to numerous sites for additional help. Nice list of helpful articles on different aspects of career management and job search techniques. 4Work is a top site that understands how to give something back.

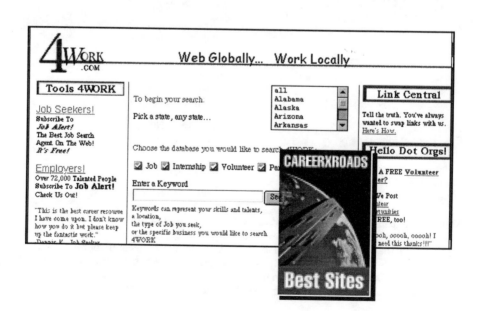

4.0 Resumes and Job Listings

www.4pt0.com/index.html

(Commercial)
e-mail: john@4.0pt0.com

Jobs? Yes
- Cost to post jobs: Free
- Cost to see jobs: Free
- Specialty: College
- Industry: All
- Location: US

Resumes? Yes
- Cost to post resumes: Free
- Cost to see resumes: Free

Feature(s)? N/A

Career Advice? No

4.0 allows college graduates to post their resumes for free. As the name implies, they ask for your GPA. Employers can post job opportunities for free and can also ask for the students GPA when they conduct a search of the resume database.

AAA Resume Service

www.infi.net/~resume

(Commercial)
Dan Carmichael, Beaman Office Building
2820 Lawndale Drive, Ste 11, Greensboro, NC 27408
800-962-4473 e-mail: resume@nr.infi.net

Jobs? No
- Cost to post jobs: N/A
- Cost to see jobs: N/A
- Specialty: All
- Industry: N/A
- Location: US

Resumes? No
- Cost to post resumes: N/A
- Cost to see resumes: N/A

Feature(s)? Career Mgm't., JSK/Resume

Career Advice? Yes

We do not typically list resume services but AAA get's the message about sharing resources. Nice list of articles and links to help the job seeker find their next opportunity. A 24 hour resume service charging $50 - $100.

Abag Globe

www.abag.ca.gov/bayarea/commerce/globe/globe.html

(Government)
Brian Kirking, Assoc. of Bay Area Governments
P.O. Box 2050, Oakland, CA 94604-2050
510-464-7900 Fax: 510-464-7970 e-mail: briank@abag.ca.gov

Jobs? Yes
• Cost to post jobs: Free
• Cost to see jobs: Free
• Specialty: All
• Industry: Government
• Location: US/W/CA/SF

Resumes? No
• Cost to post resumes: N/A
• Cost to see resumes: N/A

Feature(s)? N/A

Career Advice? Yes

Government listing of Bay Area public employment opportunities. Site gives direct contact information and salary grades. Other links that give you more detailed information on the Bay Area are also present on this site.

AboutWork

(Commercial)
Michael Rose, iVillage
170 5th Avenue, New York, NY 10010
212-604-0963 Fax: 212-604-9133 e-mail: walston@ivillage.com

Jobs? No
- Cost to post jobs: N/A
- Cost to see jobs: N/A
- Specialty: N/A
- Industry: N/A
- Location: US

Resumes? No
- Cost to post resumes: N/A
- Cost to see resumes: N/A

Feature(s)? Career Mgm't.

Career Advice? Yes

AboutWork is one of the best career management sites on the web. They do not post jobs or resumes at the site although many jobs and resumes are posted by individuals in the site's discussion groups for job hunting. Diverse, well written articles on how to get a job, manage your career, work at home or start your own dream business. A chat room is available for professionals to converse about common problems. Easy to navigate. Even has games to play when you get tired. AboutWork is one of the best in this category. Take a look.

Academe Today

www.chronicle.com

(Publisher/Trade)
Mike Snyder, The Chronicle of Higher Education
1255 23rd Street NW, Suite 700, Washington, DC 20037
800-728-2803 Fax: 202-466-1055 e-mail: circulation@chronicle.com

Jobs? Yes
- Cost to post jobs: Fee
- Cost to see jobs: Fee (Subscribe)
- Specialty: Teaching/Administration
- Industry: Education/University
- Location: US

Resumes? No
- Cost to post resumes: N/A
- Cost to see resumes: N/A

Feature(s)? N/A

Career Advice? No

All current positions listed are those published weekly in the Chronicle of Higher Education. A broad range of faculty, research, administration and executive positions. 1000+ openings are searchable by keyword and can be restricted by region. You must be a subscriber to the Chronicle to see the open positions ($75). Employers must pay for the print and internet combination.

Academic Chemistry Employment Clearinghouse

hackberry.chem.niu.edu/ChemJobText.html

(College/University)
Steven Bachrach, Northern Illinois University
e-mail: admin@hackberr.ychem.niu.edu

Jobs? Yes
- Cost to post jobs: Free
- Cost to see jobs: Free
- Specialty: Science/Chemistry
- Industry: Education/University
- Location: US

Resumes? No
- Cost to post resumes: N/A
- Cost to see resumes: N/A

Feature(s)? N/A

Career Advice? No

The Clearinghouse is a simple site. To post positions you have to e-mail them to chemjob@hackberry.chem.niu.edu. Positions will be posted for 45 days. When a position is submitted, employers receive an e-mail confirming their transmission. Nice touch. Price is right. Niche site with limited postings.

Academic Employment Network

www.academploy.com

(Commercial)
Christopher J. Gaudet
266 Gray Road, Windham, ME 04062
800-890-8283 Fax: 207-892-2614 e-mail: info@academploy.com

Jobs? Yes
- Cost to post jobs: Fee
- Cost to see jobs: Free
- Specialty: Teaching
- Industry: Education
- Location: US

Resumes? No
- Cost to post resumes: N/A
- Cost to see resumes: N/A

Feature(s)? Search by State

Career Advice? Yes

If you are looking for a position in the educational profession this is a place to add to your list. Employers pay $95 per position (30 day postings). Nice state directory for easy access to find open positions. Also information on teaching certification by each state and links to the one's that are not covered.

Academic Physician & Scientist

www.acphysci.com/aps.htm

(Association)
Martha McGarity, Academic Physician & Scientist
1185 Avenue of the Americas, New York, NY 10036
212-930-9561 Fax: 212-930-9576 e-mail: mmcgarit@nyc.lrpub.com

Jobs? Yes
- Cost to post jobs: Fee
- Cost to see jobs: Free
- Specialty: Health Care/Physician/Research
- Industry: Health Care/Education
- Location: US

Resumes? No
- Cost to post resumes: N/A
- Cost to see resumes: N/A

Feature(s)? N/A

Career Advice? No

Academic Physician & Scientist posts jobs from their magazine classified advertisements. Publication is mailed for free to every US faculty physician, scientist, senior resident and fellow at 125 US medical schools and teaching hospitals. Many senior level positions were posted on our visit. Search engine allows for easy access to find the position of your choice.

Academic Position Network

(Commercial)
Desiree Heil, 2001 Killebrew Drive
Ste. 302, Bloomington, MN 55425
612-853-9907 Fax: 612-853-0287 e-mail: apn@tc.umn.edu

Jobs? Yes
- Cost to post jobs: Fee
- Cost to see jobs: Free
- Specialty: Teaching/Academic Research
- Industry: Education
- Location: US

Resumes? No
- Cost to post resumes: N/A
- Cost to see resumes: N/A

Feature(s)? N/A

Career Advice? No

APN uses a key word search by type of position, institution and faculty description. Positions can be posted for $95. The online service claims 35,000 students and job seekers review postings each month.

AccountingNet

(Commercial)
AccountingNet
600 Stewart Street Suite 101, Seattle, WA 98101
206-441-8285 Fax: 206-441-8385 e-mail: anet@accountingnet.com

Jobs? Yes
- Cost to post jobs: Fee
- Cost to see jobs: Free
- Specialty: Finance/Accounting
- Industry: All
- Location: US

Resumes? Yes
- Cost to post resumes: Free
- Cost to see resumes: Free

Feature(s)? N/A

Career Advice? Yes

AccountingNet provides tremendous information on the accounting field. Over 500 jobs were listed on our visit. Resumes (short profiles) can be searched in detail. Recruiters pay $150 to post a job for 30 days. Site has created a discussion forum to post questions and get answers. Great start. May have a connection to major career hub.

ACM

www.acm.org/cacm/careeropps/

(Association/Publisher)
ACM
Ad Dept., 1515 Broadway, NY, NY 10036
212-869-7440 Fax: 212-869-0481 e-mail: acm-advertising@acm.org

Jobs? Yes
- Cost to post jobs: Fee
- Cost to see jobs: Free
- Specialty: IT
- Industry: Computer
- Location: US

Resumes? No
- Cost to post resumes: N/A
- Cost to see resumes: N/A

Feature(s)? N/A

Career Advice? No

Listings in the Association for Computing Machinery's (ACM) publications are posted to their website. Costs are approximately $20/line (40 characters).

ACM's Sigmod's Database Job Openings

www.acm.org/sigmod/jobs

(Association)
e-mail: sigmod@bunny.cs.uiuc.edu

Jobs? Yes
- Cost to post jobs: Free
- Cost to see jobs: Free
- Specialty: IT/Academic
- Industry: Education/University
- Location: Int'l/US

Resumes? No
- Cost to post resumes: N/A
- Cost to see resumes: N/A

Feature(s)? N/A

Career Advice? No

Sigmod only had 5 jobs posted on our most recent visit but as it is a specialty niche within the Association of Computing Machinery- there are others) and the price is free, recruiters have nothing to lose. Site archives its prior listings for months. International flavor and a University focus.

Acorn Career Counseling

www.acornresume.com

(Commercial)
Fred Nagle
8 Clay Court, Rhinebeck, NY 12572
914-876-8617 e-mail: acorn@mhv.net

Jobs? No
- Cost to post jobs: N/A
- Cost to see jobs: N/A
- Specialty: N/A
- Industry: All
- Location: US

Resumes? No
- Cost to post resumes: N/A
- Cost to see resumes: N/A

Feature(s)? Career Mgm't./Resume Service

Career Advice? Yes

Acorn Career Counseling (the Resume Doctor) gives advice on how to construct your resume. Interesting list of links to sites to post your resume for free and others for jobs to review. The Doctor posts a "defective" resume to help you analyze your own resume's strengths and weaknesses. Fred now charges $150-$300 to review your resume.

AdGuide

www.adguide.com/

(Commercial)
Adguide Publications Inc.
3722 W. 50 St., Suite 121, Minneapolis, MN 55410
800-835-4989 Fax: 612-915-1102 e-mail: adguide@adguide.com

Jobs? Yes
- Cost to post jobs: Fee
- Cost to see jobs: Free
- Specialty: College
- Industry: All
- Location: US

Resumes? No
- Cost to post resumes: N/A
- Cost to see resumes: N/A

Feature(s)? N/A

Career Advice? No

Adguide provides part-time and full time positions for college students and graduating seniors. Corporations have full page advertisements on this site with e-mail capability directly to the recruiter. Hundreds of jobs were posted on our visit within many different categories. No search engine yet, but you can easily scroll through different groupings of positions. Cost to post a position is $150 for a 3 month run. Other packages are available. A sister site can also be seen www.adguide.com/ highschool/index.html for jobs for high school students.

AdOne Classified Network

www.adone.com

(Publisher/Newspaper)
Corey Menscher, AdOne Classified Network, Inc.
361 Broadway, Suite 100, New York, NY 10013
212-965-2900 Fax: 212-334-3307 e-mail: corey@adone.com

Jobs? Yes
- Cost to post jobs: Fee
- Cost to see jobs: Free
- Specialty: All
- Industry: All
- Location: Int'l/Canada/US

Resumes? No
- Cost to post resumes: N/A
- Cost to see resumes: N/A

Feature(s)? Push to Applicant, Search by State

Career Advice? No

AdOne serves as the classified site for over 400 small market newspapers throughout the US and Canada. Most are small daily and weekly papers that have help wanted advertising. Job seekers can use an agent (Ad Hound) to identify job categories/regions and even telephone area codes to search for their next opportunity. After registering, applicants will receive e-mails listing opportunities that match their requirements. Nice product for the secondary market. Great extra value for job seekers whose desired relocation can be narrowed to an area covered by several of these small papers. This is the poor man's CareerPath.

AdSearch

www.adsearch.com

(Recruiting Related Agency)
Miller Advertising Agency
212-691-2929 e-mail: adinfo@adsearch.com

Jobs? Yes
- Cost to post jobs: Fee
- Cost to see jobs: Free
- Specialty: All
- Industry: All
- Location: US

Resumes? No
- Cost to post resumes: N/A
- Cost to see resumes: N/A

Feature(s)? N/A

Career Advice? No

Recruitment advertising agency provides a job database for their clients' openings. Applicants can search and apply online. Jobs can be placed online directly. Ads are listed for 1 month. Simple site with all levels and titles.

ADECCO

www.adia.com

(Placement Agency)
Adia Personnel Services
Redwood Shores, CA 94065
415-610-1096

Jobs? Yes
- Cost to post jobs: Fee
- Cost to see jobs: Free
- Specialty: All
- Industry: All
- Location: Int'l/US

Resumes? No
- Cost to post resumes: N/A
- Cost to see resumes: N/A

Feature(s)? N/A

Career Advice? Yes

Major placement/temporary agency with 2,400 offices in more then 40 countries. Has hundreds of positions posted through their offices with a search engine that makes it easy to find what you want. All levels/types of jobs are listed.

Adweek Online

www.adweek.com

(Publisher/Trade)
Wright Ferguson, Jr., BPI Communications Inc.
1515 Broadway, NY, NY 10036
212-536-6528 Fax: 212-536-5353 e-mail: jeffreywhi@aol.com

Jobs? Yes
- Cost to post jobs: Fee
- Cost to see jobs: Free
- Specialty: Advertising
- Industry: Advertising
- Location: US

Resumes? No
- Cost to post resumes: N/A
- Cost to see resumes: N/A

Feature(s)? N/A

Career Advice? No

Online job opportunities are listed from this weekly advertising publication. Hundreds of jobs are listed. These openings can be searched but it is somewhat cumbersome. A weekly visit may be necessary if you like it. Direct contact information is available for the job seeker.

AfricaOnline Jobs

www.AfricaOnline.com/AfricaOnline/job.html

(Commercial)
Africa Online Inc.
Africa
161-749-4021

Jobs? Yes
• Cost to post jobs: Free
• Cost to see jobs: Free
• Specialty: All
• Industry: All
• Location: Int'l/Africa

Resumes? Yes
• Cost to post resumes: Free
• Cost to see resumes: Free

Feature(s)? Diversity

Career Advice? No

Not much has changed since we last reviewed Africa Online and the site needs help. Dozens of jobs and resumes are posted but they are very difficult to find and once found, the descriptions are not clear. We hope the webmaster listens to our advice as this site has potential in a fast growing area of the world.

AgriCareers

www.agricareers.com

(Publisher/Trade)
519-843-5688 Fax: 519-843-6808 e-mail: sanedra@agricareers.om

Jobs? Yes
• Cost to post jobs: Fee
• Cost to see jobs: Free
• Specialty: All
• Industry: Agriculture
• Location: Int'l./Canada

Resumes? Yes
• Cost to post resumes: Free
• Cost to see resumes: Free

Feature(s)? N/A

Career Advice? Yes

Agri Careers is a monthly publication that posts it's print career opportunities section on this website. A career forum allows job seekers to post their resumes and ask questions of the industry. Jobs are posted by dozens of employers across the country. Site also has links to Canadian career sites.

Agricultural Job Listings

caticsuf.csufresno.edu:70/1/atinet/agjobs

(College/University)
Calif. State U. at Fresno
CA

Jobs? Yes
- Cost to post jobs: Free
- Cost to see jobs: Free
- Specialty: Science/Agriculture
- Industry: Agriculture
- Location: US/W/CA

Resumes? No
- Cost to post resumes: N/A
- Cost to see resumes: N/A

Feature(s)? Yes

Career Advice? No

Agri Careers is a monthly publication that posts it's print career opportunities section on this website. A career forum allows job seekers to post their resumes and ask questions of the industry. Jobs are posted by dozens of employers across the country. Site also has links to Canadian career sites.

AIP Physics Careers Bulletin Board

www.aip.org

(Association)
American Institute of Physics
Career Services Division, One Physics Ellipse, College Park, MD 20740
301-209-3190 Fax: 301-209-0841 e-mail: csv@aip.org

Jobs? Yes
- Cost to post jobs: Fee
- Cost to see jobs: Free
- Specialty: Science/Physics
- Industry: N/A
- Location: US

Resumes? No
- Cost to post resumes: N/A
- Cost to see resumes: N/A

Feature(s)? N/A

Career Advice? No

If you are looking for a job in physics or hoping to locate a physics major for your company opening, AIP's site needs to be in your package. The cost to submit a job is $38 (for up to 10 lines for a 4 week posting). When you enter the site you must go to Career Services to see Job Opportunities. Dozens of academic and corporate positions are listed. Direct contact information is provided and recruiters can also purchase links directly to their sites.

Airline Employment Ass't. Corps

www.avjobs.com

(Association)
T. Lahey, AEAC
P.O. Box 462151, Aurora, CO 80046
303-683-2322 Fax: 303-683-2322 e-mail: sales@aeac.com

Jobs? Yes
- Cost to post jobs: Free
- Cost to see jobs: Fee
- Specialty: All
- Industry: Aviation
- Location: US

Resumes? Yes
- Cost to post resumes: Fee
- Cost to see resumes: Free

Feature(s)? N/A

Career Advice? Yes

Great niche site for the airline industry. Members are charged $10 to join and then can post their resume and look at open positions. Employers can post openings for free. AEAC provides information on obtaining a career in the industry. Easy to use, AEAC is a must if this is your interest.

Airwaves MediaWeb

www.airwaves.com

(Commercial)
William Pfeiffer, Airwaves Media
P.O. Box 8746, Springfield, MO 65801
e-mail: wdp@airwaves.com

Jobs? Yes
- Cost to post jobs: Free
- Cost to see jobs: Free
- Specialty: Entertainment/Radio Broadcasting
- Industry: Entertainment
- Location: US

Resumes? Yes
- Cost to post resumes: Free
- Cost to see resumes: Free

Feature(s)? N/A

Career Advice? No

Airwaves MediaWeb archives old radio show scripts for it's visitors along with a free job postings and a free resume database. Great links to other radio stations and they ask for nominations for additional links. Job seekers resume includes a live e-mail hyperlink.

Alexus

(Commercial)
Troy Green, Alexus
555 Quince Orchard Road, Suite 480, Gaithersburg, MD 20878-1437
301-721-1311 Fax: 301-417-0500 e-mail: greent@alexus.com

Jobs? No
- Cost to post jobs: N/A
- Cost to see jobs: N/A
- Specialty: All
- Industry: All
- Location: US

Resumes? No
- Cost to post resumes: N/A
- Cost to see resumes: N/A

Feature(s)? RT/Aptrack

Career Advice? No

Alexus has developed technology to support web-based, applicant resume databases for private use by Alexus' clients. Employers can see all the resumes meant for them from anywhere in the world and Alexus guarantees that they will not share them with any of their other clients. They also solicit resumes from outside vendors. Simple, easy to access. Standard screens make this supplier an up and coming player in the optical scanning game. Minimal reporting capability but, Alexus is willing to do some customization. Price is relatively inexpensive. One of several new entries as an alternative to in-house applicant tracking.

All Campus In-Sites

www.allcampus.com

(Commercial)
Michelle DePue, Allcampus Media
26 Castillian Drive, Santa Barbara, CA 93117
805-968-8007 Fax: 805-968-8003 e-mail: info@marketmedia.com

Jobs? No
- Cost to post jobs: N/A
- Cost to see jobs: N/A
- Specialty: College
- Industry: All
- Location: US

Resumes? No
- Cost to post resumes: N/A
- Cost to see resumes: N/A

Feature(s)? JSK/Links

Career Advice? Yes

Commercial site with product branding and other activities for college students. Banners and recruitment postings are available. Nice list of links to other college related sites. When you get tired from all of those exams you can link to the sites that have games to play.

CAREERXROADS©
Job, Resume & Career Management Sites on the World Wide Web
• The 1998 Directory •

- 61 -

Allied Health Opportunities Directory

(Publisher/Trade)
Kathleen Czermanski, Great Valley Publishing Company
1288 Valley Forge Rd, Ste., Valley Forge, PA 19482
800-278-4400 Fax: 610-917-9041 e-mail: admin@gvpub.com

Jobs? Yes
- Cost to post jobs: Fee
- Cost to see jobs: Free
- Specialty: Health Care/Allied Health
- Industry: Health Care
- Location: US

Resumes? No
- Cost to post resumes: N/A
- Cost to see resumes: N/A

Feature(s)? N/A

Career Advice? No

This allied health care publisher posts positions and then links the applicant to the employers site for more information. Cumbersome process. About a dozen positions were listed on our last visit and they ranged from cardiovascular technologists to surgeon assistants. Obviously, the publisher is not posting all positions that appear in print.

America's Employers: The Job Seekers Home

www.americasemployers.com

(Commercial)
Rose Emerson, Career Relo Corp. of America
630 Third Avenue, New York, NY 10017
212-681-6800 Fax: 212-681-6818 e-mail: profserv@americasemployers.com

Jobs? Yes
- Cost to post jobs: Fee
- Cost to see jobs: Free
- Specialty: All
- Industry: All
- Location: US

Resumes? Yes
- Cost to post resumes: Fee
- Cost to see resumes: Fee

Feature(s)? N/A

Career Advice? Yes

Start with the guided tour for a summary of the information and services available on each "floor" - be sure to get all your job search essentials in order! The site states there are 55,000 advertised positions and a company database with over 40,000 employers for you to explore. Try their electronic networking forums where many job seekers have developed new contacts and employment leads. You can also evaluate more than 1,000 recruiters and peruse entrepreneurial options. To jumpstart your job search, take the time to post your confidential profile into their resume bank. If you'd like to participate in one of America's Employers' "real-time" job search seminars, stop into career chat to download your free chat software and check the latest schedule. Enhance your efforts by visiting Rooms With A View. Fees for employers to post on the site range from $120 for a 60 day posting to $5000 for a year long subscription. Unique to this site is a new interactive interview chat room where employers can conduct online interviews with job seekers. While these interviews do not replace face-to-face meetings, they do raise some interesting possibilities. For example this is an excellent opportunity for employers to remotely talk to a group of students prior to a campus visit and for the students to get the lowdown on a company's culture and opportunities prior to signing up for an on campus interview. Employers could advertise the time and place of their "live" meeting to students through the campus' newspaper.

America's Job Bank

www.ajb.dni.us

(Government)
US Government

Jobs? Yes
- Cost to post jobs: Free
- Cost to see jobs: Free
- Specialty: All
- Industry: All
- Location: US

Resumes? No
- Cost to post resumes: N/A
- Cost to see resumes: N/A

Feature(s)? Search by State

Career Advice? Yes

A huge searchable database of job listings from across the country developed for the government's 2,000+ employment offices. This site claims to have 400,000+ jobs. To post jobs, recruiters can forward positions through the local unemployment office or get a password and go direct. The Equal Employment Advisory Council issued the following notice in 1996: "Three of the Labor Department's offices, the OFCCP, the Office of Veteran's Affairs, and the Employment Training Administration, have agreed that using the AJB can satisfy job posting requirements under the particular regulating authority". The EEOC is running several regional seminars on the use of the AJB. Contact Annie Blackwell at 202-789-8650. Biggest flaw is how few folks are aware of this site's value. Employers should remember that job seekers will go anywhere they think they might find helpful leads. This is a big one. Another problem is that some state's provide contact info- others do not. Try their search engine. Very nice in its simplicity. Also contains useful articles on how to use the web for a job search. Long term, AJB will be a contender for top honors. It can only get better.

America's Online Help Wanted

(Commercial)
Karla Ward
2900 Delk Road, Suite 700-278, Marietta, GA 30067
770-951-0325 Fax: 770-850-0671 e-mail: ceedub@ohw.com

Jobs? Yes
- Cost to post jobs: Fee
- Cost to see jobs: Free
- Specialty: IT
- Industry: All
- Location: US

Resumes? Yes
- Cost to post resumes: Free
- Cost to see resumes: Fee

Feature(s)? N/A

Career Advice? No

America's Online Help Wanted specializes in IT recruiting and is concentrating in major US cities (Boston, Chicago, NY, Raleigh/Durham, Charlotte, LA, SF and Washington D.C.) areas. Job seekers post a listing of their skills for free and recruiters can view the data and select who they want to contact once they register. Cost to post an unlimited number of jobs is around $325 depending on the city you choose. Site claims to have lists of user groups in each state but we came up empty on each try. Also advised us that they are sending out 150-200 resumes a month. Simple niche site in an area that cannot get enough candidates and one wonders how long the wave will continue.

America's Talent Bank

(Government)
US Dept of Labor and State Gov.
e-mail: mt02633@navix.net

Jobs? No
- Cost to post jobs: N/A
- Cost to see jobs: N/A
- Specialty: All
- Industry: All
- Location: US

Resumes? Yes
- Cost to post resumes: Free
- Cost to see resumes: Free

Feature(s)? Search by State

Career Advice? No

America's Talent Bank is the government's nationwide resume database that can be searched electronically by employers to find qualified candidates for their openings. Every "One Stop" State Employment Center, where individuals looking for employment can connect, have included in their contract with the US Dept. of Labor, a commitment to implement America's Talent Bank as part of their state's overall effort to supporting the labor market. The prototype and development of ATB was piloted in 1997 by 9 states. Many major resume databases will be impacted by this system as employers and job seekers recognize its value. This is CAREERXROADS sleeper of the year.

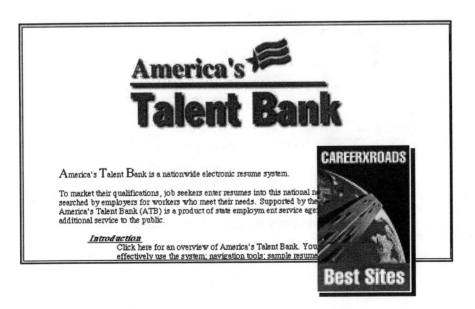

America's TV JobNetwork

www.tvjobnet.com

(Commercial)
Bruce Billow, 7250 Westfield Avenue
Pennsauken, NJ 08110
609-665-5600 Fax: 609-665-0055 e-mail: info@tvjobnet.com

Jobs? Yes
- Cost to post jobs: Fee
- Cost to see jobs: Free
- Specialty: All
- Industry: All
- Location: US/NE/NJ/PA

Resumes? Yes
- Cost to post resumes: Fee
- Cost to see resumes: Free

Feature(s)? N/A

Career Advice? Yes

This Pennsylvania/New Jersey television show lists job opportunities and gives career guidance. The show appears on Philadelphia public television on Saturday mornings and on cable stations 23 times a week. For recruiters, the resume database on their web site is free while applicants pay $19.95 for having their resume listed for six months. Employers pay $25 per job to post positions and there are packages to get your job shown on the television show. Look for more of this advertising media in your area.

American Assoc. of Fin & Accounting

www.aafa.com/

(Placement Agency)
American Assoc. of Finance & Accounting
e-mail: mrklink@marketlink.com

Jobs? Yes
- Cost to post jobs: Fee
- Cost to see jobs: Free
- Specialty: Finance/Accounting
- Industry: All
- Location: US

Resumes? No
- Cost to post resumes: N/A
- Cost to see resumes: N/A

Feature(s)? JSK & RT/Links

Career Advice? Yes

Network of 250 search firms that specialize in placing accounting/finance professionals. Site has a search engine and states that jobs are posted. However, every time we did a search, we were advised that "no jobs are listed this time". Good place to obtain a lengthy list of search firms for this field.

American Astronomical Society

(Association)
Dawn-Marie Craig, American Astronomical Society
2000 Florida Ave., Suite 400, Washington, DC 20009
202-328-2010 Fax: 202-234-2560 e-mail: aas@aas.org

Jobs? Yes
- Cost to post jobs: Fee
- Cost to see jobs: Free
- Specialty: Science/Astronomy
- Industry: Education/University
- Location: US

Resumes? No
- Cost to post resumes: N/A
- Cost to see resumes: N/A

Feature(s)? N/A

Career Advice? Yes

The American Astronomical Society has been in existence since 1899 and includes opportunities specifically for Astronomers. Many postdoctoral positions are listed from all over the world. Simple site that could use a search engine to improve it's effectiveness.

American Chemical Society Job Bank

(Association/Publisher)
Matt McCloskey, American Chemical Society
Classified Advertising, 676 East Swedesford Road, Wayne, PA 19087
610-964-8061 Fax: 610-964-8071 e-mail: mccloske@acs.org

Jobs? Yes
- Cost to post jobs: Fee
- Cost to see jobs: Free
- Specialty: Science/Chemistry
- Industry: All
- Location: US

Resumes? Yes
- Cost to post resumes: Fee
- Cost to see resumes: Free

Feature(s)? N/A

Career Advice? No

Members of the ACS can post free advertisements up to 35 words. All other positions listed are from the Chemical & Engineering News which has a $460 minimum cost per advertisement. If you are looking for chemical engineers this is the place to shop. Make sure ads listed in the C&E News get this internet component. Future plans for ACS member job seekers includes the ability to post their resumes confidentially for a $40 fee (this should be available on the web by the beginning of 1998).

American Journalism Review Online

www.newslink.org/joblink.html

(Association)
Ernie Durso, American Journalism Review
Univ. of Maryland Foundation, 8701 Adelphi Road, Adelphi, MD 20783
301-431-4771 Fax: 301-431-0097 e-mail: akrohn@ajr.umd.edu

Jobs? Yes
- Cost to post jobs: Free
- Cost to see jobs: Free
- Specialty: Journalism
- Industry: Publishing
- Location: US

Resumes? Yes
- Cost to post resumes: Free
- Cost to see resumes: Free

Feature(s)? JSK

Career Advice? No

This site is a joint venture between the American Journalism Review and NewsLink Associates, a research, consulting and publishing firm. This could be one of the best online niche sites for journalism positions. Job postings and resume postings are free. They incorporate a speedy search engine to make it easier to find what you want. On our last visit there were dozens of resumes and jobs posted and all had direct contact information. If you can place your advertisement unassisted, it is free. If you need help, there is a $50 charge. You also receive free search keywords, free reply info and if you desire a free hyperlink. Ads stay online for 30 days. Site also has 4,500 links to newspapers, magazines and news services which recruiters and job seekers may need as a resource in their hunt for the best person or opportunity.

American Physical Therapy Assoc.

apta.edoc.com

(Association)
American Physical Therapy Association
1111 North Fairfax Street, Alexandria, VA 22314
703-684-2782 Fax: 703-684-7343

Jobs? No
- Cost to post jobs: N/A
- Cost to see jobs: N/A
- Specialty: Health Care/Physical Therapy
- Industry: Health Care
- Location: US

Resumes? No
- Cost to post resumes: N/A
- Cost to see resumes: N/A

Feature(s)? Career Mgm't.

Career Advice? Yes

If you want to learn about being a physical therapist, this is the site to visit. Lots of career information including: how to obtain your license and how to join the APTA national association with over 72,000 members. Site has a search engine but it is for finding articles. There are no jobs posted. Keep watching.

American Soc. of Agricultural Eng.

asae.org/jobs

(Association)
Jackie Elowsky, ASAE
2950 Niles Road, St. Joseph, MI 49085
616-428-6324 Fax: 616-429-3852 e-mail: elowsky@asae.org

Jobs? No
- Cost to post jobs: N/A
- Cost to see jobs: N/A
- Specialty: Engineering/Agricultural
- Industry: Agriculture
- Location: US/MW

Resumes? No
- Cost to post resumes: N/A
- Cost to see resumes: N/A

Feature(s)? JSK/Links

Career Advice? No

Over 230 links to many of the common job sites but a few...are really different. Owner publishes Resource, a magazine which is geared to the engineering community but does not post jobs on their website.

American Society for Quality

www.asq.org

(Association)
ASQC
611 East Wisconsin Ave., Milwaukee, WI 53201
414-272-8575 Fax: 414-248-1948

Jobs? Yes
- Cost to post jobs: Fee
- Cost to see jobs: Free
- Specialty: QA/QC
- Industry: All
- Location: US

Resumes? No
- Cost to post resumes: N/A
- Cost to see resumes: N/A

Feature(s)? N/A

Career Advice? No

Information about ISO-9000 standards and listings for ASQC chapters is the centerpoint of this site. It took some searching to find the jobs here because they are not readily apparent from the home page. But, once found, dozens of opportunities are posted from all over the US. Positions are categorized by region and include direct contact information. Also check out their home page www.asqc.org for more information.

American Water Works Association

www.awwa.org

(Association)
Charles Berberich, American Water Works Association
6666 West Quincy Avenue, Denver, CO 80235
303-794-7711 e-mail: cberberi@awwa.org

Jobs? Yes
- Cost to post jobs: Free
- Cost to see jobs: Free
- Specialty: Environmental
- Industry: Water
- Location: US

Resumes? No
- Cost to post resumes: N/A
- Cost to see resumes: N/A

Feature(s)? Push to Applicant

Career Advice? No

A simple site that gets the job done. Jobs can be e-mailed to the AWWA site and are posted in 2-3 days for free. A tremendous amount of industry information is available as well as links to industry associations. All members registering are e-mailed ALL job openings. On our visit only 7 positions were listed but this is definitely a place to look for someone with this technical experience.

Anchorage Daily News

www.adn.com/classifieds/jobs.html

(Publisher/Newspaper)
David Kelley, Anchorage News
1001 Northway Drive, Anchorage, AK 99508
907-257-4293 e-mail: dkelley@pop.adn.com

Jobs? Yes
- Cost to post jobs: Fee
- Cost to see jobs: Free
- Specialty: All
- Industry: N/A
- Location: US/NW/AL/Anchorage

Resumes? No
- Cost to post resumes: N/A
- Cost to see resumes: N/A

Feature(s)? N/A

Career Advice? No

This site posts classified help wanted advertising. Direct contact information is just like reading the newspaper. Positions wanted are also posted and on our visit the link was not working. Simple site for a very tough market ...Alaska. An interesting feature is that you can subscribe to get the paper e-mailed to you.

the Antenna's Internet Broadcast Jobs

www.theAntenna.com

(Commercial)
theAntenna
120 Garfield Place, Suite 402, Cincinnati, OH 45202-1916
513-241-1440 Fax: 513-241-2440

Jobs? Yes
- Cost to post jobs: Free
- Cost to see jobs: Free
- Specialty: Entertainment/Broadcasting
- Industry: Entertainment
- Location: US

Resumes? No
- Cost to post resumes: N/A
- Cost to see resumes: N/A

Feature(s)? N/A

Career Advice? No

"the Antenna's Internet Broadcast Jobs" has positions in TV/cable, print journalism and even one for an "Uncle Weatherbee" (Some of us still remember who he was). Jobs can be posted for free and there were about a dozen at all levels and in many different areas on our last visit.

The Appointments Section

www.taps.com

(Commercial)
Internet App't. LTD.
United Kingdom
441-712-2195 e-mail: taps-feedback@taps.com

Jobs? Yes
- Cost to post jobs: Fee
- Cost to see jobs: Free
- Specialty: All
- Industry: All
- Location: Int'l/UK

Resumes? Yes
- Cost to post resumes: Free
- Cost to see resumes: Fee

Feature(s)? N/A

Career Advice? Yes

This UK site is shared by more than 75 corporations. Simple effective search engine lets you respond to help wanted advertisements from the newspapers regarding each of these companies or search broadly for any job that meets your career interests. Lots of features to help individuals who want to work in England.

ApView

(Commercial)
Even Brande, Aspen Tree Software, Inc.
700 Grand Avenue, P.O. Box 1347, Laramie, WY 82070
307-721-5888 Fax: 307-721-2135 e-mail: evenb@aspentree.com

Jobs? No
- Cost to post jobs: N/A
- Cost to see jobs: N/A
- Specialty: All
- Industry: All
- Location: US

Resumes? No
- Cost to post resumes: N/A
- Cost to see resumes: N/A

Feature(s)? RT/AppScreening

Career Advice? N/A

A telephone interview screening service (interactive voice recognition system) that has gone to the net. Apview features detailed pre-screening programs where employers can set the questions to keep in or screen out candidates that do not meet job criteria. While this is not a low cost solution, Apview is geared for larger organizations that are trying to organize high-volume recruiting, the use of automated screening software can reduce the labor...and cost involved in processing large numbers of applications.

Arizona Careers Online

(Commercial)
Rich Watson, Diverse Data
287-2 North Meyer Ave., Tucson, AR 85701
520-884-1320 Fax: 520-791-0955 e-mail: aztu@azstarnet.com

Jobs? Yes
- Cost to post jobs: Fee
- Cost to see jobs: Free
- Specialty: All
- Industry: All
- Location: US/SW/AR

Resumes? Yes
- Cost to post resumes: Fee
- Cost to see resumes: Free

Feature(s)? Diversity

Career Advice? Yes

Arizona Careers Online has loads of information about the area and provides links to SW colleges and job hotlines. Part of the Help Wanted-USA Network, (see Help Wanted-USA), employers can post jobs for $95/2 weeks while also searching their resume database for a fee. Cost to post a resume for several months is a hefty $89.95 but includes a service to send it to over 700 locations. If you decide to check into this ask "Where exactly is my resume going ?" (You want to know that so you have at least some control or think you do).

Asia-Net

(Commercial)
Dale Bowen-President
603 Mission Street, Santa Cruz, CA 95060
408-469-0781 Fax: 408-469-0782 e-mail: sales@asia-net.com

Jobs? Yes
- Cost to post jobs: Fee
- Cost to see jobs: Free
- Specialty: All
- Industry: All
- Location: Int'l./US

Resumes? Yes
- Cost to post resumes: Free
- Cost to see resumes: Fee

Feature(s)? Push to Applicant, Diversity/ Bi-lingual

Career Advice? No

A must see for recruiters, Asia-Net is one of our favorites as it has stayed true to it's niche and continues to expand. If you speak English and either Japanese, Chinese or Korean and are seeking employment throughout the world this is one site to visit. They claim to have 20,000+ addresses of bi-lingual professionals and will e-mail them an employer's job specification for a fee ($795 for a domestic position and $995 for an international opening). The perfect example of our maxim "Whoever has the most e-mails- wins". Dale Bowen, the site's president, was among the first to recognize the "community" he could build by obtaining permission to communicate in a narrow way and then keeping his word.

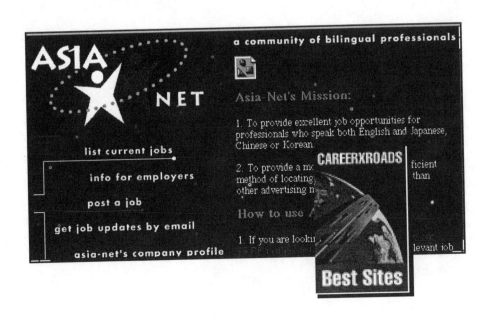

Asian Career Web

www.rici.com/acw

(Job Fair)
David Zing, International Career Information, Inc.
111 Pavonia Avenue, Jersey City, NJ 07310
800-859-8535 e-mail: dzing@rici.com

Jobs? Yes
- Cost to post jobs: Fee
- Cost to see jobs: Free
- Specialty: N/A
- Industry: N/A
- Location: Int'l/US

Resumes? Yes
- Cost to post resumes: Free
- Cost to see resumes: Fee

Feature(s)? Push to Applicant, Diversity

Career Advice? Yes

ICI is a Japanese firm with high visibility in the recruitment field in Asia. In the US, ICI conducts specialized Job Fairs for Asian nationals. ICI has enhanced its Asian Career Web site. Job seekers can have a profile matched against postings, post a resume for review and register anonymously so that employers cannot see their personal contact information.

Association for Women in Computing

www.halcyon.com/awc/

(Association)
Association for Women in Computing
41 Sutter Street, Ste. 1006, San Francisco, CA 94104
415-905-4663 e-mail: awc@acm.org

Jobs? Yes
- Cost to post jobs: N/A
- Cost to see jobs: N/A
- Specialty: IT
- Industry: All
- Location: US

Resumes? No
- Cost to post resumes: N/A
- Cost to see resumes: N/A

Feature(s)? Diversity

Career Advice? No

This gender-based web is part of a national association; there are links to local chapters in many cities whose job posting policies (and content) vary. From the recruiters standpoint, the chapters are a good resource for potential job postings and candidates. An additional feature is a short list of links to other women's technical organizations.

Association of Online Professionals

(Association)
Susan Merkel, Association of Online Professionals
7578 B Telegraph Road, Alexandria, VA 22315
703-924-9692 Fax: 703-924-9594 e-mail: meraop@aol.com

Jobs? Yes
- Cost to post jobs: Free
- Cost to see jobs: Free
- Specialty: IT/WWW/Communications
- Industry: Computer/Communications
- Location: US

Resumes? No
- Cost to post resumes: N/A
- Cost to see resumes: N/A

Feature(s)? Push to Applicant

Career Advice? No

AOP does things a little differently and will e-mail employer openings to their members. Jobs that are pushed out include: webmasters, systems operators, etc. All recruiters need to do is e-mail a description of the opening with the contact information and AOP will post it in their weekly electronic newsletter. Nice free service for AOP members.

ATI-Net

(College/University)
Saeed Awan, California Agricultural Technology Institute
2910 E. Barstow Avenue, M/S 115, Fresno, CA 93740
209-278-2361 Fax: 209-278-4849 e-mail: webmaster@atinet.org

Jobs? Yes
- Cost to post jobs: Free
- Cost to see jobs: Free
- Specialty: Science/Agriculture
- Industry: Agriculture
- Location: US

Resumes? No
- Cost to post resumes: N/A
- Cost to see resumes: N/A

Feature(s)? N/A

Career Advice? No

Advanced Technology Information Network is a unit of the California Agricultural Technology Institute at California State University, Fresno. In addition to agricultural information, the site posts dozens of jobs for professionals in education, management, research, sales & marketing. Positions cover part-time/seasonal and temporary.

Atlanta ComputerJobs Store

www.computerjobs.com

(Commercial)
Michael K. Gilfillan, The Computer Jobs Store, Inc.
2000 Powers Ferry Road, St 300, Atlanta, GA 30067
770-850-0045 e-mail: info@computerjobs.com

Jobs? Yes
- Cost to post jobs: Fee
- Cost to see jobs: Free
- Specialty: IT
- Industry: N/A
- Location: US/SE/GA/Atlanta/TX/Dallas/IL/ Chicago/Carolina

Resumes? Yes
- Cost to post resumes: Free
- Cost to see resumes: Fee

Feature(s)? N/A

Career Advice? No

Computer Jobs Store lists positions by job title. On our visit there were 1,815 jobs posted. The site also has a great list of employer profiles with contact info. Another listing of local and regional user groups includes e-mail addresses and is a great networking tool for someone looking for a job or for candidates. Similar computer stores have been created for the Carolinas, Texas and Chicago.

> www.carolina.computerjobs.com has 183 jobs listed.
> www.chicago.computerjobs.com has 373 jobs listed.
> www.texas.computerjobs.com has 826 jobs posted on our last visit. Recruiters can post a job for $30 a week but must advertise on a monthly basis to access the resume database.

Au Pair in Europe

www.princeent.com

(Placement Agency)
John/Corine Prince
P.O. Box 68056, Blakeley Postal Outlet, Hamilton, Ontario L8M3M7
905-545-6305 Fax: 905-544-4121 e-mail: aupair@princeent.com

Jobs? Yes
- Cost to post jobs: N/A
- Cost to see jobs: N/A
- Specialty: Household/Caretaker
- Industry: N/A
- Location: Int'l

Resumes? No
- Cost to post resumes: Fee
- Cost to see resumes: N/A

Feature(s)? N/A

Career Advice? No

If you want to take care of children and see Europe for the summer this is the place with an opportunity for you. Au Pair charges $295 for their services. Some interesting statistics are presented on the site regarding the different requirements and salaries between the countries in Europe. You can select from 16 different countries.

Auditions Online

www.auditions.com

(Commercial)
e-mail: stephen@auditions.com

Jobs? Yes
• Cost to post jobs: Free
• Cost to see jobs: Free
• Specialty: Entertainment
• Industry: Entertainment
• Location: US/W/CA

Resumes? No
• Cost to post resumes: N/A
• Cost to see resumes: N/A

Feature(s)? N/A

Career Advice? No

Interesting guide to acting calls in the Los Angeles and San Francisco areas. This site allows you to e-mail a casting call to the site's owners and post it for free. Auditions Online includes an actor's chatroom where you can find out the latest and greatest regarding your craft. Great concept and we were disappointed to see that it had not been updated in six months. This site "coulda been a contenda."

Augusta Chronicle

www.augustachronicle.com

(Publisher/Newspaper)
725 Broad Street, P.O. Box 1928, Augusta, GA 30902
706-724-0851 Fax: 704-724-0772

Jobs? Yes
• Cost to post jobs: Fee
• Cost to see jobs: Free
• Specialty: All
• Industry: N/A
• Location: US/SE/GA/Augusta

Resumes? No
• Cost to post resumes: N/A
• Cost to see resumes: N/A

Feature(s)? N/A

Career Advice? No

Classified job advertisements from the Sunday Augusta Chronicle are posted on this site. It is amazing that you can see Sunday's help wanted advertising on Saturday and get a leg up on your competition. Lots of graphics so be prepared for a slow view. No search engine. You have to scroll down through each ad... and they are not in alphabetical order.

Aviation Employee Placement Service

(Commercial)
Sysops, Inc.
P.O. Box 550010, Ft. Lauderdale, FL 33355
954-472-6684 Fax: 954-472-8524 e-mail: aeps@sysops.com

Jobs? Yes
- Cost to post jobs: Free
- Cost to see jobs: Fee
- Specialty: Airline Pilots
- Industry: Aviation
- Location: US

Resumes? Yes
- Cost to post resumes: Fee
- Cost to see resumes: Free

Feature(s)? N/A

Career Advice? Yes

The cost to post your resume is free... for the first 10 days and then the charge is $29.95. Corporations can post their jobs for free. Members can see current jobs while non-members can see positions that are older then 30 days. A very interesting approach to getting new members. Good niche design. More information about the activity on this site would support our push for "truth in hype" and let job-seekers who want to pay make more informed decisions.

Bakery-Net

(Commercial)
Profit.Net, Inc.
Naperville, IL 60565
e-mail: steve@bakery-net.com

Jobs? Yes
- Cost to post jobs: Free
- Cost to see jobs: Free
- Specialty: All
- Industry: Food/Bakery
- Location: US

Resumes? Yes
- Cost to post resumes: Free
- Cost to see resumes: Free

Feature(s)? N/A

Career Advice? Yes

Bakery-Net provides free services for bakery owners, managers and their advertisers. You must register to get in and they ask a ton of questions regarding what type of operation you have or will have as this is great information for the site's sponsors who are looking to sell products. You will receive a password (we hope you like pastries as one of them will be your password). All types of positions are posted and the date of posting is prominently shown. Could this site be a rising star?

BAMTA

www.mlds.arc.nasa.gov:80/BAMTA/

(Commercial)
Dr. Susie W. Chu, Broad Alliance for Multimedia Technology
e-mail: chu@mlds.arc.nasa.gov

Jobs? Yes
- Cost to post jobs: Free
- Cost to see jobs: Free
- Specialty: IT/Multimedia
- Industry: High Technology
- Location: US/W/CA

Resumes? No
- Cost to post resumes: N/A
- Cost to see resumes: N/A

Feature(s)? N/A

Career Advice? No

Broad Alliance for Multimedia Technology provides a job bank for multimedia and web technology positions. Recruiters can post jobs for free while job seekers can view them for free as well. Site has partnered with the Virtual Job Fair.

Be the Boss

www.betheboss.com

(Recruiting Related Agency)
TMP Worldwide
e-mail: btbfeedback@betheboss.com

Jobs? No
- Cost to post jobs: N/A
- Cost to see jobs: N/A
- Specialty: All
- Industry: All
- Location: US

Resumes? No
- Cost to post resumes: N/A
- Cost to see resumes: N/A

Feature(s)? JSK/Franchise

Career Advice? No

Franchise information on all types of businesses is available at this site for the prospective entrepreneur to browse. Approximately 75 businesses are linked to this site. For those who are tired of the corporate rat race, fantasizing about working for yourself and wondering what all that money you have from your "early out" will buy, here's a place to play.

BenefitsLink

www.benefitslink.com/

(Commercial)
David Rhett Parker
201 South Orange Avenue, Suite 1225, Orlando, FL 32801
407-841-3717 Fax: 407-841-3054 e-mail: erisa@benefitslink.com

Jobs? Yes
- Cost to post jobs: Fee
- Cost to see jobs: Free
- Specialty: Human Resources/Benefits
- Industry: All
- Location: US

Resumes? No
- Cost to post resumes: N/A
- Cost to see resumes: N/A

Feature(s)? Push to Applicant

Career Advice? No

If ERISA or 401K are your cup of tea, then this site could provide your next job opportunity. Benefits positions are listed here and the cost for recruiters to post is $150 for a 60 day listing. With their "Agent", BenefitsLink will push job content out to over 600 job seekers who have registered. The message board where questions can be posed about the latest benefit regulation and answers found is one of the oldest and best on the net. BenefitsLink offers helpful articles and provides an e-mail address database for anyone who chooses to register.

Best Bets for Summer Abroad

www.cie.uci.edu/~cie/staff/index.html

(College/University)
UCI Center for International Education
Univ. of California, Irvine
1010 Student Services II, Irvine, CA 92697-2476
714-824-8657 Fax: 714-824-3832 e-mail: cie@uci.edu

Jobs? Yes
- Cost to post jobs: Free
- Cost to see jobs: Free
- Specialty: College
- Industry: N/A
- Location: Int'l.

Resumes? No
- Cost to post resumes: N/A
- Cost to see resumes: N/A

Feature(s)? N/A

Career Advice? Yes

Learn about summer job opportunities abroad.

Best Jobs U.S.A.

www.bestjobsusa.com

(Recruiting Related Agency)
Gisele Matarese, Recourse Communications, Inc.
1655 Palm Beach Lakes Blvd., West Palm Beach, FL 33401
561-686-6800 Fax: 561-686-6796 e-mail: rci@bestjobsusa.com

Jobs? Yes
- Cost to post jobs: Fee
- Cost to see jobs: Free
- Specialty: All
- Industry: N/A
- Location: US

Resumes? No
- Cost to post resumes: Free
- Cost to see resumes: Fee

Feature(s)? N/A

Career Advice? Yes

Best Jobs promotes it's own job fairs and it's publication Employment Review. Employers pay $75 per job posting. Some interesting career information and surveys are listed here. The owner of the site, Recourse Communications, is in the business of publishing, recruitment advertising, executive search as well as conducting job fairs. (If one thing doesn't work, they'll sell you something else). Caveat Emptor- when you place your resume on a web site, confirm who is going to see it and where it is going to wind up. You want to have as much control as possible.

Bilingual-Jobs

www.bilingual-jobs.com

(Commercial)
Wilson Lee, International Consulting Group
P.O. Box 34069, Department 185, Seattle, WA 98124
604-264-7771 Fax: 604-264-7745 e-mail: info@e-cv.com

Jobs? Yes
- Cost to post jobs: Fee
- Cost to see jobs: Free
- Specialty: All
- Industry: All
- Location: Int'l/Europe, Asia

Resumes? Yes
- Cost to post resumes: Fee
- Cost to see resumes: Fee

Feature(s)? Push to Applicant, C/V

Career Advice? Yes

BIJ's focus is on Bilingual Careers in the Technology and Finance related industries. Push methodology delivers bilingual career openings directly to job seekers via e-mail. The cost to applicants is $120 to post a resume and $400-500 per position posted by an employer. A very interesting plan called "Pay for Results" is available to employers willing to pay $50 per qualified resume. Money back guarantee and a free newsletter to hiring personnel. This site's geographic emphasis is Europe and Asia.

Bio Online: Life on the 'Net

www.bio.com

(Commercial)
John D. Turkel, Vitadata Corporation
2855 Telegraph Ave., Suite 210, Berkeley, CA 94705
510-548-1171 Fax: 510-548-1173 e-mail: john@bio.com

Jobs? Yes
• Cost to post jobs: Fee
• Cost to see jobs: Free
• Specialty: Science/Bio
• Industry: Biotechnology/Pharmaceuticals
• Location: US

Resumes? Yes
• Cost to post resumes: Free
• Cost to see resumes: Fee

Feature(s)? N/A

Career Advice? Yes

Created by Vitadata Corporation and supported by KPMG, Covance (formerly Corning Pharmaceutical) and others, Bio Online has a standard job search engine (titles and companies), career guides, a search firm list and resume bank with free posting. Applicants can post resumes which can be sent directly to job postings. In the near future, Bio Online will have a resume bank that recruiters can view for a fee. Significant content related to the Biotech Industry is available, searchable and constantly updated. Costs range from $115 to post a job and up. A career discussion forum is being created for the job seeker. Their on-line application form makes it easy for the job seeker with excellent controls for confidentiality and distribution.

Biomedical Positions

www.informatik.uni-rostock.de/HUM-MOLGEN/positions

(College/University)
Kai Garlipp, The Netherlands Ophthalmic Res. Inst.
P.O.Box 12141, 1100 AL, Amsterdam, The Netherlands
e-mail: see notes

Jobs? Yes
• Cost to post jobs: Free
• Cost to see jobs: Free
• Specialty: Science/Biomedical/Genetics
• Industry: Higher Education/Research
• Location: Int'l./US

Resumes? Yes
• Cost to post resumes: Free
• Cost to see resumes: Free

Feature(s)? N/A

Career Advice? No

Site has a new web address which we listed and has added a search engine since our last visit. You can e-mail for more info to: garlipp@informatik.uni-rostock.de or go to the site where Kai has a mail form. There are a number of positions listed for universities and corporations all over the world. The price is right and from a recruiters standpoint you have everything to gain.

BioSpace Career Center

www.biospace.com/sd/career

(Commercial)
Timothy Fredel, Synergistic Designs, Inc.
Attn: BioSpace Career Cent, 594 Howard Street, Ste 400, San Francisco, CA 94105
415-977-1600 Fax: 415-977-1606 e-mail: missioncontrol@biospace.com

Jobs? Yes
- Cost to post jobs: Fee
- Cost to see jobs: Free
- Specialty: Science/Bio
- Industry: Biotechnology/Pharm.
- Location: Int'l./US

Resumes? No
- Cost to post resumes: N/A
- Cost to see resumes: N/A

Feature(s)? N/A

Career Advice? Yes

A long list of corporations have signed on to post their open positions in the bio sciences field. Jobs are posted by company, region of the world and title. Direct contact information is available and they would appreciate that you refer to their ad code when you reply. Date of job posting is also available. Cost to an employer is $100 per posting for 4 weeks. Very useful measure is a monthly report sent back to the employer totaling the number of visitors to their job posting. It's technically feasible for any site to provide this simple measure...and more.

The Black Collegian Online

www.black-collegian.com

(Pub./College/Diversity)
Scott Edwards, Black Collegiate Service, Inc.
140 Carodelet Street, New Orleans, LA 70130
504-523-0154 Fax: 504-523-0271 e-mail: scott@black-collegian.com

Jobs? Yes
- Cost to post jobs: Fee
- Cost to see jobs: Free
- Specialty: All
- Industry: All
- Location: US

Resumes? Yes
- Cost to post resumes: free
- Cost to see resumes: Fee

Feature(s)? Diversity

Career Advice? Yes

This is the electronic version of the Black Collegian which is a national career opportunities publication. Employers can post jobs for $55 over the cost of an ad in the magazine or $75 for the site alone. A resume database has recently been added where students and professionals can post their backgrounds (in confidence if they wish). This site has a lot of promise. (See its sister site - Minorities Job Bank)

Black Data Processing Assoc. On line!

www.bdpa.org

(Association)
Wayne Abbott, Black Data Processing Association
1111 14th Street NW, Ste 700, Washington, DC 20005
800-727-2372 Fax: 202-789-1592 e-mail: nbdpa@bdpa.org

Jobs? No
• Cost to post jobs: N/A
• Cost to see jobs: N/A
• Specialty: IT
• Industry: All
• Location: US

Resumes? No
• Cost to post resumes: N/A
• Cost to see resumes: N/A

Feature(s)? Diversity/Links

Career Advice? Yes

Link from this national site to the local chapters to find (or post) job listings. Employers should certainly investigate web advertising opportunities here. Career Fairs and information about the BDPA National Conference are available. Exploring the site, we found an interesting link to a new site- "Spectra Links", an list of web sites for people of color. As BDPA grows (it seems to be a work in progress), we will keep an eye on it through our monthly updates.

Black E.O.E Journal

www.BlackEOEJournal.com

(Publisher)
Tom Layton, Olive Tree Publishing
22845 Savi Ranch Parkway, Suite H, Yorba Linda, CA 92687
800-487-5099 Fax: 714-974-8213 e-mail: beoeresume@aol.com

Jobs? No
• Cost to post jobs: N/A
• Cost to see jobs: N/A
• Specialty: N/A
• Industry: N/A
• Location: US

Resumes? Yes
• Cost to post resumes: Free
• Cost to see resumes: Fee

Feature(s)? Diversity

Career Advice? Yes

There are no jobs or resumes on the site itself. This is an employment magazine which focuses on college and experienced professionals. E.O.E. collects resumes from many different sources and passes the ones that match onto their clients and advertisers. You must place a help wanted ad in the publication to get the service. The cost for the resume match service is free and they make sure that everyone who places an ad in their journals receives resumes that match their requirements.

Bloomberg Online

www.bloomberg.com/fun/jobs.html

(Publisher/Financial)
Bloomberg Financial Markets
100 Business Park Drive, P.O. Box 888, Princeton, NJ 08542
800-448-5678 e-mail: jobs@bloomberg.com

Jobs? Yes
- Cost to post jobs: Fee
- Cost to see jobs: Free
- Specialty: Finance/Wall Street
- Industry: Financial
- Location: Int'l/US

Resumes? Yes
- Cost to post resumes: Free
- Cost to see resumes: Free

Feature(s)? N/A

Career Advice? Yes

If you are looking for a Wall Street or financial position this is among the easiest places to go. Recruiters in corporations who are clients of Bloomberg can post positions for free. Jobs are categorized by type of position in the US and, for international openings, they are listed by country. There is a special category for openings over $100K. Executive recruiters can list their firms contact information on the "Help Pages" for free. Job seekers can post their resume for free on this site and it will be categorized either by years of experience for domestic openings or by interest in international positions. Definitely worth a visit and, as the site grows and ads positions, they will certainly need a search engine. Actually, they need it now. If you are trying to get here from Bloomberg's home page (bloomberg.com), make sure you go to "Who/What/Where/When" or you will have a hard time finding the career opportunities section.

Boldface Jobs

www.boldfacejobs.com

(Commercial)
Tom Martinell
8033 N. 3rd Place, Phoenix, AZ 95020
602-861-8982 Fax: 602-861-8992 e-mail: jobs@boldfacejobs.com

Jobs? Yes
- Cost to post jobs: Free
- Cost to see jobs: Free
- Specialty: All
- Industry: N/A
- Location: US

Resumes? Yes
- Cost to post resumes: Free
- Cost to see resumes: Free

Feature(s)? N/A

Career Advice? No

You can post jobs and resumes for free (until they say differently). On our last visit there were 75 listings with direct contact information. A well laid out home page with icons makes it easy to view openings. Boldface Jobs' search engine is an added feature to speed the process. Site needs more traffic and more focus for growth. This is more a marketing challenge than a web design issue.

Boston Globe

www.boston.com

(Publisher/Newspaper)
Kim Green, Boston Globe
135 Morrissey Blvd., Boston, MA 02107
617-929-2167 e-mail: k_green@globe.com

Jobs? Yes
- Cost to post jobs: Fee
- Cost to see jobs: Free
- Specialty: All
- Industry: N/A
- Location: US/NE/MA/Boston

Resumes? No
- Cost to post resumes: N/A
- Cost to see resumes: N/A

Feature(s)? N/A

Career Advice? Yes

Newspaper help-wanted classifieds are posted on their site. This publisher also participates in CareerPath (see CareerPath). List of links to online resume banks and for fun, you can look at the resumes of famous people. Site also includes career management articles.

Boston Herald Job Find

www.jobfind.com

(Publisher/Newspaper)
Boston Herald
P.O. Box 289, Boston, MA 02106
617-426-4545 e-mail: jobfind@jobfind.com

Jobs? Yes
- Cost to post jobs: Fee
- Cost to see jobs: Free
- Specialty: All
- Industry: All
- Location: US/NE

Resumes? Yes
- Cost to post resumes: Free
- Cost to see resumes: Fee

Feature(s)? N/A

Career Advice? Yes

The Boston Herald has taken classifieds to the next step with a very good search engine that makes life easy for the job seeker by targeting states and job titles where the ads are placed. This site will also take your resume and keep it in a confidential database while responding only to the jobs you select. Employers can pay $75 to post their jobs on the web directly and are not required to place an ad in the classified section of the Herald's print edition. One of the few publishers to design quality service into their site. Unfortunately on a financial basis, they continue to "shoot themselves in the foot" as they set up sites that compete with rather than enhance their related products.

Boston Job Bank

(Commercial)
Charles Jukiewicz, Jr., Information Unlimited
110 Church Street, Westwood, MA 02090
e-mail: charles@cybercom.net

Jobs? Yes
• Cost to post jobs: Fee
• Cost to see jobs: Free
• Specialty: All
• Industry: All
• Location: US/NE/MA/Boston

Resumes? No
• Cost to post resumes: N/A
• Cost to see resumes: N/A

Feature(s)? N/A

Career Advice? No

The owner, Charles, works on faith and asks $20 from each employer who posts a job for 4 weeks. He will post your job if he receives your check or not. He would appreciate that you send it within 2 weeks. A job listing form is on the site so you can post yourself. Job seekers have direct contact information on this site. This is the job site version of share ware.

Branch Out

(Commercial)
David Ronick, Brainstorm
150 Fifth Avenue, Suite 216, New York, NY 10011
212-627-0059 e-mail: feedback@branchout.com

Jobs? Yes
• Cost to post jobs: Fee
• Cost to see jobs: Free
• Specialty: College
• Industry: All
• Location: US

Resumes? No
• Cost to post resumes: N/A
• Cost to see resumes: N/A

Feature(s)? N/A

Career Advice? Yes

Branch Out is a unique site. For individuals who have attended either, Brown, Yale, Duke, Stanford, Harvard, MIT, Dartmouth, Penn, Columbia, U. of Chicago, Berkeley, Cornell, Princeton, Michigan or Northwestern this is a place where these colleges' graduates can connect and share information. From BranchOut, you can find jobs, classifieds for buying/selling items, a yellow pages for finding people in areas of common interest or need (that are alumnae of course) and simply "network" to your hearts content. Employers can post jobs for a $100 each and you also get two free postings. Positions are kept on the site for 4 weeks. Neat "community" model bringing people together from 15 major universities. This idea has powerful possibilities. These people are exploring the power of the net and you can expect other communities in the future.

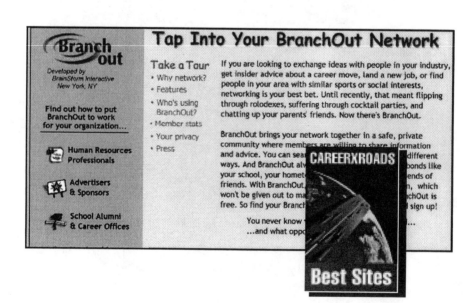

Brave New World

www.newwork.com

(Publisher/Newspaper)
Gary Johnson, New York News
e-mail: gjohnson@pclink.com

Jobs? No
• Cost to post jobs: N/A
• Cost to see jobs: N/A
• Specialty: All
• Industry: All
• Location: US

Resumes? No
• Cost to post resumes: N/A
• Cost to see resumes: N/A

Feature(s)? Career Mgm't.

Career Advice? Yes

Brave New World collects articles from major publications all over the world on work related issues. The information is updated on a daily basis with a synopsis of each article and a link to the document as well.

BridgePath Employment Services

www.bridgepath.com

(Commercial)
Auren Hoffman
2039 Shattuck Avenue, Suite 406, Berkeley, CA 94704
510-644-0608 Fax: 510-848-0351 e-mail: mail@bridgepath.com

Jobs? Yes
• Cost to post jobs: Fee
• Cost to see jobs: Free
• Specialty: College
• Industry: All
• Location: US

Resumes? Yes
• Cost to post resumes: Free
• Cost to see resumes: Fee

Feature(s)? Push to Applicant

Career Advice? No

BridgePath has collected e-mail addresses from over 800 colleges & universities. Two search engines allow recruiters to select specific degrees and/or the year graduated. Employers can narrow candidates by GPA, languages spoken, etc. Employers are advised how many "candidates" their query found. For $1.50 an e-mail they can then send a personal message to the potential candidates. We love push technology although we question if they have 800 colleges signed up as we only saw 30 on their individual list. Watch this site. Much applause for a unique design. As a student, I would use it. Obvious flaw though is how you, the employer, can audit what they do and, how they, BridgePath, can assure or certify that the criteria submitted by the students is accurate. Lots of work to do here but success could have a superb payoff.

BRINT (@BRINT)

www.brint.com

(Government)
US Government
e-mail: feedback@brint.con

Jobs? No
• Cost to post jobs: N/A
• Cost to see jobs: N/A
• Specialty: N/A
• Industry: All
• Location: US

Resumes? No
• Cost to post resumes: N/A
• Cost to see resumes: N/A

Feature(s)? JSK/Research

Career Advice? No

Job Seeker's, but especially recruiters may find this Business Research in Information and Technology site a valuable tool for checking out contemporary business and management issues related to information processes, information systems and information technologies. The latest articles on all the emerging technology ideas and elements as well as the companies that develop them can be accessed from this address.

Building Industry Exchange

www.building.org

(Association)
e-mail: feedback@building.org

Jobs? Yes
• Cost to post jobs: Free
• Cost to see jobs: Free
• Specialty: All
• Industry: Construction
• Location: US

Resumes? Yes
• Cost to post resumes: Free
• Cost to see resumes: Free

Feature(s)? N/A

Career Advice? No

The Building Industry Exchange is a non-profit information exchange center of Internet resources for the building industry. Connections to companies, job resources and a small resume database. Easy access to the jobs and resumes that are listed here.

Bullseye Job Shop

(Commercial)
e-mail: gcbristow@interoz.com

Jobs? No
• Cost to post jobs: N/A
• Cost to see jobs: N/A
• Specialty: N/A
• Industry: N/A
• Location: US

Resumes? No
• Cost to post resumes: N/A
• Cost to see resumes: N/A

Feature(s)? JSK/Links

Career Advice? No

Lots of links to potential job sites on the web and in newsgroups. Like throwing darts at a target.

Business Job Listing

www.cob.ohio-state.edu/~fin/jobslist.htm

(University)
Tim Opler, Ohio State University
Fisher College of Business, Ohio
Fax: 614-292-2418 e-mail: opler.l@osu.edu

Jobs? Yes
• Cost to post jobs: Free
• Cost to see jobs: Free
• Specialty: Business
• Industry: N/A
• Location: US

Resumes? No
• Cost to post resumes: N/A
• Cost to see resumes: N/A

Feature(s)? Yes

Career Advice? Yes

Job listings from corporations that are posted at Ohio State University's Fisher College of Business site. Dozens of links to company job pages and other potential job opportunity web sites. When school is in session, we would not expect fresh job openings to be posted.

California Career and Employment Center

(Commercial)
Central Coast Employment Center
P.O. Box 2107, Monterey, CA 93942
Fax: 408-626-6156 e-mail: cces@netcom.com

Jobs? No
- Cost to post jobs: Fee
- Cost to see jobs: N/A
- Specialty: All
- Industry: webcom.com/career/welcome.html
- Location: US/W/CA

Resumes? Yes
- Cost to post resumes: Fee
- Cost to see resumes: Free

Feature(s)? Yes

Career Advice? No

CCEC concentrates on the West coast and charges $75 to post positions. Site has package deals with other major web sites. Features include a resume talent bank that is free to employers. Candidate contact information is public. Cost is $30 to post your resume locally (you will be given a live e-mail response link). The price to post your resume to the WorldWide talent bank is $60 and for $90 CCEC will electronically distribute your resume to over 700 resume databases. We strongly recommend you check sites like this out before you spend your $$$.

California Job Bank

(Association)
California Society of Newspaper Editors
3108 Adams Street, Alameda, CA 94501
510-337-1832 e-mail: beckyday@csne.org

Jobs? Yes
- Cost to post jobs: Fee
- Cost to see jobs: Free
- Specialty: Journalism
- Industry: Publications
- Location: US/CA

Resumes? No
- Cost to post resumes: N/A
- Cost to see resumes: N/A

Feature(s)? Yes

Career Advice? No

This site has remained true to form since our last visit. Jobs are posted for free for members of CSNE while others are charged $25 (in California and Nevada; outside the area, the rate is $50). Listings of jobs with full contact information and job descriptions are available. As an added touch, the date is posted next to the title line. If you are looking for a west coast journalism position this is still the place to go. Aren't niches great?

Can Work Net

www.hrdc.ingenia.com/cwn/english/main.html

(Non-Profit)
e-mail: cwn-feedback@ingenia.com

Jobs? No
- Cost to post jobs: N/A
- Cost to see jobs: N/A
- Specialty: All
- Industry: All
- Location: Int'l/Canada

Resumes? No
- Cost to post resumes: N/A
- Cost to see resumes: N/A

Feature(s)? JSK/Links

Career Advice? Yes

Lots of information on the future outlook for Canadian careers. Can Work Net provides over 1,300 links ranging from sites that emphasize career development to those that offer financial help.

Canadian Job Source

www.irus.rri.uwo.ca/~jlaw/national.html

(Commercial)
Jeff Lawrence

Jobs? Yes
- Cost to post jobs: N/A
- Cost to see jobs: N/A
- Specialty: All
- Industry: All
- Location: Int'l/Canada

Resumes? No
- Cost to post resumes: N/A
- Cost to see resumes: N/A

Feature(s)? Push to Applicant

Career Advice? Yes

Canadian Job Source has added hundreds of links since our last review but the basic premise remains the same. The site links to Canadian job information, recruiters, companies and job banks. You can register and receive job announcement updates for free from a service called JobSat. The problem we have with this site is that some of the links may not have been checked in over a year.

Career Action Center

www.careeraction.org/CACpublic/intro.html

(Non-Profit)
10420 Bubb Road, Suite 100, Cupertino, CA 95014
408-253-3200 Fax: 408-257-6400 e-mail: request@careeraction.org

Jobs? No
- Cost to post jobs: N/A
- Cost to see jobs: N/A
- Specialty: All
- Industry: All
- Location: US/W/CA

Resumes? No
- Cost to post resumes: N/A
- Cost to see resumes: N/A

Feature(s)? Career Mgm't.

Career Advice? Yes

Career Action Center provides first class services in career counseling. Categories include: career self-assessment, marketing, career fitness etc. The center carries books on career management and posts a listing of workshops. If you need help in getting your career back on track, visit CAC. Annual memberships are $145, and individual sessions are available for a fee.

Career America

www.careeramerica.com

(Placement Agency)
Cheryl Wayne, Phoenix Professionals
P.O. Box 4081, Mamouth Lakes, CA 93546
619-934-3566 Fax: 619-934-1838 e-mail: technet@qnet.com

Jobs? Yes
- Cost to post jobs: Fee
- Cost to see jobs: Free
- Specialty: All
- Industry: All
- Location: US

Resumes? Yes
- Cost to post resumes: Fee
- Cost to see resumes: Free

Feature(s)? Yes

Career Advice? No

You always have to wonder when the owner is on both sides of the fence. This site is owned by a recruitment agency that charges job seekers $40 to post a resume. They also charge employers $100 to post a position.

Career Board

(Placement Agency)
Dennis Geisler, Staffing Solutions Enterprises
27 Chagrin Boulevard, Suite 300, Cleveland, Ohio 44122
216-595-2200 Fax: 216-595-2227 e-mail: dgeisler@careerboard.com

Jobs? Yes
- Cost to post jobs: Fee
- Cost to see jobs: Free
- Specialty: All
- Industry: All
- Location: US/MW/OH

Resumes? Yes
- Cost to post resumes: Free
- Cost to see resumes: Fee

Feature(s)? N/A

Career Advice? Yes

CareerBoard is a regionalized niche job site showcasing opportunities in the Cleveland and Akron Ohio areas. Jobs are posted and coded so you have to go back to the site to get the contact information. Employer cost to post jobs is $75. Resumes can be posted for free. If you place your resume on the site then you can e-mail it to any job listed by clicking on their "send" button. Nice feature.

CareerBuilder

(Commercial)
Stephen Abel, NetStart, Inc.
11495 Sunset Hills road, Reston, VA 20190
703-709-1001 Fax: 703-709-1004 e-mail: info@netstartinc.con

Jobs? Yes
- Cost to post jobs: Fee
- Cost to see jobs: Free
- Specialty: All
- Industry: All
- Location: US

Resumes? No
- Cost to post resumes: N/A
- Cost to see resumes: N/A

Feature(s)? Push to Applicant

Career Advice? Yes

First developed by NetStart, Inc. as an intranet product, TeamBulder was CareerBuilder's internal cousin where an employer could post internal positions and giver access to their employees. NetStart's services quickly expanded to a web site, CareerBuilder, where employers with Teambuilder could easily move their openings "out"- onto the web. CareerBuilder is now only one of the sites NetStart has packaged in this way.

CareerBuilder is a "push" site. Job seekers complete a short online form specifying areas of interest, location, salary etc. When new jobs are posted that fit specific requirements, job seekers are notified via e-mail. This is only available to clients who have purchased their software at this time but more services should be available when CAREERXROADS (1998) is published. The site also pushes out advice and other job resources information. A powerful marketing engine seems to be behind this site. We see them everywhere- conferences, trade shows and more...even drive time radio in major markets. If the money holds out this site could emerge a winner. Great design. Great strategy.

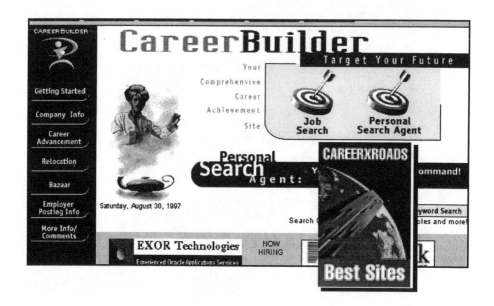

Career Center for Workforce Diversity

(Publisher/Trade)
John Miller, EOP, Inc.
150 Motor Pkwy, Hauppauge, NY 11788
516-273-0066 e-mail: info@eop.com

Jobs? Yes
• Cost to post jobs: Fee
• Cost to see jobs: Free
• Specialty: All
• Industry: N/A
• Location: US

Resumes? No
• Cost to post resumes: N/A
• Cost to see resumes: N/A

Feature(s)? Diversity

Career Advice? Yes

Owner publishes "Equal Opportunity", "Women Engineer", "Minority Engineer", "Careers and the Disabled" and "Workforce Diversity" magazines. All help-wanted advertisers are supplied free links to their site. Solid, helpful articles regarding the world of workforce diversity.

Career Channel

(College/University)
Michael Breu, Rice CSC - MS 521
6100 Main, Houston, TX 77054
713-527-4055 e-mail: breu@rice.edu

Jobs? Yes
• Cost to post jobs: N/A
• Cost to see jobs: N/A
• Specialty: College
• Industry: N/A
• Location: Int'l./US

Resumes? No
• Cost to post resumes: N/A
• Cost to see resumes: N/A

Feature(s)? Career Mgm't.

Career Advice? Yes

This site could be a model for other colleges to follow on how to create an interesting theme. Excellent graphic design. The site is set up like a TV studio with content at different "channels". The content however is a little thin. Internships are posted and several career links are available.

Career China

(Commercial)
Ya Li, Global Communications Services Inc.
3130 Rt. 10 West, Denville, NJ 07834
201-989-0501 Fax: 201-328-9216 e-mail: yli@glcs.com

Jobs? Yes
• Cost to post jobs: Fee
• Cost to see jobs: Free
• Specialty: All
• Industry: All
• Location: Int'l/China

Resumes? Yes
• Cost to post resumes: Fee
• Cost to see resumes: Fee

Feature(s)? Diversity

Career Advice? Yes

Career China offers openings in mainland China, Taiwan, Hong Kong, Singapore, and a few other points on the Pacific Rim. Employers are charged $30 per opening or $300 per month for unlimited postings. The job seeker can post their resume for $15. Resumes (350) were coded when we visited so you must go back to the "mainland" to get more information on the applicants. The Pacific Rim is a hot area and this site will likely become a player in that region.

CareerCity

(Commercial)
Paul Huekell, Adams Media Corporation
260 Centre St., Holbrook, MA 02343
800-872-5627 Fax: 617-767-2055 e-mail: huekell@careercity.com

Jobs? Yes
• Cost to post jobs: Fee
• Cost to see jobs: Free
• Specialty: All
• Industry: N/A
• Location: US

Resumes? Yes
• Cost to post resumes: Free
• Cost to see resumes: Fee

Feature(s)? N/A

Career Advice? Yes

Career City is a "Career Hub" and is trying (too hard) to do it all for everyone. This site, owned by a reputable publisher, claims it has 125,000 jobs which is the same claim it made last year. A great search engine and direct contact information for jobs that are posted are included in the design. Resumes can be posted electronically and are kept for 4 months. A large list of links to newsgroups is available as is career management information. You need to become a member to get the full benefits of this site and various levels of sponsorship are also available.

Career Command Center

www.CareerCommandCenter.com

(Commercial)
Greg Franchina, WorldBase, Inc.
4301 N. Fairfax Drive, Suite 1062, Arlington, VA 22203
703-892-0717 Fax: 703-892-0705 e-mail: support@worldbaseinc.com

Jobs? Yes
- Cost to post jobs: Fee
- Cost to see jobs: Free
- Specialty: IT
- Industry: High Technology
- Location: US

Resumes? Yes
- Cost to post resumes: Free
- Cost to see resumes: Fee

Feature(s)? N/A

Career Advice? No

Career Command Center concentrates on IT/IS applicant resumes. You can post your resume for free and employers pay $100 to pull resumes from the site. Recruiters see profiles and then can pull resumes. Site is looking to push openings out to job seekers in the near future.

Career Counseling-Lite

www.execpc.com/~cclite/

(Commercial)
Dr. Brent Evans, VOC-EVAL Associates, Inc.
Wisconsin
e-mail: cclite@execpc.com

Jobs? No
- Cost to post jobs: N/A
- Cost to see jobs: N/A
- Specialty: All
- Industry: All
- Location: US

Resumes? No
- Cost to post resumes: N/A
- Cost to see resumes: N/A

Feature(s)? Career Mgm't.

Career Advice? Yes

Career Counseling Lite provides 48 hour response to your career questions at no charge. The Dr. must be into motorcycles as he uses them to get your motor running. CCL has links to other career sites and before you leave on your cyber travels you can pick up a t-shirt with their CC-Lite logo.

Career Crafting

(Commercial)
Howard Sambol, Encompass
27 Regina Way, San Rafael, CA 94903
415-472-3383 Fax: 415-472-3384 e-mail: CareerCrft@aol.com

Jobs? No
- Cost to post jobs: N/A
- Cost to see jobs: N/A
- Specialty: All
- Industry: All
- Location: US

Resumes? No
- Cost to post resumes: N/A
- Cost to see resumes: N/A

Feature(s)? Career Mgm't.

Career Advice? Yes

Career Crafting has several interesting articles to help you get a jump start on your job search. We especially liked "10 Secrets to Effective Communication in the Workplace" and "Winning in a World Without Jobs". Owner of the site also sells career management courses and has a free Q&A session located on AOL.

Career Doctor

www.career-doctor.com

(Recruiting Related Agency)
Barry Deutsch, CJA-The Adler Group
5757 W. Century Blvd., Suite 700, Los Angeles, CA 90045

Jobs? Yes
- Cost to post jobs: Fee
- Cost to see jobs: Fee
- Specialty: All
- Industry: N/A
- Location: US

Resumes? Yes
- Cost to post resumes: Free
- Cost to see resumes: Fee

Feature(s)? Career Mgm't.

Career Advice? Yes

One of the few recruitment agencies we have placed in this edition. We like the discussion group that allows people to talk about career related issues. Great effort giving back. Barry supports many professional activities behind the scenes. Career Doctor maintains excellent articles on how to boost your career.

CAREERXROADS©
Job, Resume & Career Management Sites on the World Wide Web
• The 1998 Directory •

- 101 -

Career Espresso/Emory University

www.sph.emory.edu/studentservice/career.html

(College/University)
John Youngblood Jr., Emory University Career Services
e-mail: jyoungb@emory.edu

Jobs? No
- Cost to post jobs: N/A
- Cost to see jobs: N/A
- Specialty: Public Health
- Industry: All
- Location: US

Resumes? No
- Cost to post resumes: N/A
- Cost to see resumes: N/A

Feature(s)? JSK/Links

Career Advice? Yes

Career Espresso is the successor to John Youngblood's "Career Paradise" site from the 1997 directory. This quality niche is for Public Health graduates. Link from here to top public health sites and to the Internship Exchange. Many more things to come as John is a master at creating a flavorful website.

Career Exchange

www.careerexchange.com/

(Commercial)
Jason Moreau, CorpNet InfoHub Ltd.
Unit E-7950 Huston Road, Delta, B.C., Canada V4G 1C2
604-940-2754 Fax: 604-940-2840 e-mail: develop@corpinfohub.com

Jobs? Yes
- Cost to post jobs: Fee
- Cost to see jobs: Free
- Specialty: IT
- Industry: All
- Location: Int'l/Canada/US

Resumes? Yes
- Cost to post resumes: Free
- Cost to see resumes: Fee

Feature(s)? N/A

Career Advice? Yes

Clients posting positions at CareerExchange receive resumes for their effort. About 2,100 positions are listed and nearly 60% are US jobs. Job seekers can send their online resume directly to the recruiter. An effective key word search engine adds to the convenience of using this site. Positions are for Canada or the US and primarily in IT areas but, many jobs in other specialties are also available. Employer cost to post jobs is in the $17-35 range for 30 days.

Career Exposure

www.careerexposure.com

(Commercial)
Amy Garofalo McMahon, Career Exposure, Inc.
503-525-8498 e-mail: bizmail@careerexposure.com

Jobs? Yes
- Cost to post jobs: Fee
- Cost to see jobs: Free
- Specialty: All
- Industry: All
- Location: US

Resumes? No
- Cost to post resumes: N/A
- Cost to see resumes: N/A

Feature(s)? N/A

Career Advice? Yes

Career Exposure sorts job openings by industry and then presents the job seeker with profiles on corporations with links for more information. Easy to follow. Employers pay $450 per month. Job seekers can link to the job opportunities for free.

CareerFile

www.careerfile.com

(Placement Agency)
Cynthia Welch, Search & Placement Services, Inc.
P.O. Box 3331, Clock Tower Bus. Park, Pittsfield, MA 01202
413-499-2498 Fax: 413-448-5673 e-mail: careerfile@taconic.net

Jobs? Yes
- Cost to post jobs: Free
- Cost to see jobs: Free
- Specialty: All
- Industry: N/A
- Location: Int'l./US

Resumes? Yes
- Cost to post resumes: Free
- Cost to see resumes: Fee

Feature(s)? N/A

Career Advice? No

Career File is a library of executive, managerial and technical talent . Employers can browse the site and search through resumes. The site is designed to protect the candidate's confidentiality...somewhat. Employers are charged $6.95 to obtain candidates contact information. You need to register as a job seeker to gain access to the employer job information.

Career Internetworking

(Commercial)
Career Internetworking
5255 Yonge Street, Suite 711 P.O. Box 17, North York, Ontario, Canada
416-229-2666 Fax: 416-229-2943

Jobs? Yes
- Cost to post jobs: Fee
- Cost to see jobs: Free
- Specialty: All
- Industry: All
- Location: Int'l/Canada/US

Resumes? No
- Cost to post resumes: N/A
- Cost to see resumes: N/A

Feature(s)? N/A

Career Advice? Yes

Career Internetworking includes helpful articles on how to get a job and prepare your resume. Recruiters pay $100 to post a position for one month. Other packages are available. Site lists "hot jobs" in a separate page and has a career forum for job seekers to discuss common problems and issues. This Canadian site is easy to view and follow and will only get better with time.

CareerLab

(Author)
William Frank
304 Inverness Way South, STE 465, Englewood, Colorado 80112
303-790-0505 Fax: 303-790-0606 e-mail: comments@careerlab.com

Jobs? No
- Cost to post jobs: N/A
- Cost to see jobs: N/A
- Specialty: All
- Industry: All
- Location: US

Resumes? No
- Cost to post resumes: N/A
- Cost to see resumes: N/A

Feature(s)? Career Mgm't.

Career Advice? Yes

Career Lab makes templates for cover letters available to job seekers as well as other documents related to job hunting. Good design despite the emphasis on selling the site owner's book. But then, you have to make a living somehow and people who live in glass houses... A very nice touch is that Mr. Frank will answer questions related to cover letters for free via e-mail.

Career Link USA

(Commercial)
Mickey Tyler, CareerLink USA, Inc.
4915 E. State St., Rockford, IL 61108
800-667-5465 Fax: 815-227-5482 e-mail: hrlinks@aol.com

Jobs? Yes
• Cost to post jobs: Fee
• Cost to see jobs: Free
• Specialty: All
• Industry: All
• Location: US

Resumes? Yes
• Cost to post resumes: Fee
• Cost to see resumes: Free

Feature(s)? N/A

Career Advice? No

It costs a job seeker $35 to post their resume and it will stay in the database for one year (your contact information is available to the recruiter). Jobs are coded and you can send your resumes via the website directly to the employer who pay $175 to post a position. CareerLink seems to concentrates on the Mid West and Washington DC for job openings.

Career Magazine

www.careermag.com

(Commercial)
Gary Resnikoff, NCSJobline, Inc.
4775 Walnut Street, Suite 2A, Boulder, CO 80301
303-440-5110 Fax: 303-440-3386 e-mail: gary@careermag.com

Jobs? Yes
• Cost to post jobs: Fee
• Cost to see jobs: Free
• Specialty: All
• Industry: All
• Location: US

Resumes? Yes
• Cost to post resumes: Free
• Cost to see resumes: Free

Feature(s)? Diversity, Search by State

Career Advice? Yes

Career Magazine maintains a searchable index of 19 job related newsgroups as one of its many services. Career articles, resume databases and company positions are searchable by location, skill and title as well as by date posted and are instantly available to the job applicant. Employer prices are $95 to post a position for 4 weeks. An unlimited job posting subscription is available and prices vary depending upon whether you post directly or have NCS do it for you as with other services. This is one of the most flexible and successful sites on the internet. A directory of executive recruiters (15 categories) is also an excellent tool for the job seeker. Great diversity content suggests that CareerMag be checked out for its active links as well and, while most sites are just looking to expand their WWW site's services, CareerMagazine has set its sights on a broader horizon- PC-to-PC interviewing. Not the subject of this review but the thinking that went into creating this "turnkey" system for remote interview screening of applicants was brilliant and deserves a special staffing award for its innovation. We hope it succeeds (See our June '97 Update).

Career Mart

(Recruiting Related Agency)
BSA Advertising
360 Lexington Avenue, New York, NY 10017
212-599-6606 e-mail: careermart@mcimail.com

Jobs? Yes
• Cost to post jobs: Fee
• Cost to see jobs: Free
• Specialty: N/A
• Industry: N/A
• Location: US

Resumes? Yes
• Cost to post resumes: Free
• Cost to see resumes: Fee

Feature(s)? Push to Applicant

Career Advice? Yes

This site looks like it has it all and then some. CareerMart pushes job openings to applicants for free, makes a chatroom available for discussions, includes a search engine that offers great choices and has great graphics. Unfortunately this last really slows you down. Employers pay in the $100 range to post job opportunities on the BSA recruitment advertising agency's site. Graphics are beautiful but you may want to look at this site by hitting the text only button so you can move along crisply. You can post your resume for free but recruiters must pay to see them. It's surprising with all this going for it, that the owners have spent so little effort to market CareerMart to more job seekers and employers.

CareerMosaic

www.careermosaic.com

(Recruiting Related Agency)
Jeffrey Hodes, Bernard Hodes Advertising
555 Madison Avenue, NY, NY 10022
800-624-7744 Fax: 212-486-4049 e-mail: sales@careermosaic.com

Jobs? Yes
• Cost to post jobs: Fee
• Cost to see jobs: Free
• Specialty: All
• Industry: All
• Location: Int'l/US

Resumes? Yes
• Cost to post resumes: Free
• Cost to see resumes: Free

Feature(s)? Search by State, Diversity, Career Mgm't.

Career Advice? Yes

Career Mosaic is one of the original "Career Hubs" of the web and continues to be one of the best and brightest stars in the recruiting market today. With it's sister sites: healthopps.com, college connection.com, and it's international sites it continues to expand without pausing to rest on its laurels. For recruiters this site continues be one of the few major sites allowing resumes to be both seen and posted for free. Employer cost to post individual open positions is $150 for a 30 day run. CareerMosaic will post all its jobs to usenet groups as added value. A sophisticated search engine drills into this job database by date, company name, title and location making this a place job seekers find easy to return to often. No push technology, but you have to remember this is owned by a recruitment advertising firm. Their obvious objective is to get you to return as often as possible so employers view the "hit" numbers which must be as high as the sky. Recruiters should always ask to see "search numbers" rather then hits as they can be misleading and the more generic the site the more important it is to know details of those searches e.g. by keyword, location etc. to see if job seekers for your openings continue to flock here. Add in a strong knowledge of how to market their service and CM continues to be one of the most visible sites on the web for job seekers and recruiters.

Career NET (Career/NET)

www.careernet.com

(Commercial)
616-344-0019 e-mail: careerinfo@careernet.com

Jobs? No
- Cost to post jobs: N/A
- Cost to see jobs: N/A
- Specialty: IT
- Industry: All
- Location: US

Resumes? Yes
- Cost to post resumes: Free
- Cost to see resumes: Fee

Feature(s)? N/A

Career Advice? No

Everything here is free. Watch for fees in the future. Search options speed up the job seekers ability to find leads fast. Once you register as an employer, you can review resumes with direct contact information. CareerNET needs a little help organizing as we had a great deal of difficulty posting a position - yet the owners say it can be done. Cost to post jobs is around $100, while the site provides different packages to also view their 100,000 resume profiles.

Career Opportunities in Singapore

www.singapore-careers.com

(Commercial)
Singapore Econ. Dev. Board, Int'l Manpower Programme
210 Twin Dolphin Drive, Redwood City, CA 94065
Fax: 415-591-1328 e-mail: joboffer@newsserver.technet.sg

Jobs? Yes
- Cost to post jobs: Fee
- Cost to see jobs: Free
- Specialty: All
- Industry: All
- Location: Int'l./Singapore

Resumes? No
- Cost to post resumes: Free
- Cost to see resumes: N/A

Feature(s)? N/A

Career Advice? No

Dozens of local and International corporations post jobs here. Candidates can use a resume form to apply directly. Site gives you general information about the openings and the name of the corporation. Positions posted were in many different fields. Additional information on the cost of living in this country is also available.

CareerPath.com

www.careerpath.com

(Publisher/Newspaper)
Mary Kay, CareerPath.com
523 W. Sixth Street, Suite 515, Los Angeles, CA 90014
213-623-0200 Fax: 213-623-0244 e-mail: advertising@careerpath.com

Jobs? Yes
- Cost to post jobs: Fee
- Cost to see jobs: Free
- Specialty: All
- Industry: N/A
- Location: US

Resumes? Yes
- Cost to post resumes: Free
- Cost to see resumes: Fee

Feature(s)? Yes

Career Advice? Yes

More than 50 daily newspapers, including the country's most well known (Chicago Tribune, New York Times, LA Times, etc.), have built a common repository for their classified, help-wanted ads (in addition to their own web sites). Now, with over 250,000 "fresh" openings from the nation's largest newspapers, CareerPath.com can make a credible claim as the number 1 stop for the nation's job seekers (especially when they learn that most of these leads are available a day before they appear in print). Some issues still exist: a few individual papers require an additional fee before posting to the 'Net while others offer everything in their paper as added value and, many newspapers are still unable to convert their most expensive help wanted display ads to an internet posting. CareerPath.com has also created and recently introduced a resume database service. Employers can contact professionals on CareerPath.com's staff who will conduct resume searches while protecting the job seekers contact information. Qualified candidates are e-mailed the company's job profile, asked if they are interested in the position and invited to apply. An e-mail is then sent from CareerPath.com to the employer with the candidates filed resume. A new self-service model may be available later in '98 that will maintain the job seeker's confidentiality. Currently, CareerPath.com charges employers $1,500 for 10-20 qualified candidates. As this site moves forward with plans for contracting directly with companies to post positions automatically from the companies' web sites, we wonder whether the number of ads needed in print will decrease but, for recruiters and especially job seekers, this site will continue to attract the highest volume of traffic. Should CareerPath.com decide to place the openings that are scheduled to appear in print in the member papers on Sunday as they are received, thereby meeting a recruiter's sense of urgency, this site could dominate their market.

CAREERXROADS©
Job, Resume & Career Management Sites on the World Wide Web
• The 1998 Directory •

Career Resource Center

(Commercial)
Marc D. Snyder, Career Resource Center
2508 Fifth Avenue, Ste. 147, Seattle, WA 98121
206-233-8672 Fax: 206-727-7970 e-mail: marcds@careers.org

Jobs? No
- Cost to post jobs: N/A
- Cost to see jobs: N/A
- Specialty: All
- Industry: All
- Location: US

Resumes? No
- Cost to post resumes: N/A
- Cost to see resumes: N/A

Feature(s)? JSK/Links

Career Advice? Yes

Links, links and more links to all your career needs. From career "gems" (best sites), employer sites, job sites, education sites and career management sites. If you have the time, this site is worth a visit.

CareerShop

(Commercial)
Janis Davis, Tenkey Interactive Inc.
5422 Carrier Drive, Suite 201, Orlando, FL 32819
800-639-2060 Fax: 407-352-1462 e-mail: sales@careershop.com

Jobs? Yes
- Cost to post jobs: Fee
- Cost to see jobs: Free
- Specialty: All
- Industry: All
- Location: US

Resumes? Yes
- Cost to post resumes: Free
- Cost to see resumes: Fee

Feature(s)? N/A

Career Advice? No

At Career Shop, employers post positions & job seekers post their resume. This site claims 6,682 applicants in their database (July '97). The site provides a link to an IT salary survey and claims to have an online job fair (really just links to employers who have posted jobs by major location). Jobs are posted for 60 days for free. Career Shop will also list your jobs with other sites or newsgroups, and will provide a link to an employer's site for $95 a month. Company logo is $595 per month and you can also obtain a recruiting package that gives you radio and advertisements in an interactive, online magazine. This site needs to make it easier to find what you want but they have an interesting approach.

CareerSite

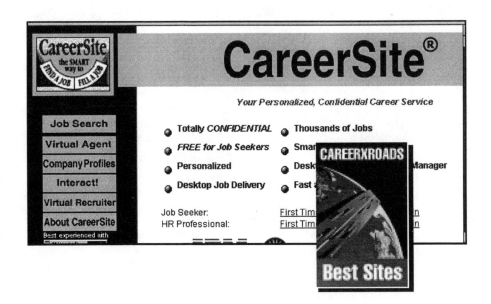

www.careersite.com

(Commercial)
Seth Peets, Virtual Resources Corporation
310 Miller Avenue, Ann Arbor, MI 48103
313-213-9500 Fax: 313-213-9011 e-mail: seth@careersite.com

Jobs? Yes
- Cost to post jobs: Fee
- Cost to see jobs: Free
- Specialty: All
- Industry: All
- Location: US

Resumes? Yes
- Cost to post resumes: Free
- Cost to see resumes: Fee

Feature(s)? Push to Applicant

Career Advice? Yes

Applicants who register at CareerSite can have newly posted openings automatically searched by keywords and forwarded to an e-mail address (virtual agent's desktop). Confidentiality is maintained when employers search the resume database and simply see a "blind" snapshot of the applicant. You are the only one who can release your contact info as you will be e-mailed that an employer has an interest in you. Job seekers can also apply for positions directly through this site. Cost to post jobs is around $100. This is one of the best thought through designs on the web. CareerSite has partnered with several other web sites and serves as their "engine". We hope they survive the coming shakeout.

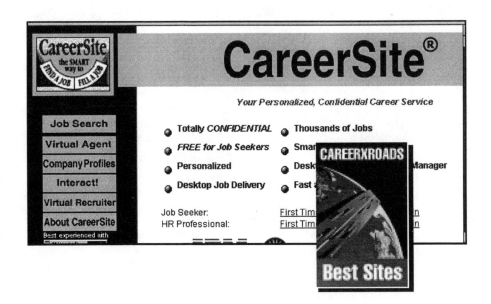

The Career Spot

(Publisher/Newspaper)
Catherine Daley, Ft. Lauderdale Sun Sentinel
200 East Las Olas Blvd., Fort Lauderdale, FL 33301
305-356-4000 Fax: 305-356-4093

Jobs? Yes
- Cost to post jobs: Fee
- Cost to see jobs: Free
- Specialty: All
- Industry: N/A
- Location: US/SE/FL/Ft. Lauderdale

Resumes? No
- Cost to post resumes: N/A
- Cost to see resumes: N/A

Feature(s)? N/A

Career Advice? Yes

Help wanted advertising from this Florida daily newspaper and CareerPath participant. Search engine allows you to narrow down your criteria in a helpful, logical fashion. Employers pay an additional $1/line to have their jobs posted on the web. Please note that company help-wanted display ads are not posted on the web.

Career Talk

(Commercial)
Joe Stimac, Seaton Corp.
P.O. Box 3096, Lawrence, KS 66047
e-mail: career@idir.net

Jobs? No
- Cost to post jobs: N/A
- Cost to see jobs: N/A
- Specialty: All
- Industry: N/A
- Location: US

Resumes? No
- Cost to post resumes: N/A
- Cost to see resumes: N/A

Feature(s)? Career Mgm't.

Career Advice? Yes

The owner writes a syndicated career column. You can pose questions to him via the web and he will e-mail responses to you. This site also markets video based training programs called "Winning Career Strategies". Links to numerous major websites are also listed.

Career Toolbox

(Commercial)
Chivas Regal
800-244-8271

Jobs? No
- Cost to post jobs: N/A
- Cost to see jobs: N/A
- Specialty: All
- Industry: All
- Location: US

Resumes? No
- Cost to post resumes: N/A
- Cost to see resumes: N/A

Feature(s)? Career Mgm't., JSK/Links

Career Advice? All

We still do not understand why Chivas Regal supports a career site but, with their recently added search engine to hundreds of placement agencies, it is worth a visit. Articles on handling career issues through their "Virtual Mentor" include a test to see how you do. Well done. Their objective is to get you to complete a customer survey and, if you do, they will send you a free disc with more career tips.

Career Transitions

www.bfservs.com:80/bfserv.html

(Commercial)
Tony Davidson, Best-BF Services, Inc.
P.O. Box 2698, Covington, GA 30210
770-787-1141 Fax: 770-385-0381 e-mail: tndavdsn@aol.com

Jobs? No
- Cost to post jobs: N/A
- Cost to see jobs: N/A
- Specialty: N/A
- Industry: N/A
- Location: US

Resumes? No
- Cost to post resumes: N/A
- Cost to see resumes: N/A

Feature(s)? JSK/Links

Career Advice? Yes

Career Transitions provides dozens of links to other job related web sites. If you click on the last link, you will also get an extended list of sites with career assistance. All in all, very straightforward.

CareerWeb

(Publisher)
Chelsy Carter, Landmark Communications, Inc.
150 W. Brambleton Avenue, Norfolk, VA 23510
800-871-0800 Fax: 757-623-5942 e-mail: info@cweb.com

Jobs? Yes
- Cost to post jobs: Fee
- Cost to see jobs: Free
- Specialty: N/A
- Industry: N/A
- Location: US/Int'l

Resumes? Yes
- Cost to post resumes: Free
- Cost to see resumes: Fee

Feature(s)? Push to Applicant

Career Advice? Yes

CareerWeb will push new jobs to candidates via e-mail but this is the first site that we have seen that charges the job seeker ($25 for 3 months) for the service. CareerWeb claims over 5,000 job openings in 200+ companies. Jobs that are posted for $115 each to CareerWeb are reposted on Yahoo classifieds. A solid list of articles and links to help the job seeker rounds out this site. Landmark Communications, the publisher, has spent an enormous amount to get to this site in among the first tier but CareerWeb still needs some extra spice to put it over the top.

Careers & Jobs

(Commercial)
Internet Information Associates, Inc.
1009 E. Capitol Expressway, Suite #304, San Jose, CA 95121
e-mail: careersjobs@usa.net

Jobs? No
- Cost to post jobs: N/A
- Cost to see jobs: N/A
- Specialty: All
- Industry: All
- Location: US

Resumes? No
- Cost to post resumes: N/A
- Cost to see resumes: N/A

Feature(s)? JSK/Links

Career Advice? No

Careers & Jobs has several hundred links to job and resume sites. A share ware model, the owner asks for a contribution of $5-$25 if you get any value here. Dreamland.

Careers in Management Consulting

(College/University)
Steve Ravine, Fisher College of Business
Ohio State University
e-mail: ravine@cob.ohio-state.edu

Jobs? No
- Cost to post jobs: N/A
- Cost to see jobs: N/A
- Specialty: Finance/Business
- Industry: All
- Location: US/MW

Resumes? No
- Cost to post resumes: N/A
- Cost to see resumes: N/A

Feature(s)? Yes

Career Advice? Yes

Resources include a useful list of links for professionals interested in the world of finance.

Careers On-Line

(University/Government)
Tim Fitzgerald, U. of Minnesota, Disability Services
12 Johnston Hall, 101 Pleasant St., SE, Minneapolis, MN 55455
612-626-9649 e-mail: careers@disserv.stu.umn.edu

Jobs? Yes
- Cost to post jobs: Free
- Cost to see jobs: Free
- Specialty: All
- Industry: All
- Location: US/MW/MN

Resumes? Yes
- Cost to post resumes: Free
- Cost to see resumes: Free

Feature(s)? Diversity

Career Advice? Yes

This site continues to amaze us. Careers On-line provides job search and employment information to people with disabilities (jobs and resumes are now posted here as well). This is a cooperative effort of U. of Minnesota's Disability Services and US Dept. of Education. Job accommodation information and many links to other useful sites.

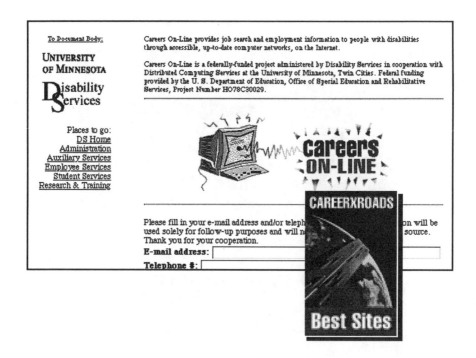

CAREERXROADS

(Commercial)
Mark Mehler/Gerry Crispin, MMC Group
P.O. Box 253, Kendall Park, NJ 08824
908-821-6652 Fax: 908-821-1343 e-mail: mmc@careerxroads.com

Jobs? No
- Cost to post jobs: N/A
- Cost to see jobs: N/A
- Specialty: N/A
- Industry: N/A
- Location: Int'l./US

Resumes? No
- Cost to post resumes: N/A
- Cost to see resumes: N/A

Feature(s)? Push to Applicant, Career Mgm't.

Career Advice? Yes

What can we say. If you are reading this book, this is where we "archive" all our updates. If you still haven't sent an e-mail to us to register for free updates each month, DO IT NOW. We won't be selling banners or spamming you with strange e-mail opportunities. We do want to keep in touch. Check out our "New" listing of seminars and speaking engagement dates. CAREERXROADS is traveling across the US giving seminars to HR Professionals on "Staffing and the Internet."

Carolina Career Center

www.webcom.com/~nccareer/

(Commercial)
Rich Schreyer, Career Confections of the Cent. Carolinas
8508 Park Road #308, Charlotte, NC 28210
704-399-7888 e-mail: nccareer@aol.com

Jobs? Yes
- Cost to post jobs: Fee
- Cost to see jobs: Free
- Specialty: All
- Industry: All
- Location: US/SE/NC

Resumes? Yes
- Cost to post resumes: Fee
- Cost to see resumes: Fee

Feature(s)? N/A

Career Advice? Yes

Resumes can be posted to this site for free while for $25 they will also post it to the Carolina Talent Bank. For $75 they will post your resume to over 500+ organizations. CCC lists the 500 places and they are all over the lot. You can also find a state job telephone hotline listing.

Casting Net

www.castingnet.com

(Commercial)
The Casting Net
333 Washington Blvd, Suite 121, Marina Del Rey, CA 90292
e-mail: castinfo@castingnet.com

Jobs? Yes
- Cost to post jobs: Free
- Cost to see jobs: Fee
- Specialty: Entertainment/Actor
- Industry: Entertainment
- Location: US

Resumes? Yes
- Cost to post resumes: N/A
- Cost to see resumes: N/A

Feature(s)? N/A

Career Advice? No

Actors & actresses pay $19.95 a month to become a member and see positions listed by posting date, location and role. Jobs are posted for free.

Cell Press Online

www.cellpress.com

(Publisher/Trade)
Cell Press
1050 Massachusetts Avenue, Cambridge, Mass 02138
617-661-7057 Fax: 617-661-7061 e-mail: online@cell.com

Jobs? Yes
- Cost to post jobs: Fee
- Cost to see jobs: Free
- Specialty: Science
- Industry: All
- Location: Int'l./US

Resumes? Yes
- Cost to post resumes: Free
- Cost to see resumes: Free

Feature(s)? N/A

Career Advice? No

Cell and its sister magazines owned by the same publisher post jobs and resumes on this web site. Candidates can post resumes for free. All jobs and resumes have direct contact information. Dozens of scientific positions.

CAREERXROADS©
Job, Resume & Career Management Sites on the World Wide Web
• The 1998 Directory •

- 119 -

Chase Professionals

www.chasepro.com

(Recruiting Related Agency)
David Williams, Chase Professionals, Inc.
888-992-4273 e-mail: Sales@ChasePro.com.

Jobs? Yes
- Cost to post jobs: Fee (See Note)
- Cost to see jobs: Free
- Specialty: All
- Industry: All
- Location: US

Resumes? Yes
- Cost to post resumes: Free
- Cost to see resumes: Fee (See Note)

Feature(s)? Push to Applicant

Career Advice? No

For managers in a serious hunt for qualified applicants, Chase Professionals has developed a resume database with a twist. Employers can see a modified profile of the candidates for free and are charged $50 when they want the contact data... but only when the candidate has agreed to release the information. Candidates post their job skills and background information at no charge. A 100% confidential service, candidates are free to choose when to, or when not to, reveal their identity. While posting jobs was free at the time of our review, visitors were notified that new rates are in the offing.

Chattanooga Publishing

www.chatpub.com

(Publisher/Newspaper)
Chattanooga Free-Press
400 E. 11th Street, Chattanooga, TN 37401
423-756-6900

Jobs? Yes
- Cost to post jobs: Fee
- Cost to see jobs: Free
- Specialty: All
- Industry: N/A
- Location: US/S/TN/Chattanooga

Resumes? No
- Cost to post resumes: N/A
- Cost to see resumes: N/A

Feature(s)? N/A

Career Advice? No

Newspaper classified section for the Chattanooga Free Press and the Chatanooga Times. There is no extra charge for placing ads on the web site.

Chicago Software Newspaper

www.chisoft.com

(Publisher/Trade Magazine)
Jeffrey Hunt, Chicago Software Newspaper
2N Riverside Plaza, Ste 2400, Chicago, IL 60606
800-352-0931 Fax: 617-926-1919 e-mail: info@chisoft.com

Jobs? Yes
- Cost to post jobs: Fee
- Cost to see jobs: Free
- Specialty: IT
- Industry: N/A
- Location: US/MW/IL/Chicago/MA/Boston/GA/
  Atlanta/NY

Resumes? No
- Cost to post resumes: N/A
- Cost to see resumes: N/A

Feature(s)? N/A

Career Advice? No

When you enter this site you will scroll down to CareerCat to find close to 700 jobs posted to this monthly tabloid mailed directly to 10,000 software professionals. The cost to post an advertisement in this IT publication will end up on the net as added value. Jobs are primarily located in the IL area. The publication is also distributed to schools for free. For the web site alone the cost is$50 to post on CareerCat for 90 days. Hyper links and e-mail for employers are added at no charge. The publisher will be opening Boston, NY and Atlanta "software editions by 1998.

Chicago Sun Times

www.suntimes.com

(Publisher/Newspaper)
401 N. Wabash Ave.
Chicago, IL 60611
312-321-3000 e-mail: webmaster@suntimes.com

Jobs? Yes
- Cost to post jobs: Fee
- Cost to see jobs: Free
- Specialty: All
- Industry: N/A
- Location: US/MW/IL/Chicago

Resumes? No
- Cost to post resumes: N/A
- Cost to see resumes: N/A

Feature(s)? Push to Applicant

Career Advice? No

Newspaper classified advertisements are available from a well designed search engine. The Chicago Sun Times site has also included a registration notification and claims they will e-mail you position information that matches your skills. Requests remain active for 30 days. If this really works (and we're in the middle of checking it out) this would put the Chicago Sun Times way ahead of its publisher brethren.

Chicago Tribune

www.chicago.tribune.com/career

(Publisher/Newspaper)
Harry Phillips, Chicago Tribune
401 N. Michigan Ave., Chicago, IL 60611
312-222-4211 e-mail: hphillips@tribune.com

Jobs? Yes
- Cost to post jobs: Fee
- Cost to see jobs: Free
- Specialty: All
- Industry: All
- Location: US/MW/IL/Chicago

Resumes? No
- Cost to post resumes: N/A
- Cost to see resumes: N/A

Feature(s)? N/A

Career Advice? Yes

Chicago Tribune classifieds are searchable at CareerPath. If you go to the above URL, click on jobs and it will take you to CareerPath.

Christian Jobs Online

www.christianjobs.com

(Commercial)
P.O. Box 51111
Colorado Springs, CO 80949-1111
719-592-1081 Fax: 719-592-0633 e-mail: info@christianjobs.com

Jobs? Yes
- Cost to post jobs: Fee
- Cost to see jobs: Free
- Specialty: All
- Industry: All
- Location: US

Resumes? Yes
- Cost to post resumes: Free
- Cost to see resumes: Fee

Feature(s)? N/A

Career Advice? No

This is one link too far. On the other hand, there is room for an honest difference or two. It's just that it's too easy to see how quickly this approach to staffing can get out of hand. Christian Jobs Online attaches a special logo for anyone who "signs" a "statement of faith". Obviously this helps like minds find one another. Hmmm. 30 concurrent listings for 6 months will set you back $2,200. Individual listings: $75/each listing. A "Mini-Page", link to your home page, and/or resume information not included.

Cincinnati Employment Classifieds

careerfinder.gocinci.net

(Publisher/Newspaper)
Kathy Drews, Cincinnati Enquirer/Post
513-768-8349

Jobs? Yes
- Cost to post jobs: Fee
- Cost to see jobs: Free
- Specialty: All
- Industry: All
- Location: US/MW/OH/Cincinnati

Resumes? No
- Cost to post resumes: N/A
- Cost to see resumes: N/A

Feature(s)? N/A

Career Advice? No

Help wanted classifieds on-line. You can search the ads for the last week with a search engine that is easy tc use. The site also participates in CareerPath.

CitySurf

www.citysurf.com

(Commercial)
CitySurf
6846 South Canton, Ste. 400, Tulsa, OK 74136
918-492-1170 Fax: 918-492-6676 e-mail: info@citysurf.com

Jobs? No
- Cost to post jobs: N/A
- Cost to see jobs: N/A
- Specialty: N/A
- Industry: N/A
- Location: US

Resumes? No
- Cost to post resumes: N/A
- Cost to see resumes: N/A

Feature(s)? JSK RT/M&L

Career Advice? No

A very cool site for moving and relocation. Find out more about locations through out the US. Tons of information ranging from where to pick apples to how to find the best zoos. Somewhat limited when we tested sports in NY and found only minor league teams. What is NY without info on the major teams. Tough ignoring the Yankees.

CLNET

(College/University)
Richard Chabran, Chicano Studies Research Center
54 Haines Hall, University of Calif., Los Angeles 90024
e-mail: salinas@latino.sscnet.ucla.edu

Jobs? Yes
- Cost to post jobs: Free
- Cost to see jobs: Free
- Specialty: All
- Industry: All
- Location: US/W/CA

Resumes? No
- Cost to post resumes: N/A
- Cost to see resumes: N/A

Feature(s)? Diversity

Career Advice? Yes

On our most recent visit, this site had only 10 jobs posted for positions throughout the US. Direct contact information was posted. Primarily connected to the Southern California Hispanic community, CLNET has lot's of local content regarding Latino organizations and educational resources. Niche site. Nice job.

Coach's Nationwide Job Board

www.coachhelp.com/jobs.htm

(Commercial)
Warren Swann, Comprehensive On-line Access to Coaching Help
P.O. Box 76, Allen, TX 75013
800-339-9652 e-mail: wbswann@mymail.net

Jobs? Yes
- Cost to post jobs: Free
- Cost to see jobs: Free
- Specialty: Sports Coaching/Football
- Industry: Education/HS & College
- Location: Int'l/US

Resumes? No
- Cost to post resumes: N/A
- Cost to see resumes: N/A

Feature(s)? Search by State

Career Advice? No

Coach's Nationwide Job Board is for football coaches who are looking for jobs in high school or college. Positions are listed by state and you can email to the job of your choice. Coaches have approached Warren Swann, the owner, to collect resumes he plans to add this feature as we go to press- possibly for free or a small fee. Company has a product and services directory which is where the money is made. Simple, easy and cool site to view.

CollegeCentral Network

www.collegecentral.com

(Commercial)
Stuart Nachbar, College Central Network
41 West 28th Street, 9th Fl, NY, NY 10001
212-714-1731 Fax: 212-714-1688 e-mail: stuart@collegecentral.com

Jobs? Yes
• Cost to post jobs: Fee
• Cost to see jobs: Free
• Specialty: All/College
• Industry: All
• Location: US

Resumes? Yes
• Cost to post resumes: Free
• Cost to see resumes: Fee

Feature(s)? N/A

Career Advice? Yes

Unique feature of this college site is that the posted positions are e-mailed to school career service centers. This low cost on-line job posting service was designed to one up JobTrak and charges $15 for 30 schools (30 days). No fee for gov't & non-profit organizations. We like the fact that different pages are not only named for their function but also have uniquely registered URLs e.g. Employer Central

http://www.employercentral.com, Student Central
http://www.studentcentral.com.

Career Services Central and Alumni Central follow the same approach. College Central additional services include a resume database that the student can modify and export to other sites. We also like the fact that students and alumni merely log on and declare their school without having to go to their school's career services department to obtain a special password. Student Central and Alumni Central offer free resume entry, resume update and job search services. We encourage exploring this site's value in your strategy.

College Connection

(Commercial)
Bernard Hodes Advertising
555 Madison Avenue, New York, NY 10022
212-758-2600

Jobs? Yes
- Cost to post jobs: Fee
- Cost to see jobs: Free
- Specialty: College
- Industry: All
- Location: US

Resumes? Yes
- Cost to post resumes: Free
- Cost to see resumes: Free

Feature(s)? Career Mgm't.

Career Advice? Yes

A good start and a nice new site for college seniors or recent graduates. Resume writing tips, articles about the hidden job market and long lists of jobs with employers. Recruiters need to check out the owner (See CareerMosaic) for costs.

College Grad Job Hunter

www.collegegrad.com

(Commercial)
Brian Kreuger, College Grad Job Hunter
6910 W. Brown Deer Road, Suite 201, Milwaukee, WI 53223
414-675-9100 Fax: 414-675-9111 e-mail: webmaster@execpc.com

Jobs? Yes
- Cost to post jobs: Fee
- Cost to see jobs: Free
- Specialty: All/College
- Industry: All
- Location: US

Resumes? No
- Cost to post resumes: N/A
- Cost to see resumes: N/A

Feature(s)? JSK/Salary

Career Advice? Yes

College Grad Job Hunter is geared for the college market and visitors can see all positions posted with direct contact information. Job postings are for 90 days and cost $250 ($550 for 1 year). E-mail and hyperlinks are included in those prices. Articles designed to help the job seeker make the right choice for their first employer are available. A salary calculator gives the college grad an idea of what they are worth in different parts of the country and a new internship section has recently been added. Well organized, Job Hunter has the goods to bring job seekers back.

CollegeNet

www.collegenet.com

(Commercial)
CollegeNet
One SW Columbia, Ste. 100, Portland, OR 97258
e-mail: pat@unival.com

Jobs? No
- Cost to post jobs: N/A
- Cost to see jobs: N/A
- Specialty: College/Admissions
- Industry: Education
- Location: US

Resumes? No
- Cost to post resumes: N/A
- Cost to see resumes: N/A

Feature(s)? N/A

Career Advice? Yes

College Net is geared for the person entering college. The site has comprehensive info on scholarships and financial aid. You can apply to 34 universities on line. Although a little off the beaten track when it comes to sites we normally review, there are interesting ideas here for everyone trying to build a user friendly environment on the web.

College News Online

www.collegenews.com

(Publisher/Newspaper)
Chris Brannen, Central Newspaper, Inc.
The Willoughby Tower St.1616, 8 South Michigan Avenue, Chicago, IL 60603
312-263-5388 Fax: 312-263-6095 e-mail: webteam@collegenews.com

Jobs? Yes
- Cost to post jobs: Fee
- Cost to see jobs: Free
- Specialty: College
- Industry: All
- Location: US

Resumes? No
- Cost to post resumes: N/A
- Cost to see resumes: N/A

Feature(s)? N/A

Career Advice? Yes

College News is geared for the student market. Primarily a print publication in the Chicago marketplace, they are trying it out in Philadelphia, NY and Boston. The web component is new and positions are posted with direct contact information. Career information and links to other sites will be up in the future. This is a work in progress and their objective is to expose students to web sites via their marketing mag.

Colorado Jobs Online

www.coloradojobs.com/about/html

(Commercial)
Randy Rose
2110 Hollow Brook Drive, Colorado Springs, CO 80918
719-590-7400 e-mail: rroses@jobdigest.om

Jobs? Yes
- Cost to post jobs: Fee
- Cost to see jobs: Free
- Specialty: All
- Industry: All
- Location: US/W/CO

Resumes? Yes
- Cost to post resumes: Free
- Cost to see resumes: Free

Feature(s)? N/A

Career Advice? No

Colorado Jobs Online has positions and resumes in all disciplines. Employer cost to post a job is $15 for a 30 day listing. Interesting search engine asks questions when you do your initial search (you are asked if you want to look under a sub heading for a more detailed content). Employers see a brief candidate profile and then can link to get the entire document.

The Columbus Dispatch

www.dispatch.com

(Publisher/Newspaper)
Pam Coffman, The Columbus Dispatch
5300 Crosswind Drive, Columbus, OH 43228
614-461-8803 Fax: 614-461-8525 e-mail: pcoffman@dispatch.com

Jobs? Yes
- Cost to post jobs: Fee
- Cost to see jobs: Free
- Specialty: All
- Industry: N/A
- Location: US/MW/OH/Columbus

Resumes? No
- Cost to post resumes: N/A
- Cost to see resumes: N/A

Feature(s)? N/A

Career Advice? Yes

Nice design element when you discover a classified button at the top right side of the home page. Help wanted ads (just not the display ads) are available 7 days a week. A resume builder is included to help job seekers put their best foot forward. Job hunting tips are helpful. A simple search engine gets the job done. This site also participates in CareerPath.

Community Career Center

www.nonprofitjobs.org/

(Commercial)
Gino Maini, Enterprise Inc
2160 W. Charleston, Suite L345, Las Vegas, NV 89102
702-259-6570 Fax: 702-259-0244 e-mail: info@nonprofitjob.org

Jobs? Yes
- Cost to post jobs: Fee
- Cost to see jobs: Free
- Specialty: All
- Industry: Non-Profit
- Location: US

Resumes? Yes
- Cost to post resumes: Fee
- Cost to see resumes: Fee

Feature(s)? N/A

Career Advice? No

When a site promotes non-profit organizations, it usually does not provide other services. The owners here provide structured telephone interviews of candidates, reference checking and a "characteristic" assessment - all for a fee. The site posts jobs and resumes of member organizations but we are wondering about the word non-profit. All types of jobs are posted. Resumes can only be seen by member companies. To post a resume, job seekers pay $25 for6 months. To post a job, recruiters pay for $125 for 60 days.

Computer Science Jobs in Academia

www.cs.brandeis.edu:80/~zippy/academic-cs-jobs.html

(College/University)
Patrick Tufts, Brandeis University
e-mail: zippy@cs.brandeis.edu

Jobs? No
- Cost to post jobs: Free
- Cost to see jobs: Free
- Specialty: IT/University
- Industry: Education/University
- Location: US

Resumes? No
- Cost to post resumes: N/A
- Cost to see resumes: N/A

Feature(s)? JSK/Links

Career Advice? Yes

Links to many US University faculty jobs in Computer Science. Great resource for job seekers on a mission.

Computer World's IT Careers

www.computerworld.com

(Publisher/Trade/Agent)
Jay Savell, Computerworld
500 Old Connecticut Path, Framingham, MA 01701
800-343-6474 Fax: 508-620-7739 e-mail: jay_savell@cw.com

Jobs? Yes
- Cost to post jobs: Fee
- Cost to see jobs: Free
- Specialty: IT
- Industry: Computer
- Location: US

Resumes? Yes
- Cost to post resumes: Free
- Cost to see resumes: N/A

Feature(s)? Push to Applicant

Career Advice? Yes

Computer World's help wanted classifieds are on the web. Every few months we see new features and improvements. A far cry from the primitive version they had just two years ago. Job seekers "register" their skills in a database and the publication's push agent, "CareerMail", will e-mail any positions that match the applicant's background on a daily basis. An extensive listing of career related articles can be keyword searched. Employer packages are available for corporate advertisers. Numerous links to employers are setup on a US map for ease of access. This last is a very nice feature.

Connect to Jobs

www.cabrillo.cc.ca.us/connect/index.html

(College/University)
Lyn Hood, Cabrillo College
Career Planning & Placement, 6500 Soquel Drive, Aptos, CA 95003
408-479-6540 e-mail: lyhood@cabrillo.cc.ca.us

Jobs? No
- Cost to post jobs: N/A
- Cost to see jobs: N/A
- Specialty: All
- Industry: All
- Location: US/W/CA

Resumes? No
- Cost to post resumes: N/A
- Cost to see resumes: N/A

Feature(s)? JSK/Links

Career Advice? Yes

A long list of links with helpful information for the job seeker. Site includes a list of local links for California job sites.

Contract Employment NACCB

www.computerwork.com

(Association)
NAACB
e-mail: webmaster@resourcecenter.com

Jobs? Yes
- Cost to post jobs: Fee
- Cost to see jobs: Free
- Specialty: IT
- Industry: All
- Location: US

Resumes? Yes
- Cost to post resumes: Free
- Cost to see resumes: Fee

Feature(s)? N/A

Career Advice? No

The National Association of Computer Consultant Businesses is a nationwide group made up of more than 300 companies. This site lists contract and regular positions. Direct contact information to member organizations is available. Links to other chapters who may also assist you in your job search can be found here.

Contract Employment Weekly

www.ceweekly.com

(Publisher/Trade)
Jerry Erickson, C.E.Publications
P.O. Box 97000, Kirkland, WA 98083
425-823-2222 Fax: 425-821-0942 e-mail: publisher@ceweekly.com

Jobs? Yes
- Cost to post jobs: Fee
- Cost to see jobs: Fee
- Specialty: IT
- Industry: All
- Location: US

Resumes? Yes
- Cost to post resumes: Free
- Cost to see resumes: Fee

Feature(s)? N/A

Career Advice? Yes

A weekly publication for computer contract service firms. If you register you can see some of the posted jobs for free but to see them all you must pay a fee. Employers pay print advertising costs plus $5 to place their opportunity on this web site.

Contract Employment Connection

iquest.com/~ntes/index.html

(Commercial)
National Technical Employment Services
309 Taylor Street, Scottsboro, AL 35768
205-259-6837 e-mail: info@ntes.com

Jobs? Yes
- Cost to post jobs: Fee
- Cost to see jobs: Free
- Specialty: IT
- Industry: All
- Location: US

Resumes? Yes
- Cost to post resumes: Free
- Cost to see resumes: Fee

Feature(s)? N/A

Career Advice? Yes

CEC's site continues as one of the main online players for advertising contract IT employment opportunities. CEC claims if you e-mail your resume in ASCII or mail it on a floppy, they'll make it available to every technical service firm in the US. Positions are listed from Hotflash magazine. IT/IS positions. In addition, they have a long listing of available contract recruiters. A very interesting idea and we love the marketing implications of that one. If you are a contract recruiter and handle IT openings, can't hurt to be here.

Cool Works

(Commercial)
Bill Berg, Cool Works
P.O.Box 272, Gardiner, MN 59030
406-848-2380 e-mail: greatjobs@coolworks.com

Jobs? Yes
• Cost to post jobs: Fee
• Cost to see jobs: Free
• Specialty: Sports/Outdoors/College
• Industry: Recreation/Hospitality
• Location: US

Resumes? No
• Cost to post resumes: N/A
• Cost to see resumes: N/A

Feature(s)? N/A

Career Advice? No

Cool Works is an inspiration to us all. The site's owner, Bill Berg, posts jobs from national parks, cruise lines, camps, and even jobs for RVers. He claims to have over 24,000 positions listed. Employers pay $40 per posting. All the unique content makes this site worth a visit. If you are looking for a job that is definitely camping by the mainstream, this is the place to go.

Cool Works (SM) *Linking to more than 34,000 Jobs in Great Places*

Check out what it takes to live and work in the kinds of places that most people only get to visit.

What's New

Jobs in National Parks

Ski Jobs

Cruise Jobs

Help Wanted NOW!

CAREERXROADS

Best Sites

Corporate Aviation Resume Exchange

scendtek.com/care

(Commercial)
Richard Johnson, ScendTek Internet Corp.
804 Park Hill Drive, Euless, TX 76040
800-611-3565 e-mail: rdjohn@scendtek.com

Jobs? No
- Cost to post jobs: No
- Cost to see jobs: Free
- Specialty: Airline Pilots
- Industry: Aviation
- Location: US

Resumes? Yes
- Cost to post resumes: Free
- Cost to see resumes: Free

Feature(s)? N/A

Career Advice? No

Easy to use format allows you to save your resume to the site for free. Check sheet designed to make it easy for pilots to fill in the information. 692 pilots' resumes listed. Links to other aviation sites are also included.

Corporate Offsite Resume Database

204.183.166.3/CORD

(Commercial)
Ward Christman, Online Opportunities
422 W. Lincoln Highway, Suite 422, Exton, PA 19341
610-873-6811 e-mail: Carol@jobnet.com

Jobs? No
- Cost to post jobs: N/A
- Cost to see jobs: N/A
- Specialty: All
- Industry: All
- Location: US

Resumes? No
- Cost to post resumes: N/A
- Cost to see resumes: N/A

Feature(s)? RT/Online database

Career Advice? Yes

Would you like to give your managers access to resumes from anywhere in the world? This system allows employers with a modem to dial up and see their corporation's specific resumes. This service also has automated e-mail reply capability. Site demo is worth a look. Call the owner for this private online resume database alternative. See JobNet for other services.

Cowley Job Centre

www.cowleys.com/au/public/jobs.htm#cowleys

(Commercial)
Scott Williams, Cowley Online
P.O. Box 341, Armidale 2350, Australia
e-mail: cowleys@cowleys.com.au

Jobs? Yes
• Cost to post jobs: Free
• Cost to see jobs: Free
• Specialty: All
• Industry: All
• Location: Int'l/Australia

Resumes? No
• Cost to post resumes: N/A
• Cost to see resumes: N/A

Feature(s)? N/A

Career Advice? Yes

If you need to post positions in Australia, the Cowley Job Centre does it simply and for free. Job seekers can e-mail responses back to the employer after reviewing a short "brief" about the position. A long list of links to Australian job sites and newsgroups are featured along with considerable non-job related content. You can also find contact information on over 10,000 Australian business web sites and over 832,000 businesses. Lots of general info on Australia located here as well.

Creative Freelancers Online

www.freelancers.com

(Recruiting Related Agency)
Marilyn Howard, Creative Freelancers
99 Park Avenue #210A, New York, NY 10016
888-398-9500 e-mail: cfonline@freelancers.com

Jobs? Yes
• Cost to post jobs: Free
• Cost to see jobs: Free
• Specialty: Creative and Graphic Arts
• Industry: Entertainment
• Location: US

Resumes? Yes
• Cost to post resumes: Free
• Cost to see resumes: Free (See Note)

Feature(s)? N/A

Career Advice? No

Site provides job listings and resumes (all coded) for professionals with freelance talent in both the Entertainment and fine art's. These include: illustrators, designers, computer artists, writers, directors etc. Resumes can be entered for free via e-mail but the recruiter does not see the contact information. If you hire someone there is a $50 charge. Site is owned by a temporary employment agency. Simple, easy to find what you want and worth a visit.

Crystallography Worldwide

www.unige.ch/crystal/w3vlc/crystal.index.html

(College/University)
Lachlan Cranswick, University of Geneva
e-mail: lachlan@dmp.csiro.au

Jobs? Yes
- Cost to post jobs: Free
- Cost to see jobs: Free
- Specialty: Science/Crystallography
- Industry: Education/University
- Location: Int'l/US

Resumes? No
- Cost to post resumes: N/A
- Cost to see resumes: N/A

Feature(s)? N/A

Career Advice? No

Employers can post jobs with an online form for this specialty- crystallography. The site lists career centers around the world that can help job seekers find an opportunity.

Cultural Human Resource Council

www.culturenet.ca/chrc/ehpchrc.htm

(Association)
Cultural Human Resource Council
17 York Street #201, Ottawa, Canada K1N 9J6
613-562-1535 Fax: 613-562-2982 e-mail: info@culturalhrc.ca

Jobs? Yes
- Cost to post jobs: Free
- Cost to see jobs: Free
- Specialty: College/Internship
- Industry: All
- Location: US

Resumes? No
- Cost to post resumes: N/A
- Cost to see resumes: N/A

Feature(s)? N/A

Career Advice? No

The Council brings people together to address the development needs of people in the arts in Canada. Internships are listed and there is a $50 application fee to apply.

Cyberspace Jobs

www.best.com:80/~lianne/

(Commercial)
Lianne Thompson
465 Utah #3, San Francisco, CA 94110
415-431-4076 e-mail: lianne@best.com

Jobs? No
• Cost to post jobs: N/A
• Cost to see jobs: N/A
• Specialty: IT/Web
• Industry: All
• Location: US

Resumes? No
• Cost to post resumes: N/A
• Cost to see resumes: N/A

Feature(s)? JSK/Links

Career Advice? Yes

Interesting information on 17 areas of jobs in cyberspace with detailed job descriptions and salary information. Once you find the type of job you desire, the site will then take you to corporations that have those types of openings. You have to do the work from there.

The Dallas Morning News

www.dallasnews.com

(Publisher/Newspaper)
Lilia Jones, Dallas Morning News
P.O. Box 655237, Dallas, TX 75265
214-977-8611 Fax: 214-977-7850 e-mail: ljones@dallasnews.com

Jobs? Yes
• Cost to post jobs: Fee
• Cost to see jobs: Free
• Specialty: All
• Industry: All
• Location: US/SW/TX/Dallas

Resumes? No
• Cost to post resumes: N/A
• Cost to see resumes: N/A

Feature(s)? N/A

Career Advice? No

Daily and Sunday classified advertisements. site includes an interesting search engine where you can put in words for jobs that you DO NOT want to see. Saves time.

Definitive Internet Career Guide; The

phoenix.placement.oakland.edu/career/Guide.htm

(College/University)
Oakland University
e-mail: placement@oakland.edu

Jobs? No
- Cost to post jobs: N/A
- Cost to see jobs: N/A
- Specialty: All
- Industry: All
- Location: US

Resumes? No
- Cost to post resumes: N/A
- Cost to see resumes: N/A

Feature(s)? JSK/Links

Career Advice? No

The Definitive Internet Career Guide has one of the longest and best lists of links to job, resume and career management sites on the web. You can scroll or search by the alphabet. Happy hunting.

Deja News

www.dejanews.com

(Commercial)
Stephanie Tirloni, 5407-B Clay Avenue
Austin, TX 78756
512-451-0433 Fax: 512-459-0298 e-mail: stirloni@dejanews.com

Jobs? No
- Cost to post jobs: N/A
- Cost to see jobs: N/A
- Specialty: All
- Industry: All
- Location: US

Resumes? No
- Cost to post resumes: N/A
- Cost to see resumes: N/A

Feature(s)? RT & JSK/Search Engine

Career Advice? No

Excellent tool for job seekers looking to drill into the newsgroups for jobs and for recruiters looking for specific resumes from the same source. This newsgroup search engine is a fundamental tool for your kitbag.

The Denver Post Online

www.denverpost.com

(Publisher/Newspaper)
Todd Engdahl
1560 Broadway, Denver, CO 80202
303-825-2525 Fax: 303-820-1369 e-mail: tengdahl@denverpost.com

Jobs? Yes
- Cost to post jobs: Fee
- Cost to see jobs: Free
- Specialty: All
- Industry: N/A
- Location: US/W/CO/Denver

Resumes? No
- Cost to post resumes: N/A
- Cost to see resumes: N/A

Feature(s)? N/A

Career Advice? No

Help wanted newspaper classifieds. Publisher participates in CareerPath (See CareerPath).

DesignSphere Online

www.dsphere.net/comm/jobs.html

(Commercial)
Irene Woerner, Cogent Software, Inc.
221 E. Walnut St., Suite 215, Pasadena, CA 91101
818-585-2788 Fax: 818-585-2785 e-mail: exposure@dsphere.com

Jobs? Yes
- Cost to post jobs: Free
- Cost to see jobs: Free
- Specialty: IT/Multimedia/Graphic Arts
- Industry: All
- Location: US

Resumes? Yes
- Cost to post resumes: Free
- Cost to see resumes: Free

Feature(s)? N/A

Career Advice? No

Site has changed its address and added graphics since our last visit. A little slow coming in. Jobs and resumes for the graphic arts field are free to post and free to see. All contact information is included.

DICE

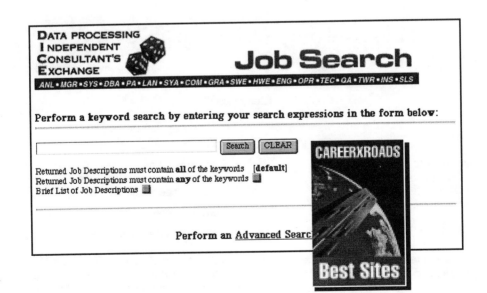

www.dice.com

(Commercial)
J. Peterson, D & L Online
P.O.Box 7070, Des Moines, IA 50309
515-280-1144 Fax: 515-280-1452 e-mail: sales@dlinc.com

Jobs? Yes
- Cost to post jobs: Fee
- Cost to see jobs: Free
- Specialty: IT
- Industry: All
- Location: US

Resumes? Yes
- Cost to post resumes: Free
- Cost to see resumes: Fee

Feature(s)? N/A

Career Advice? No

Dice caters to the data processing, engineering and technical writing fields. Site claims 2,000 jobs are posted each day with over 22,000 open jobs that are less than 30 days old. All jobs have direct contact information. The job seeker fills out their questionnaire for free and with over 600 companies you should be getting some calls. Unlimited job postings are in the $500 per month range. Niche site that does a good job and knows how to promote its services.

Digital City South Florida

southflorida.digitalcity.com

(Publisher/Newspaper)
Catherine Daley, Sun-Sentinel
200 East Las Olas Blvd., Fort Lauderdale, FL 33301-2293
954-459-2297 Fax: 954-459-2288 e-mail: cdaley@digitalcity.com

Jobs? Yes
- Cost to post jobs: Fee
- Cost to see jobs: Free
- Specialty: All
- Industry: All
- Location: US/SE/FL

Resumes? No
- Cost to post resumes: N/A
- Cost to see resumes: N/A

Feature(s)? N/A

Career Advice? No

Available on the net and through AOL, Digital cities plans to rollout to nearly 100 cities by the end of 1997. Currently in 13 cities, DC offers employers the opportunity to link directly to their company site and offers profiles and postings. (See also Career Spot) On our first visit to this site all we saw were ads from the Florida Sun-Sentinel. Still a work in progress, Digital cities needs some thought on its design to be effective in recruitment.

Direct Marketing World Job Center

www.dmworld.com

(Commercial)
Mainsafe Marketing Information
1113 Channing Way, Ste. 11, Berkeley, CA 94702
e-mail: jobs@wweb.mainsail.com

Jobs? Yes
- Cost to post jobs: Free
- Cost to see jobs: Free
- Specialty: Marketing
- Industry: All
- Location: US

Resumes? Yes
- Cost to post resumes: Free
- Cost to see resumes: Free

Feature(s)? N/A

Career Advice? Yes

Jobs and resumes can be posted for free to this direct marketing site. The most effective element on this small site emphasizes the recently posted positions. There were over 200 jobs to choose when we reviewed which was double the number available from our '97 review. Simple niche.

Diversity Careers Online

www.diversitycareers.com

(Publisher/Trade)
Janet Penn, Diversity/Careers in Eng. & Information Technology
P.O. Box 557, Springfield, NJ 07081
201-912-8555 Fax: 201-912-8599 e-mail: diversity@worldnet.att.net

Jobs? Yes
• Cost to post jobs: Fee
• Cost to see jobs: Free
• Specialty: Engineering/IT
• Industry: All
• Location: US

Resumes? Yes
• Cost to post resumes: Free
• Cost to see resumes: Fee

Feature(s)? Diversity

Career Advice? Yes

This publication comes out in print 6 times a year for minority technical professionals. Online, Diversity Careers provides links to those companies advertising in their publication. Resumes can be posted for free and are then sent to the companies that advertise in print.

DoctorLink

www.doctorlink.com

(Commercial)
e-mail: drlink@doctorlink.comor

Jobs? Yes
• Cost to post jobs: Free
• Cost to see jobs: Free
• Specialty: Health Care/MD
• Industry: Health Care
• Location: US/NW/WA

Resumes? Yes
• Cost to post resumes: Free
• Cost to see resumes: Free

Feature(s)? No

Career Advice? No

The Doctor is in and there are several dozen medical positions and resumes posted on this site. Long list of links to many medical foundations and information on many illnesses. Articles about medical issues with children give this site added value. Site is always under construction.

Drake Beam Morin

www.dbm.com/dbm.html

(Recruiting Related Agency)
Steve Hoffman
100 Park Avenue, Third Floor, New York, NY 10017
800-326-0033

Jobs? Yes
- Cost to post jobs: Free
- Cost to see jobs: Free (See Note)
- Specialty: All
- Industry: All
- Location: US

Resumes? Yes
- Cost to post resumes: Free
- Cost to see resumes: Free

Feature(s)? N/A

Career Advice? Yes

Employers should register at this online site of one of the largest outplacement firms in the country in order to get access to DBM's candidate resume database. This is a new feature that certainly can't hurt any recruiter. Employers are invited to post their jobs but unfortunately, DBM only makes them available to their "clients". We can't blame them but it does mean responses will be restricted.

e-Math American Mathematical Society

www.ams.org/committee/profession/employ.html

(Association)
American Mathematical Society
P.O. Box 6248, Providence, RI 02940
800-321-4267 Fax: 401-455-4000 e-mail: emp-info@ams.org

Jobs? Yes
- Cost to post jobs: Fee
- Cost to see jobs: Free
- Specialty: Science/Mathematics
- Industry: Education
- Location: US

Resumes? Yes
- Cost to post resumes: Free
- Cost to see resumes: Free

Feature(s)? Push to Applicant

Career Advice? No

If you need a math wizard, this niche site allows recruiters to post positions for 60 days for $120. Site will e-mail openings to its subscribers for free. These positions are published through the American Mathematical Society whose journal accepts classified ads as well.

E-span

(Recruiting Related Agency)
Barbara Ruess, J. B. Laughrey, Inc.
8440 Woodfield Crossing Blvd., Ste 170, Indianapolis, IN 46240
800-682-2901 e-mail: info@espan.com

Jobs? Yes
- Cost to post jobs: Fee
- Cost to see jobs: Free
- Specialty: All
- Industry: All
- Location: US

Resumes? Yes
- Cost to post resumes: Free
- Cost to see resumes: Fee

Feature(s)? Diversity, Search by State

Career Advice? Yes

Resume Mail is E-Span's "push" technology which allows companies to enter their requirements once and then receive weekly e-mails of resumes posted which match their requirements. As one of the larger career hubs, e-span maintains 10,000+ job listings and claims 30,000 searches a day. With more than 5000 sources of employment related information and a focus on tools, services, resources for job seekers and recruiters, e-span remains one of the net's best. This site is now under the same ownership as Nationwide Advertising.

Eagleview

(Commercial)
Amanda Roy
1601 Trapelo Road, Waltham, MA 02154-7300
617-672-6000 Fax: 617-672-6019 e-mail: evi@eagleview.com

Jobs? Yes
- Cost to post jobs: Fee
- Cost to see jobs: Free
- Specialty: All
- Industry: N/A
- Location: US

Resumes? Yes
- Cost to post resumes: Free
- Cost to see resumes: Fee

Feature(s)? Push to Applicant

Career Advice? Yes

Eagleview matches company jobs with a job seekers background and then e-mails the results. Job seekers can post resumes for free or, if you need confidentiality, it will cost $100. Employer pays $10,000 for access to their resume database and then pays a 5% recruitment fee if a candidate is hired. If you want Eagleview to do the resume searching for you the charge is 15%. If you want contract recruiters they can provide them as well. Database has over 5,000 resumes- strictly in IT. Eagleview claims over 100 clients. We have a hunch these costs will change in '98. Very focused in the Northeast but looks to expand nationwide. We can't reconcile the costs noted above versus the models we see as successful long term. So, even though their clients all give them high marks, we haven't included them this year among the "best of the best".

Eastern & European JobBANK

(Commercial)
Philip Atkinson, Scala ECE
Budapest
361-327-5805 Fax: 361-266-5701 e-mail: philip.atkinson@scala.hu

Jobs? Yes
- Cost to post jobs: Free
- Cost to see jobs: Free
- Specialty: All
- Industry: All
- Location: Int'l/US

Resumes? Yes
- Cost to post resumes: Free
- Cost to see resumes: Free

Feature(s)? N/A

Career Advice? No

If you want to look for candidates in Eastern and Central Europe this site had 24 jobs listed and over 220 resumes that could be seen for free.

Edphysician

www.edphysician.com/

(Commercial)
Ralph Single
P.O. Box 1361, Derry, New Hampshire 03038
603-437-2989 Fax: 603-437-2989 e-mail: info@edphysician.com

Jobs? Yes
• Cost to post jobs: Free
• Cost to see jobs: Free
• Specialty: Health Care/MD/Emergency Room
• Industry: Health Care
• Location: US

Resumes? No
• Cost to post resumes: N/A
• Cost to see resumes: N/A

Feature(s)? Search by State

Career Advice? No

Job opportunities for emergency room doctors. Ed Physician has upgraded its graphics and the new look makes it easy to navigate and conduct a search. A state directory allows you to search for jobs by location with direct contact information.

Education Jobs Marketplace

www.edjobs.com

(Commercial)
Mike Schackel, President, Education Jobs Marketplace
4060 Muirfield Place, Lompoc, CA 93436
805-733-4626 e-mail: admin@edjobs.com

Jobs? Yes
• Cost to post jobs: Fee
• Cost to see jobs: Free
• Specialty: Teaching
• Industry: Education
• Location: Int'l./US

Resumes? Yes
• Cost to post resumes: Fee
• Cost to see resumes: Free

Feature(s)? Search by State

Career Advice? No

Education Jobs Marketplace is a new site catering to school teachers and the boards that hire them all over the world. Search engine gives you the ability to look by state, job level or specialty. Cost to post your resume is $20 while employers pay $50 to post a position for 30 days and $2 for each additional month the job is listed. Other packages are available. Give this site some time to gain it's "education" as we did not find any jobs posted here on our visit.

Educator's Network EDNET

pages.prodigy.com/CA/luca52a/bagley.html

(Commercial)
Karla Freedman, Educator's Network-EDNET
5426 Woodlake Avenue, Woodland Hills, CA 91367
818-999-9432 Fax: 818-999-5134 e-mail: luca52a@prodigy.com

Jobs? Yes
- Cost to post jobs: Fee
- Cost to see jobs: Free
- Specialty: Teaching
- Industry: Education/K-12
- Location: US/W/CA

Resumes? No
- Cost to post resumes: N/A
- Cost to see resumes: N/A

Feature(s)? N/A

Career Advice? Yes

There were over 285 teaching positions vacant in the Southern CA area listed here when we visited and EDNET plans to expand to the rest of the state (21 other postings). Jobs are posted within 48 hours and you can place your initial openings for 3 months for free. If you want to continue the cost is $300 for the next 12 month period. Good Q&A regarding how to get a job in the CA school system. Search results show the type of position and the school district. You have to do the rest. Long list of links to school districts.

El Nueuvo Herald digital

www.elherald.com

(Publisher/Newspaper)
Lois Gonzalez, Miami Herald
Miami, FL
305-376-3150 e-mail: business@herald.com

Jobs? Yes
- Cost to post jobs: Fee
- Cost to see jobs: Free
- Specialty: All
- Industry: All
- Location: US/SE/FL/Miami

Resumes? No
- Cost to post resumes: N/A
- Cost to see resumes: N/A

Feature(s)? Diversity

Career Advice? No

Hispanic edition of the Miami Herald. Classified section is posted on this web site. Site can be read in Spanish or English- you have your choice. Smart move.

Electric Power NewsLink

www.powermag.com

(Publisher/Trade)
Jeff Chufar, McGraw-Hill/Power
11 West 19th Street, 2nd Floor, New York, NY 10011
330-478-4037 e-mail: powermag@mindspring.com

Jobs? Yes
- Cost to post jobs: Fee
- Cost to see jobs: Free
- Specialty: Engineering/Power
- Industry: Utility/Power
- Location: US

Resumes? No
- Cost to post resumes: N/A
- Cost to see resumes: N/A

Feature(s)? N/A

Career Advice? No

On some sites you have to have a crystal ball to find their employment listings. This could be one of them. When you enter this site you need to click on Electric Power NewsLink and then all the way at the bottom is a link to employment listings. Positions listed are advertised in Power, a McGraw-Hill magazine.

Electronic Engineering Times

techweb.cmp.com/eet/823/

(Publisher/Trade)
Lynette McGill Hodge, CMP Media Group
(See TechWeb)
800-598-7689 e-mail: lhodge@cmp.com

Jobs? Yes
- Cost to post jobs: Fee
- Cost to see jobs: Free
- Specialty: IT/Engineering
- Industry: Computer
- Location: US

Resumes? No
- Cost to post resumes: N/A
- Cost to see resumes: N/A

Feature(s)? N/A

Career Advice? Yes

Companies can post ads to the EETimes web site for $150 whether an ad is running in the publication or not. The same ad is automatically posted to Career Mosaic for 30 days. Since Career Mosaic is also a $150 cost, it seems logical to always place your ad in EETimes to get the "twofer".

Electronic News On-Line

www.sumnet.com/enews

(Publisher/Trade Magazine)
Diana Basso, Electronic News
2 5th Avenue, 4th Floor, New York, NY 10001
800-883-6397 Fax: 212-545-5455 e-mail: jobs@employmentedge.com

Jobs? Yes
- Cost to post jobs: Fee
- Cost to see jobs: Free
- Specialty: Engineering/Elect.
- Industry: Electronics
- Location: US

Resumes? No
- Cost to post resumes: N/A
- Cost to see resumes: N/A

Feature(s)? Yes

Career Advice? No

Ads are posted weekly from the Electronic News ($125/inch) and are put on their web site at no extra charge. Employer links are available. Everything from technician to CEO listed during our stopover.

Employers Applicant Bank

eab.datastar.net/eab.html

(Commercial)
Multimedia Resume Services
P.O. Box 1911, Picayune, MS 39466
e-mail: mmresume@datastar.net

Jobs? Yes
- Cost to post jobs: Fee
- Cost to see jobs: Free
- Specialty: All
- Industry: All
- Location: US

Resumes? Yes
- Cost to post resumes: Free
- Cost to see resumes: Free

Feature(s)? Push to Employer

Career Advice? Yes

Employers Applicant Bank is designed so that employers can match posted positions with the site's resume database. Resumes are then forwarded as part of the package ($115 for 30 days). Resumes can be seen for free. The job seeker can add a picture and/or an audio message to their virtual resume if they choose (and we think that might be a crazy thing to do unless you are an actor).

EmployMed

www.njnet.com/~embbs/job/jobs.html

(Commercial)
Ash Nashed, M.D., Triple Star Systems
10 Swackhamer Road, Whitehouse Station, NJ 08889
908-469-7129 e-mail: ashrafn@aol.com

Jobs? Yes
• Cost to post jobs: Fee
• Cost to see jobs: Free
• Specialty: Health Care/MD
• Industry: Health Care
• Location: US

Resumes? No
• Cost to post resumes: N/A
• Cost to see resumes: N/A

Feature(s)? Search by State

Career Advice? No

EmployMed covers all medical specialties for MDs. Recruiters pay $50 to post a position for two months. Site states they will have your job up within 48 hours. Other pricing packages are available. Search by state (not all of them) and various skill categories.

Employment Channel

www.employ.com

(Publisher/Cable)
J.W. McKinnon, The Employment Channel
152 Madison Avenue, New York, NY 10016
e-mail: administrator@employ.com

Jobs? Yes
• Cost to post jobs: Fee
• Cost to see jobs: Free
• Specialty: All
• Industry: N/A
• Location: US/NE/NY/NYC

Resumes? Yes
• Cost to post resumes: Free
• Cost to see resumes: Fee

Feature(s)? Push to Applicant

Career Advice? Yes

If you can stay up until midnight, Channel 31 in the NY/NJ area posts jobs of all types on their web site and lists them on their hour long TV program. Positions can be seen on this web site anytime. Business must be good because they claim to be expanding into Boston, Phil., SF and LA. Resumes can also be posted for free and seen by companies who pay to post jobs. A live chat room is planned for the future. Not quite ready for prime time yet. TV costs will set you back $1000 plus.

Employment Opportunities in Water Resources

www.uwin.siu.edu/announce/jobs/

(College/University)
Southern Illinois University
e-mail: webmaster@siu.edu

Jobs? Yes
• Cost to post jobs: Free
• Cost to see jobs: Free
• Specialty: Environmental/Water
• Industry: Water
• Location: US

Resumes? No
• Cost to post resumes: N/A
• Cost to see resumes: N/A

Feature(s)? N/A

Career Advice? Yes

Southern Illinois University has put up this specialty site to post jobs for academic and non-academic positions in water resources. Lots of industry information as well as a listing of seminars in related topics. How can we resist. We've often thought sites like this were all wet.

Employment Post

world.net/emp-post/about.html

(Publisher/Newspaper)
Australia
022-415-888

Jobs? Yes
• Cost to post jobs: Fee
• Cost to see jobs: Free
• Specialty: All
• Industry: All
• Location: Int'/Australia

Resumes? No
• Cost to post resumes: N/A
• Cost to see resumes: N/A

Feature(s)? N/A

Career Advice? No

Employment Post states it is the first newspaper in Australia to place positions on the Internet. If you put an ad in the newsprint version you receive the web for free. Search engine works well. Site is clean and simple.

Employnet

employnet-inc.ksi.com/index.htm

(Recruiting Related Agency-Group)
Jim Chrisholm, 111 Broadway
Floor 8, New York, NY 10006
212-634-0604 Fax: 212-634-0611 e-mail: resume@employnet-inc.com

Jobs? No
• Cost to post jobs: N/A
• Cost to see jobs: N/A
• Specialty: All
• Industry: N/A
• Location: US

Resumes? Yes
• Cost to post resumes: Fee
• Cost to see resumes: Free

Feature(s)? N/A

Career Advice? No

Employnet claims over 600 recruitment firms use their resume database (resumes are scanned). Recruiters use a dial up system to get to the database. Site charges $49 for the job seeker to post a resume. Interesting career articles.

Engine Room

www.iweb.co.uk/iwsearch.html#map

(Commercial)
i web
United Kingdom
e-mail: jobs@iweb.co.uk

Jobs? Yes
• Cost to post jobs: Fee
• Cost to see jobs: Free
• Specialty: All
• Industry: All
• Location: Int'l/UK

Resumes? Yes
• Cost to post resumes: Free
• Cost to see resumes: Fee

Feature(s)? Push to Applicant

Career Advice? No

International sites are not as responsive to our inquiries as sites in the US. We cannot tell if engine room is a headhunter posting client opportunities or a Commercial service. Job seekers have many ways to cut this job database and quickly find the job they seek. In addition, applicants can quickly point and click to record their interests and skills and have Engine Room match and send leads via e-mail. Great design.

EngineeringJob Source

(Publisher/Newspaper)
Jean Eggertsen
2016 Manchester #24, Ann Arbor, MI 48104
313-971-6995 Fax: 313-677-4386 e-mail: advertise@engineerjobs.com

Jobs? Yes
• Cost to post jobs: Fee
• Cost to see jobs: Free
• Specialty: Engineering
• Industry: All
• Location: US/MW

Resumes? No
• Cost to post resumes: N/A
• Cost to see resumes: N/A

Feature(s)? Push to Applicant

Career Advice? No

Engineering Job Source has two free weekly online job publications that they e-mail to visitors who register. The publications are engineering & technical positions in Michigan and Illinois provided by employers who pay $50 per position.

Engineering Jobs

www.engineeringjobs.com

(Commercial)
Wayne Black, Engineering Jobs
P.O. Box1195, El Cerrito, CA 94530
510-237-3323 Fax: 510-237-3324 e-mail: feedback@engineeringjobs.com

Jobs? Yes
• Cost to post jobs: Free
• Cost to see jobs: Free
• Specialty: Engineering
• Industry: All
• Location: US

Resumes? Yes
• Cost to post resumes: Free
• Cost to see resumes: Free

Feature(s)? N/A

Career Advice? No

Corporations link their openings for engineering positions from this site. Applicants can have a link to their full resume from a short profile on Engineering Jobs. Resumes are sorted by specialty and there are dozens of them to choose from. Corporations pay for placing banner ads.

CAREERXROADS©
Job, Resume & Career Management Sites on the World Wide Web
• The 1998 Directory •

- 153 -

Engineering News Record

www.enr.com

(Publisher/Trade)
Mark Barreca, The McGraw-Hill Companies
1221 Avenue of the Americas, 41st Floor, New York, NY 10020
800-458-3842 Fax: 212-512-2074 e-mail: mark_barreca@mcgraw-hill.com

Jobs? Yes
- Cost to post jobs: Fee
- Cost to see jobs: Free
- Specialty: Engineering/Civil/Design
- Industry: Construction
- Location: Int'l./US

Resumes? No
- Cost to post resumes: N/A
- Cost to see resumes: N/A

Feature(s)? Yes

Career Advice? Yes

Positions are posted from this national weekly publication geared to the construction, environmental, architectural and design engineering industry. Ads can be seen for three weeks from date of issue. Search engine allows sorting by title, keyword and state to make it easy to quickly hone in on your next opportunity. Direct contact information is available.

Entry Level Job Seeker Assistant

members.aol.com/Dylander/jobhome.html

(Commercial)
Joseph E. Schmalhofer
e-mail: Dylander@aol.com

Jobs? Yes
- Cost to post jobs: N/A
- Cost to see jobs: N/A
- Specialty: College
- Industry: N/A
- Location: US

Resumes? Yes
- Cost to post resumes: Free
- Cost to see resumes: Free

Feature(s)? Career Mgm't.

Career Advice? Yes

Good things stay the same and this site's owner keeps up to date. The Entry Level Job Seeker Assistant is free to all who post jobs and resumes alike. Emphasizing the recent college graduate, this site has a list of company links and information on how to post your resume to the web. Keep it up.

The Environmental Careers Organization

www.eco.org

(Association)
Celine Pering, The Environmental Careers Organization, Inc.
179 South Street, Boston, MA 02111
617-426-4375 Fax: 617-423-0998 e-mail: cpering@eco.org

Jobs? Yes
- Cost to post jobs: Free
- Cost to see jobs: Free
- Specialty: Environmental/Internship
- Industry: All
- Location: US

Resumes? No
- Cost to post resumes: N/A
- Cost to see resumes: N/A

Feature(s)? N/A

Career Advice? Yes

Environmental internship positions are listed at locations all over the US. Openings are coded and you can apply online. Postings are free. Good career information and a list of links to environmental sites are also here. Why the site codes the jobs is something we don't understand. All you have to do is ask the candidate where they found out about the job and the recruiter will surely advertise again. This site could be more user friendly.

Environmental Careers World

www.environmental-jobs.com

(Commercial)
757-727-7895 Fax: 757-727-7904 e-mail: ecwo@environmental-jobs.com

Jobs? Yes
- Cost to post jobs: Fee
- Cost to see jobs: Free
- Specialty: Environmental
- Industry: All
- Location: US

Resumes? No
- Cost to post resumes: N/A
- Cost to see resumes: N/A

Feature(s)? N/A

Career Advice? Yes

Environmental Careers World posts positions and gives career advice here. Recruiters pay $69 for a 30 day run and, if you are a non-profit organization, you get to pay only $39. A link is an additional $25. Jobs in numerous environmental fields are posted. A few career articles can also be seen and, if you register, you will receive a copy of their publication.

EPage Greater NYC Classifieds

ep.com

(Commercial)
Brad Waller
P.O. Box 2356, Redondo Beach, CA 90278
310-792-0128 Fax: 310-792-0128 e-mail: epage@ep.com

Jobs? Yes
- Cost to post jobs: Fee
- Cost to see jobs: Free
- Specialty: All
- Industry: All
- Location: US

Resumes? No
- Cost to post resumes: N/A
- Cost to see resumes: N/A

Feature(s)? N/A

Career Advice? No

Your "local" classifieds section is here- ever kind of classifieds. Posting costs $8 with contact information. If you are looking for antiques, cars or anything else your heart desires along with help wanted, you might find it at EPage. It looks as if the owners are trying to change their design. We think it might be a good idea. We don't believe models like this will have longevity. You'll find Epage in nearly every city.

Equipment Leasing Association Online

www.elaonline.com

(Association)
Denise L. James, Equipment Leasing Association
1300 N. 17th Street, Suite 1010, Arlington, VA 22209
703-527-8655 Fax: 703-527-2649 e-mail: ela@elamail.com

Jobs? Yes
- Cost to post jobs: Fee
- Cost to see jobs: Free
- Specialty: Leasing
- Industry: Equipment Leasing
- Location: US

Resumes? No
- Cost to post resumes: N/A
- Cost to see resumes: N/A

Feature(s)? N/A

Career Advice? All

The name says it all regarding the types of jobs and career opportunities listed at this site. Cost to post a position is still $295 for six weeks for ELA members or$495 for non-members. All types of positions are listed for this industry with direct contact information available on the web.

Escoffier On Line - Employment Resources

www.escoffier.com/nonscape/employ.shtml

(College/University)
George Cook, Escoffier On Line
P.O. Box 225, Sea Cliff, NY 11579
516-676-8507 e-mail: webmaster@escoffier.com

Jobs? Yes
- Cost to post jobs: Free
- Cost to see jobs: Free
- Specialty: Food/Chefs
- Industry: Hospitality
- Location: Int'l/US

Resumes? Yes
- Cost to post resumes: Free
- Cost to see resumes: Free

Feature(s)? N/A

Career Advice? No

Escoffier on Line is run by the New York Institute of Technology Culinary Arts Program. Site lists positions all over the world for chefs ("working", executive, pastry, baker, food & beverage managers or any food service employment). Resumes are also posted and you can respond directly online with the advertisement placed in your e-mail so there is no question what you are responding to. Site also provides a list of links to jobs in the food service business. Easy to view. This is a well constructed site. Not big enough for a search engine...yet.

Exec-U-Net

www.execunet.com

(Recruiting Related Agency)
Dave Opton, Exec-U-Net, Inc.
25 Van Zant Street, Norwalk, CT 06855
800-637-3126 Fax: 203-851-5177 e-mail: execunet@execunet.com

Jobs? Yes
- Cost to post jobs: Free
- Cost to see jobs: Fee
- Specialty: All
- Industry: N/A
- Location: ALL

Resumes? No
- Cost to post resumes: N/A
- Cost to see resumes: N/A

Feature(s)? N/A

Career Advice? Yes

One of the pioneers in networking and business leads, Exec-U-Net offers an online executive job listing report. Job leads are generated from members as well as companies and search firms for positions with a minimum salary level of $75,000. Originally developed to focus on its group meetings that are held monthly throughout the US, members pay $110 (3 months) to $290 (12 months) to receive job leads in the mail or now...on the net. (Only fee paid subscribers can obtain listings. Employers or Search firms can list jobs at no charge). Member rules prevent sharing with other job seekers and the net has interesting security features.

ExecuBank

(Recruiting Related Agency)
Byron House, Front Street, Arnold, Nottingham NG5 7EG England
(0115) 920 1200 e-mail: sales@execubank.com

Jobs? Yes
- Cost to post jobs: Free
- Cost to see jobs: Fee
- Specialty: All/Executive
- Industry: All
- Location: Int'l./UK

Resumes? Yes
- Cost to post resumes: Fee
- Cost to see resumes: Free

Feature(s)? No

Career Advice? No

Execubank connects third party recruiters and outplacement organizations to place candidates. Recruiters can use this service for free to post jobs and obtain resumes from the site's database. Information is transferred via floppy, hard copy or updated on the net on a daily basis.

Execubank

www.execujobs.com

(Recruiting Related Agency)
RealBank
295 Greenwich Street, Suite 149, New York, NY 10009
212-344-2118 Fax: 212-344-2539 e-mail: execu@execujobs.com

Jobs? Yes
- Cost to post jobs: Fee
- Cost to see jobs: Free
- Specialty: Finance/Banking
- Industry: Finance/Banking
- Location: US/E/NY/NYC

Resumes? Yes
- Cost to post resumes: Free
- Cost to see resumes: Free

Feature(s)?

Career Advice? No

Execubank has finance, legal, marketing and sales executive openings. Free to employers to post positions. Site creates confidential profiles and forwards contact information to applicants. Job posting $95.

EZaccess

www.ezaccess.com

(Recruiting Related Agency)
Mike Silvester
1000 Marina Blvd, Suite 550, Brisbane, CA 94005
415-869-2535 Fax: 415-869-2591 e-mail: mike.silvester@ezaccess.com

Jobs? No
• Cost to post jobs: N/A
• Cost to see jobs: N/A
• Specialty: All
• Industry: All
• Location: US

Resumes? No
• Cost to post resumes: N/A
• Cost to see resumes: N/A

Feature(s)? RT/resume database

Career Advice? No

EZaccess supplies applicant tracking software. Employers input resumes via scanning, the Internet, or fax. EZaccess has extensive reporting capability and is easily customized.

Federal Job Announcement Search

www.fedworld.gov

(Government)
National Technical Information Service
U.S. Department of Commerce, Springfield, VA 22161
703-487-4650 e-mail: webmaster@fedworld.gov

Jobs? Yes
• Cost to post jobs: (See Note)
• Cost to see jobs: Free
• Specialty: All
• Industry: Government
• Location: US

Resumes? No
• Cost to post resumes: N/A
• Cost to see resumes: N/A

Feature(s)? N/A

Career Advice? No

Federal Job Announcement Search is an excellent site to browse for government openings. More than 1,500 U.S. Government openings are posted and updated daily. Nearby, the FLIT Supreme Court Database allows full-text searches of 7,407 Supreme Court decisions. Only one employer gets to post here.

Federal Jobs Digest

www.jobsfed.com

(Publisher/Trade)
FJD Hotline
310 North Highland Avenue, Ossining, NY 10562
800-824-5000 Fax: 914-762-5695 e-mail: webmaster@jobsfed.com

Jobs? Yes
- Cost to post jobs: (See Note)
- Cost to see jobs: Fee (See Note)
- Specialty: All
- Industry: Government
- Location: US

Resumes? Yes
- Cost to post resumes: See Note
- Cost to see resumes: See Note

Feature(s)? N/A

Career Advice? No

Federal Jobs Digest claims more federal vacancies than any other source. Indications are that 3,693 vacancies were listed at the site on our last visit. This site charges $40 to advise you which jobs will match your qualifications. You send them your resume via the web and they do a search of the federal job database to match your skills with current openings. Still takes 3-4 weeks to get back to you. Could use some help.

Fin Career Global Financial Careers

www.fincareer.com

(Recruiting Related Agency)
John Chetelat, Domine & Partners
75 Cannon Street, London, England 5BN
441-719-290101 e-mail: webmaster@fincareer.com

Jobs? Yes
- Cost to post jobs: Fee
- Cost to see jobs: Free
- Specialty: Finance/Executive
- Industry: Finance
- Location: Int'l./US

Resumes? No
- Cost to post resumes: N/A
- Cost to see resumes: N/A

Feature(s)? N/A

Career Advice? No

Fincareer places people in top level finance positions throughout the world. What makes this site unique is that they post positions on their web site with direct contact information for some of the largest corporations in the world. Job seekers can see this information for free and they are not soliciting resumes. Company deals with global and investment banks, insurance and asset management firms. Site provides interesting data on the top firms in these fields.

Finding A Job

www.dbisna.com/dbis/jobs/vjobhunt.htm

(Commercial)
Dun and Bradstreet Information Services
800-738-4638 e-mail: employers@dbisna.com

Jobs? No
• Cost to post jobs: N/A
• Cost to see jobs: N/A
• Specialty: N/A
• Industry: N/A
• Location: Int'l/US

Resumes? No
• Cost to post resumes: N/A
• Cost to see resumes: N/A

Feature(s)? JSK/Company Research

Career Advice? Yes

An information provider still trying to find the power of the web. When you use their search engine (if you can find it amidst the clutter of all the flashing banners, you get minimal information on the company you are researching). You may be better off paying a service like D&B or Hoover or checking out their free info at these and other sites.

Finding and Getting a Job

edie.cprost.sfu.ca/~gophers/find.html

(College/University)
Quinn Merio
e-mail: melanson@sfu.co

Jobs? No
• Cost to post jobs: N/A
• Cost to see jobs: N/A
• Specialty: All
• Industry: N/A
• Location: US

Resumes? No
• Cost to post resumes: N/A
• Cost to see resumes: N/A

Feature(s)? Career Mgm't.

Career Advice? Yes

Interesting career management articles that are short and to the point. A focused list of links to Canadian and other US major web sites rounds out a nicely thought out resource for job seekers.

Finishing.com

(Commercial)
Ted Mooney
14 Fiddlers Elbow, Kinnellon, NJ 07405
201-838-1346 Fax: 973-283-0766 e-mail: tmooney@intac.com

Jobs? Yes
- Cost to post jobs: Free
- Cost to see jobs: Free
- Specialty: Finishing
- Industry: Manufacturing
- Location: US

Resumes? No
- Cost to post resumes: N/A
- Cost to see resumes: N/A

Feature(s)? N/A

Career Advice? No

The place to go for the "finishing" industry. Lots of content and contact information. A "chat room" has been added so jobseekers can network. Briefly written job opportunities can be posted for free and a surprising number were posted here.

Food and Drug Packaging Online

(Publisher/Trade)
Carol Young Orlando, Food & Drug Packaging
18724 W. Osage, Mundeliein, IL 60060
847-949-9604 e-mail: caroleo@fdp.com

Jobs? Yes
- Cost to post jobs: Fee
- Cost to see jobs: Free
- Specialty: Engineering/Packaging
- Industry: Manufacturing
- Location: US

Resumes? No
- Cost to post resumes: N/A
- Cost to see resumes: N/A

Feature(s)? N/A

Career Advice? No

Web version of the classified pages of the Food & Drug Packaging magazine appear on this page. Jobs have direct contact information. You must register (free) before being able to enter the site. Site includes an interesting section, "Let's Talk", where professionals can post day-to-day packaging problems and solutions.

Forty Plus (Northern Calif.)

web.sirius.com/~40plus/#contact

(Association)
Forty Plus
7440 Earhart Road, Oakland, CA 94603
510-430-2400 Fax: 510-430-1750 e-mail: 40plus@fortyplus.org

Jobs? No
- Cost to post jobs: N/A
- Cost to see jobs: N/A
- Specialty: All
- Industry: N/A
- Location: US/W/CA

Resumes? Yes
- Cost to post resumes: Fee
- Cost to see resumes: Free

Feature(s)? Diversity

Career Advice? No

This group has continued to improve since our last edition but they still aren't meeting their potential. Members of forty plus post brief bio's of their background and allow some employers to e-mail for more information. Most employers have to go to the site to request additional data. Awkward model. Job seeker must be a member of 40+ to participate in the resume database. This site has links to other 40+ groups around the US.

Frasernet

www.frasernet.com

(Association/Diversity)
George Fraser, Success Guide
e-mail: fraser@frasernet

Jobs? Yes
- Cost to post jobs: Fee
- Cost to see jobs: Free
- Specialty: All
- Industry: N/A
- Location: US

Resumes? Yes
- Cost to post resumes: Free
- Cost to see resumes: Fee

Feature(s)? Diversity

Career Advice? Yes

This site holds great promise but still confuses us. Interesting opportunities, a business card exchange, a chatroom with features geared to the minority community all have "entrepreneur" stamped on them. Jobs are posted with direct contact information. Frasernet charges a small fee for posting positions and everything else is free. Unless we missed it (and we tried) there seemed to be no easy way to communicate with the owners to find out what the fees are. We also have a problem with sites that ask you to agree with their "philosophy" (no matter how positive) and sign an agreement to that effect before joining.

FuneralNet

www.funeralnet.com/classifieds/index.html

(Commercial)
Michael Turkiewicz, FuneralNet
6902 SE 18th Street, Portland, OR 97202
800-721-8166 e-mail: info@funeralnet.com

Jobs? Yes
• Cost to post jobs: Free
• Cost to see jobs: Free
• Specialty: Mortuary
• Industry: Funeral
• Location: US

Resumes? Yes
• Cost to post resumes: Free
• Cost to see resumes: Fee

Feature(s)? Push to Applicant

Career Advice? No

Hard to imagine this as a growth industry but apparently the business of dying needs some extra help. Funeral Net (talk about a niche) has everything you need. Recruiters (I can't imagine specializing in this) can post jobs for free and e-mail links are only $49. Candidates can post a profile for free (they are highlighted in green- is that the color of embalming fluid?). Date of posting is on the profile so recruiters know how "fresh" the information is. Please-no Bella Lugosi jokes or we'll be dead meat. Owner's main business is creating websites for the funeral industry and is providing a real service here.

Future Access Employment Guide

futureaccess.com:80/employ.html

(Commercial)
Future Access
P.O. Box 584, Saratoga, CA 95071-0584
408-867-3719 e-mail: webmaster@futureaccess.com

Jobs? Yes
• Cost to post jobs: Fee
• Cost to see jobs: Free
• Specialty: All
• Industry: All
• Location: US

Resumes? Yes
• Cost to post resumes: Free
• Cost to see resumes: Free

Feature(s)? N/A

Career Advice? No

Future Access is a simple site where you can post your resume and see jobs for free. Employers pay $10 to post positions. Employer contact information and a search engine designed to speed up finding openings are available for visitors.

Future Med

(Commercial)
Suite 94, #305-4625 Varsity Drive N.W., Calgary, Alberta, Canada T3A OZ9
e-mail: 102562.632@compuserve.com

Jobs? No
- Cost to post jobs: N/A
- Cost to see jobs: N/A
- Specialty: Health Care
- Industry: Health Care
- Location: Int'l/US

Resumes? No
- Cost to post resumes: N/A
- Cost to see resumes: N/A

Feature(s)? JSK/Links

Career Advice? No

Future Med includes a nice list of medical job site links and newsgroups that are definitely worth exploring. Visitors are asked to buy a book that details health care employment opportunities overseas. A search engine has been added that allows you to review 28 health care career categories and link to potential employers and other medical information.

Future Resource Systems

(Commercial)
Future Resource Systems, Inc.
503 Plainsboro Road, P.O. Box 3206, Princeton, NJ 08543
609-734-9100 Fax: 609-734-8490 e-mail: futurejob@webb.com

Jobs? Yes
- Cost to post jobs: Fee
- Cost to see jobs: Free
- Specialty: All
- Industry: All
- Location: Int'l./US

Resumes? Yes
- Cost to post resumes: Free
- Cost to see resumes: Fee

Feature(s)? Yes

Career Advice? Yes

Future Resource Systems is owned by a recruitment agency. Employers are asked to pay $1,000 per year to join the site and an additional $100 per job. Candidates send their resume directly to the employer's e-mail, fax or snail mail address. Employers can have candidates send responses to the site for $250 (thereby protecting the Employer's confidentiality). All advertisements are for 30 days. Future Resource Systems will also conduct a confidential search for you for $1,000 using their database. All jobs posted on our visits were coded and responses went back to the site. Positions are grouped by financial, computer specialties, service or graphics. Some jobs were old and we might have a few more questions before getting involved here.

Future Tech Careers

www.advancehtc.com

(Publisher/Trade)
Tom Cole, Montgomery Newspapers
290 Commerce Drive, Fort Washington, PA 19034
215-542-0200 Fax: 215-643-0166 e-mail: tcole@advancehtc.com

Jobs? Yes
- Cost to post jobs: Fee
- Cost to see jobs: Free
- Specialty: IT
- Industry: All
- Location: US/E/PA

Resumes? No
- Cost to post resumes: N/A
- Cost to see resumes: N/A

Feature(s)? N/A

Career Advice? Yes

Future TechCareers (formerly Advance HiTechCareers) is a direct mail publication advertising high tech positions in the Delaware Valley, Philadelphia and New Jersey area. Applicants can review openings and subscribe to the publication for free. Direct contact information is listed on the site for each job opening. Employers placing ads in this publication get the internet component for free.

Georgia Job Bank

www.mindspring.com/~exchange/jobbank/ga/jobs.html

(Commercial)
JobBank
3232 Cobb Parkway, Ste. 611, Atlanta, GA 30339
404-815-0770 e-mail: resume@jobbankusa.com

Jobs? No
- Cost to post jobs: N/A
- Cost to see jobs: N/A
- Specialty: All
- Industry: N/A
- Location: US/SE/GA

Resumes? Yes
- Cost to post resumes: Free
- Cost to see resumes: Fee

Feature(s)? N/A

Career Advice? No

The Georgia JobBank is a resume distribution service and part of JobBank USA's network (see their listing). If you send your resume to them via e-mail they will distribute it to organizations looking to hire employees with your qualifications. Snail mail will cost you $24.95. Watch where your resume goes and ask where it is going. You need to know.

GeoWeb for GIS/GPS/RS

(Commercial)
Henry Hoffman, GeoWeb
1271 Country Place Circle, Houston, TX 77079
713-994-9903 Fax: 713-988-0071 e-mail: geoweb@ggrweb.com

Jobs? Yes
- Cost to post jobs: Free (See Notes)
- Cost to see jobs: Free
- Specialty: IT/Geographic Systems
- Industry: All
- Location: US

Resumes? Yes
- Cost to post resumes: Fee
- Cost to see resumes: Free

Feature(s)? Push to Applicant

Career Advice? Yes

Employers can post jobs for $150 each for two months on this site or for free if you accept the restriction that they will be shared with GeoWeb's members only. Job Seekers become members and get to post their resume, have it sent to agencies and potential employers and see open positions for $49.99 a year. Openings are e-mailed on a daily basis. Recruiters can see resumes for free and contact candidates directly.

GetAJob!

(Commercial)
510-829-2682

Jobs? Yes
- Cost to post jobs: Fee
- Cost to see jobs: Free
- Specialty: All
- Industry: All
- Location: US

Resumes? No
- Cost to post resumes: N/A
- Cost to see resumes: N/A

Feature(s)? N/A

Career Advice? Yes

Get a Job! has a search engine in need of fine tuning. Positions are listed in alpha order and by function but this last is not in any order. Employer contact information is listed and the job specs are easy to understand. Different rate packages range from $1,000 a year for unlimited postings to monthly memberships of $25 or simply pay $5 a job. A list of career management articles is available. Look into their free trial job posting.

Get Me A Job

www.getmeajob.com

(Commercial)
Wayne Diu Productions
1229 Walkley Road, Ottawa, ON, Canada K1V6P9
e-mail: webmaster@getmeajob.com

Jobs? Yes
- Cost to post jobs: Free
- Cost to see jobs: Free
- Specialty: All
- Industry: All
- Location: Int'l/Canada/US

Resumes? Yes
- Cost to post resumes: Free
- Cost to see resumes: Free

Feature(s)? N/A

Career Advice? No

GetMeAJob is a new site which has resumes and jobs that can be posted and seen for free at this time. You can purchase a banner for $500 which will link to your site. As a start up, this is a clean, neat design and all pages were easy to get to. No search engine.

Getting A Job

www.americanexpress.com/student/

(Commercial)
American Express University

Jobs? Yes
- Cost to post jobs: N/A
- Cost to see jobs: Free
- Specialty: College/Internships
- Industry: N/A
- Location: US

Resumes? No
- Cost to post resumes: N/A
- Cost to see resumes: N/A

Feature(s)? N/A

Career Advice? Yes

Long list of internship programs with non-profit organizations make this a site we would visit if we were still in college. Good articles on keeping your finances in order with interesting career pieces as well. The section called the "Money Pit" is one of our favorites and it advises you on how to finance college and supplies a budget calculator ("budget" and "college" do not seem to go together these days). Content is well done and worth a visit from students or parents.

Getting Past Go: A Survival Guide for College

www.lattanze.loyola.edu/:80/mongen/home.html

(Commercial)
Chris Webb, Monumental General Insurance Group
1111 N. Charles St., Baltimore, MD 21201
410-685-5500 Fax: 410-347-8693 e-mail: bduncan@lattanze.loyola.edu

Jobs? No
- Cost to post jobs: N/A
- Cost to see jobs: N/A
- Specialty: College
- Industry: N/A
- Location: US

Resumes? No
- Cost to post resumes: N/A
- Cost to see resumes: N/A

Feature(s)? Career Mgm't.

Career Advice? Yes

Lots of unique content for the college grad seeking their first job. Learn first hand everything from what it is like living in a different part of the country to how to get health insurance. Practical advice that we all need. This site's list of links to the web includes annotations about what you will find and how it will help you in your job search. The basics are here and the basics never go out of style.

Global Careers

www.globalcareers.com

(Commercial)
Global Career Services, Inc.
555 Fifth Avenue, 8th Floor, NY, NY 10017
888-323-3066 Fax: 212-599-4684 e-mail: info@globalcareers.com

Jobs? Yes
- Cost to post jobs: Fee
- Cost to see jobs: Free
- Specialty: All
- Industry: Transportation; Int'l Bus.
- Location: Int'l/US

Resumes? Yes
- Cost to post resumes: Free
- Cost to see resumes: Free

Feature(s)? N/A

Career Advice? No

Niche site in transportation and International business. Basic rate for posting jobs is $100 per opening. Also available is a 90 day trial for $300 including10 job postings or 1 year membership for $900/30 job postings. You must be a subscriber to see the contact information on the resumes posted. An online resume application makes it easy for the job seeker to record skills into the database. Jobs can be viewed at no cost. In the future global finance careers may be added.

Global Job Services

www.job-searcher.com

(Recruiting Related Agency)
Dee Tomczyk, Global Job Services
1001 N. Pasadena #25, Mesa, AZ 85201
602-655-1790 Fax: 602-655-1722 e-mail: admin@job-searcher.com

Jobs? Yes
- Cost to post jobs: N/A
- Cost to see jobs: N/A
- Specialty: N/A
- Industry: N/A
- Location: Int'l/US

Resumes? Yes
- Cost to post resumes: N/A
- Cost to see resumes: N/A

Feature(s)? RT JSK/Research

Career Advice? Yes

Global Job Services has undergone a major overhaul, but there never was nor will there be a job database (reference to our 1997 directory). Their clients are international and while there is no resume posting either, there is a wealth of career advice. This site's claim to fame is that they will cruise the web for job seekers or recruiters to find where talent and opportunity connect. For the job seeker there are 3 search plans to choose from: $140 for 9 weekly searches, $95 for 6 weeks, $50 for 3 weeks. Recruiters are charged $50 an hour or a $50 sign up fee with an additional 25% of any fee you receive (at the successful conclusion of your search). GJS conducts searches based on candidate skills and interest. In the real world all of this comes down to one word-"researcher".

Good Works

www.essential.org/goodworks/

(Association)
Good Works
P.O. Box 19405, Washington, DC 20036
e-mail: ei@essential.org

Jobs? Yes
- Cost to post jobs: N/A
- Cost to see jobs: N/A
- Specialty: All
- Industry: Non-Profit
- Location: US

Resumes? No
- Cost to post resumes: N/A
- Cost to see resumes: N/A

Feature(s)? N/A

Career Advice? Yes

Good Works is the national directory for social change organizations and public interest careers. Jobs can be posted by e-mailing them to goodjobs@essential.org. These openings can be seen by the job seeker who can contact an employer directly. Great niche.

Gopher for Windows

www.go4win.com

(Commercial)
Ken Peck, Kenneth Peck Associates
e-mail: kenpeck@ix.netcom.com

Jobs? No
- Cost to post jobs: N/A
- Cost to see jobs: N/A
- Specialty: All
- Industry: All
- Location: US

Resumes? No
- Cost to post resumes: N/A
- Cost to see resumes: N/A

Feature(s)? RT/Web Search Tool

Career Advice? Yes

This site claims to be a computer based recruiting system for search firms and human resource departments. Site also has a recruiter's handbook with over 40 pages of recruiting tips but when we tried to drill through on several occasions we failed each time. We have not tried this system but will look at it again in our updates. We always like to advise on new toys on the market and, if this has helpful capabilities, it may be worth a look.

Gordon Group Home Page

www.owt.com/jobsinfo/jobsinfo.htm

(Commercial)
Bob Gordon, Partenariat CanWorkNet Partnership
4th Floor, Place du Portage, Ottawa, Ontario, Canada K1A0J9
819-994-3556 e-mail: gordons@owt.com

Jobs? No
- Cost to post jobs: N/A
- Cost to see jobs: N/A
- Specialty: All
- Industry: All
- Location: Int'l/Canada/US

Resumes? No
- Cost to post resumes: N/A
- Cost to see resumes: N/A

Feature(s)? JSK/Links

Career Advice? Yes

Over 115 links to jobs and career management resources are listed. Also provides connections to the major search engines.

Great Summer Jobs

(Commercial)
Susan Greenberg, Peterson's
202 Carnegie Center, Princeton, NJ 08540
800-338-3282 Fax: 609-243-9150 e-mail: crism@petersons.com

Jobs? Yes
- Cost to post jobs: Fee
- Cost to see jobs: Free
- Specialty: College/Summer
- Industry: Recreation
- Location: US

Resumes? No
- Cost to post resumes: N/A
- Cost to see resumes: N /A

Feature(s)? N/A

Career Advice? Yes

Great Summer Jobs lists Summer Camp openings across the US. You need to list positions early in the winter prior to the upcoming summer season as the site claims it gets thousands of job listings. Also listed is information on the types of jobs, what you can expect in salary from these positions and a well written piece on what camp directors are looking for in prospective counselors.

Greentree Systems, Inc.

(Commercial)
Greentree Systems, Inc.
201 San Antonio Circle #120, Mountain View, CA 94040
800-348-8845 Fax: 415-948-8879 e-mail: info@greentreesystems.com

Jobs? No
- Cost to post jobs: N/A
- Cost to see jobs: N/A
- Specialty: All
- Industry: All
- Location: US

Resumes? No
- Cost to post resumes: N/A
- Cost to see resumes: N/A

Feature(s)? RT/Resume Database

Career Advice? No

Greentree Systems provides applicant tracking and resume scanning software for recruiters who need to get the paperwork off their desks. This windows based system tracks job applicants, produces reports and makes it easy for recruiters to find resumes in a flash. Priced for the mid market client they continue to improve and, when you are looking to put in an optical scanning system this is one that should be considered.

Hard@Work

(Commercial)
Dennis Murphy, Hard@Work, Inc.
210 Commerce Boulevard, Round Rock, TX 78664
800-580-5421 Fax: 512-255-7523 e-mail: demwit@hardatwork.com

Jobs? No
- Cost to post jobs: N/A
- Cost to see jobs: N/A
- Specialty: All
- Industry: All
- Location: US

Resumes? No
- Cost to post resumes: N/A
- Cost to see resumes: N/A

Feature(s)? Push to Applicant

Career Advice? Yes

If you want to have some fun, take a trip to Hard@work's "Water Cooler" where people gather to share their opinions on different work issues. Play "Stump the Mentor" to see intriguing HR questions and equally unusual commentary. At the "Rock Pile" pick your HR question of the day. Lots of fun, interesting topics and the owners respond to all questions. Hard@Work pushes an online newsletter directly to its fans and it's all free. Take a break and chill out.

Hartford Courant

www.courant.com

(Publisher/Newspaper)
285 Broad Street, Hartford, CT 06115
800-524-4242 Fax: 860-241-3864

Jobs? Yes
- Cost to post jobs: Fee
- Cost to see jobs: Free
- Specialty: All
- Industry: All
- Location: US/NE/CT

Resumes? No
- Cost to post resumes: N/A
- Cost to see resumes: N/A

Feature(s)? N/A

Career Advice? No

We always like it when a newspaper puts their classified help wanted link right up front on the home page so it is easy to find. Hartford Courant participates in CareerPath.

HeadHunter.NET

(Commercial)
Warren Bare, Software Technology Corp
1430 Boundary Blvd., Suwanee, GA 30174
770-813-8892 Fax: 770-495-6363 e-mail: feedback@headhunter.net

Jobs? Yes
- Cost to post jobs: Free
- Cost to see jobs: Free
- Specialty: IT
- Industry: All
- Location: US

Resumes? Yes
- Cost to post resumes: Free
- Cost to see resumes: Free

Feature(s)? Push to Applicant

Career Advice? No

HeadHunter has a very attractive model. Posting an opening as a basic service is free at this IT job site. For a $450 annual fee, your company can join the site's "friends" program. This allows an employer to set up a link from HeadHunter to their website. In addition, visually, the company's openings will be listed in bold type and when job seekers sort company positions using the site's search engine, openings from companies in the "friends" program are listed before any others.

As a job seeker you can keep your identity confidential so your present employer will not be able to see your information. Openings that match a candidates interests are e-mailed to a preferred address.

Jobs listed on HeadHunter are also posted to more than 75 newsgroups. Direct contact information is available. Salary ranges for open positions are also available at the employer's option. Headhunter sells banner advertising and seems to be doing quite well and is aggressively marketing it's services. Fast rising newcomer this year.

HEALTH BANK USA

www.healthbankusa.com

(Commercial)
HealthBankUSA
295 Greenwich Street, Suite 149, New York, NY 10007
212-344-2118 Fax: 212-751-3797 e-mail: careers@healthbankusa.com

Jobs? Yes
• Cost to post jobs: Fee
• Cost to see jobs: Free
• Specialty: All
• Industry: All
• Location: US

Resumes? Yes
• Cost to post resumes: Fee
• Cost to see resumes: Free

Feature(s)? N/A

Career Advice? No

Health care positions and candidate profiles are listed. Recruiters pay $25 to post a position. Candidates can have a confidential profile listed for free. Profiles of candidates can be viewed by employers for free.

Health Care Jobs

(Commercial)
Paul Erickson, Health Care Jobs Online
338 Winnebago Rod, Lake Winnebago, MO 64034
816-537-5511 Fax: 816-537-8493 e-mail: Paul@qni.com

Jobs? Yes
• Cost to post jobs: Fee
• Cost to see jobs: Free
• Specialty: All
• Industry: Health Care
• Location: US

Resumes? No
• Cost to post resumes: N/A
• Cost to see resumes: N/A

Feature(s)? N/A

Career Advice? No

Health Care Jobs includes opportunities for hospitals, healthcare corporations and long term facilities. Cost to post jobs is $50 for a 30 day run. Anything related to health care is here. There are a few direct links to hospital employment pages.

Health Careers Online

(Commercial)
Richard Sierra, Sierra Recruitment Service, Inc.
2611 N. Hiatus Road, #129, Cooper City, FL 33026
800-322-1463 Fax: 954-680-0995 e-mail: info@healthcareers-online.com

Jobs? Yes
• Cost to post jobs: Fee
• Cost to see jobs: Free
• Specialty: Health Care
• Industry: Health Care
• Location: US

Resumes? No
• Cost to post resumes: N/A
• Cost to see resumes: N/A

Feature(s)? N/A

Career Advice? Yes

Fairly large database of positions listed for a variety of health care field careers. Health Careers Online provides links to the employers and a well thought out search engine makes the process easy. Split screen design makes helps the visitor to quickly navigate around the site. Jobs are posted within 24 hours of receipt at a cost of $125 for 30 days. The layout of open positions at the site gives title, specialty and location along with links to more content. A worthwhile addition to your package of niche sites.

Health Opps

(Recruiting Related Agency)
Career Mosaic
555 Madison Ave., New York, NY 10022
800-624-7744 Fax: 212-486-4049 e-mail: mgroutage@careermosaic.com

Jobs? Yes
• Cost to post jobs: Fee
• Cost to see jobs: Free
• Specialty: Health Care
• Industry: Health Care
• Location: US

Resumes? Yes
• Cost to post resumes: Free
• Cost to see resumes: Free

Feature(s)? N/A

Career Advice? Yes

Resource information at this site includes a calendar of health meetings, a list of licensure boards and career opportunities for physicians, nurses, physical therapists and risk management specialists. I'm going to go out on the limb here and wonder aloud if anyone truly believes that many physicians will be hired via online posting but hey, Health Opps isn't the only site making the attempt. Health Opps is the sister of Career Mosaic and has an easy to use design that makes navigating the content here a snap.. Direct contact information is available for resumes and jobs. Resumes show the month when they were originally posted.

Healthcare Careers

(Commercial)
Robert Truog
58 ½ Main Street, Suite 101, Fairfield, IA 52556
515-472-0998 Fax: 515-472-3007 e-mail: truog@lisco.com

Jobs? Yes
• Cost to post jobs: Fee
• Cost to see jobs: Free
• Specialty: Health Care
• Industry: Health Care
• Location: US

Resumes? No
• Cost to post resumes: N/A
• Cost to see resumes: N/A

Feature(s)? Search by State

Career Advice? Yes

Health care job sites are expanding rapidly on the web and this is another site that does a good job in an increasingly competitive field. Positions are listed in various health care categories and all openings include employer contact information. Positions are listed by region and then by state. Recruiters can post positions (on a trial basis) for free. It takes as long as a week for the postings to go live. The rate card bases its costs on the volume of jobs posted. For example, 1-15 jobs can be posted for $85 per month. Other packages are available.

Heart

(Commercial)
Sandhya Dave, Heart Advertising Network, Inc.
5150 El Camino Real, Ste D33, Los Altos, CA 94022
415-903-5800 Fax: 415-903-5848 e-mail: sandhya@career.com

Jobs? Yes
- Cost to post jobs: Fee
- Cost to see jobs: Free
- Specialty: All
- Industry: All
- Location: Int'l/US

Resumes? Yes
- Cost to post resumes: Free
- Cost to see resumes: Fee

Feature(s)? Search by State, Career Mgm't.

Career Advice? Yes

Heart offers on-line "Virtual Job Fairs", charging $5000 for the privilege. We suggest employers call references and ask for success rates before you sign up but you would be hard pressed to find a better job site design with a vision of future possibilities. Heart deserves a look. Jobs are posted with direct contact information. Job seekers post their resumes for free. Resumes are e-mailed to the corporations that post jobs. Heart has added an international component to the site.

CAREERXROADS©

Helpwanted.com

(Commercial)
Recruitment On_Line, Inc.
771 Boston Post Road, Marlboro, MA 01752
508-485-1230 Fax: 508-481-9616 e-mail: editor@helpwanted.com

Jobs? Yes
- Cost to post jobs: Fee
- Cost to see jobs: Free
- Specialty: All
- Industry: All
- Location: US

Resumes? Yes
- Cost to post resumes: Free
- Cost to see resumes: Fee

Feature(s)? N/A

Career Advice? No

Help Wanted is a general job site with a large number of jobs posted and links to corporation's jobs pages. Resumes can be posted for free and are available to "clients" who receive a password. Recruiters have a choice of packages. You can pay $600 per year to post 15 jobs per month or simply pay a flat $10 per job. Newly added here is a long listing of employment agencies who may help job seekers.

Help Wanted USA

(Commercial)
James Gonyea, Gonyea and Associates, Inc.
1151 Maravista Drive, New Port Richey, FL 34655
813-372-1333 Fax: 813-372-0394 e-mail: gonyeaasoc@aol.com

Jobs? Yes
- Cost to post jobs: Fee
- Cost to see jobs: Free
- Specialty: All
- Industry: All
- Location: US

Resumes? Yes
- Cost to post resumes: Fee
- Cost to see resumes: Free

Feature(s)? N/A

Career Advice? Yes

Help Wanted USA is an icon on the web for recruiting or finding a job. One of the pioneer sites, HW-USA and it's sister- Internet Career Connection still offers a good value but some of the early marketing pizzaz seems to have faded. The database for this site is built through a network of independent sites in cities throughout the country. Jobs can be posted for $75 each or you can post up to 30 ads for one month for $300. A unique approach is their super volume discount where you will be sent a software program to prepare ads offline and then upload them to their service. When you send the file you will be invoiced $50 for each 100 ads you place ($.50 per ad). These are posted for 2 weeks but, for the price, if you are doing high volume recruiting, this is definitely worth a look. HW-USA can also be viewed through AOL. The charge to post your resume is $25 for six months.

HireWire

www.hirewire.com

(Commercial)
Barbara Gorla, Recruitment Media
CASS Communications, 3880 Murphy Canyon Road, San Diego, CA 92123
800-378-3700 Fax: 619-505-8290 e-mail: help@college.com

Jobs? No
- Cost to post jobs: N/A
- Cost to see jobs: N/A
- Specialty: College
- Industry: All
- Location: US

Resumes? No
- Cost to post resumes: N/A
- Cost to see resumes: N/A

Feature(s)? RT/Banners

Career Advice? Yes

Brand new site with an interesting college concept that provides loads of information. Hire Wire has a marketing gimmick that is one of the best we have seen. Good resume assistance that evaluates each aspect of your writing and walks you through it step by step. Ten rules of interviewing and the art of negotiating are things that even the experienced job seeker should read. As a graduate, when you register and give Hire Wire the name of your alma mater you are then linked to your school's home page. Check out the "College Club" This is where Hire Wire works with employers to connect them to their targeted colleges. Interesting concept and worth a visit. Essentially this site can eventually help organize and drive college candidates directly to company sites. Only downside is this doesn't come cheap and could set you back $2000 per school.

Hispanic Network Magazine

members.aol.com/hnmagazine/index.html

(Publisher/Trade)
Ramona Santana, Olive Tree Publications
5928 Broadway, Suite 305, San Antonio, TX 78209
800-433-9675 Fax: 909-924-1139 e-mail: hnmagazine@juno.com

Jobs? Yes
- Cost to post jobs: N/A
- Cost to see jobs: N/A
- Specialty: All
- Industry: All
- Location: US

Resumes? Yes
- Cost to post resumes: N/A
- Cost to see resumes: N/A

Feature(s)? Diversity

Career Advice? No

Recruiters can match their openings at a cost of $825 (and more) to reach diversity candidates. Site also provides a resume matching service. They collect resumes (sent in from their print publication) and have an internal software program to match your specs against their database. This is a print model using the web to advertise itself.

HollywoodWeb

www.hollywoodweb.com

(Commercial)
Brett Crosby, HOLLYWOODWEB
555 Rose Suite 1, Venice, CA 90291
310-392-3636 e-mail: bc@hollywoodweb.com

Jobs? Yes
- Cost to post jobs: Free
- Cost to see jobs: Free
- Specialty: Entertainment/All Areas
- Industry: Entertainment
- Location: US

Resumes? Yes
- Cost to post resumes: Free
- Cost to see resumes: Free

Feature(s)? N/A

Career Advice? No

More and more acting web sites are getting it. Here is another opportunity for actors, actresses, technicians and others interested in a career in show business. Actors who are union members can post their picture and their background for all to see for free. Contact information is here for some people but surprisingly, not for others. Site has different sections for writers, directors, actors/actresses, technicians, models etc. that make it easy to navigate.

Hongkong Jobs

www.hkjobs.com

(Commercial)
Hong Kong
e-mail: ads@hkjobs.com

Jobs? Yes
- Cost to post jobs: Fee
- Cost to see jobs: Free
- Specialty: All
- Industry: All
- Location: Int'l/Hong Kong

Resumes? Yes
- Cost to post resumes: Free
- Cost to see resumes: Fee

Feature(s)? N/A

Career Advice? No

With everything going on in Hong Kong, this site continues to add services and interesting features. Employers can post a position for $200HK for 1-2 weeks. Resumes posted to this site can be viewed only by those that pay to post jobs. A new feature has been added where job seekers can post a short profile of their skills. This service is free and has an e-mail direct response mode that also protects confidentiality. Over 200 jobs were posted.

Hong Kong Standard

jobmarket.hkstandard.com/online/job/hksjob.htm

(Publisher/Newspaper)
Hong Kong Standard Newspapers Ltd.
Hong Kong
852-279-98833 e-mail: jobmarket@hkstandard.com

Jobs? Yes
- Cost to post jobs: Fee
- Cost to see jobs: Free
- Specialty: All
- Industry: All
- Location: Int'l/Hong Kong

Resumes? Yes
- Cost to post resumes: Free
- Cost to see resumes: Fee

Feature(s)? N/A

Career Advice? No

Hong Kong newspaper has a search engine that allows quick access to its classified help wanted positions. Candidates search by company, agency or by title. Site also provides an online resume form to speed direct replies. Interesting questions about your marital status and age. Cultural differences notwithstanding, this would be a tough sell in many countries in this day and age. (The contact telephone # is correct even though it has an extra digit).

Hoovers

www.hoovers.com

(Commercial)
Hoover's, Inc.
1033 La Posada Drive, Ste. 250, Austin, TX 78752
512-374-4563 e-mail: info@hoovers.com

Jobs? No
- Cost to post jobs: N/A
- Cost to see jobs: N/A
- Specialty: All
- Industry: All
- Location: Int'l./US

Resumes? No
- Cost to post resumes: N/A
- Cost to see resumes: N/A

Feature(s)? RT/S-E, JSK/S-E

Career Advice? No

When you are looking for quick company profiles to target prospective employers or are just scanning the competition, Hoovers online resources are among the easiest to use on the web. Basic information is free, or subscribe for more in-depth access for $9.95 per month.

Hospital Web

neuro-www.mgh.harvard.edu/hospitalweb.nclk

(College/University)
John Lester
e-mail: lester@helix.mgh.harvard.edu

Jobs? No
- Cost to post jobs: N/A
- Cost to see jobs: N/A
- Specialty: Health Care
- Industry: Health Care
- Location: Health Care

Resumes? No
- Cost to post resumes: N/A
- Cost to see resumes: N/A

Feature(s)? Search by State, JSK/Links

Career Advice? No

Hospital Web lists links to US and International hospitals by state. They list thousands of facilities and you then have to find the jobs page for the one you want. Let your fingers do the scrolling.

Hospitality Net

www.hospitalitynet.nl/

(Commercial)
Henri Roelings, Hospitality Net
Akersteenweg 31, Maastricht, Netherlands 6226 HR
310-433-626600 Fax: 310-433-626770 e-mail: info@hospitalitynet.nl

Jobs? Yes
- Cost to post jobs: Free
- Cost to see jobs: Free
- Specialty: All
- Industry: Hospitality
- Location: Int'l./US

Resumes? Yes
- Cost to post resumes: Free
- Cost to see resumes: Free

Feature(s)? N/A

Career Advice? No

Hospitality Net's owner has carved out a well designed international industry niche where jobs and resumes are posted for free. Site provides industry content, dates for future industry events and a vendor showcase. Site's main income is from selling banners.

Hot Jobs

(Commercial)
Ginna Basinger, Otec Inc.
24 West 40th Street, 11th floor, New York, New York 10128
212-302-0060 Fax: 212-840-0397 e-mail: ginna@hotjobs.com

Jobs? Yes
- Cost to post jobs: Fee
- Cost to see jobs: Free
- Specialty: IT
- Industry: All
- Location: US

Resumes? Yes
- Cost to post resumes: Free
- Cost to see resumes: Fee

Feature(s)? N/A

Career Advice? Yes

Hotjobs is a slick, online IT employment site with several interesting features and services in addition to its specialty focus. A self-service site, Hotjobs allows company subscribers to enter, edit and delete openings as well as search its "Hot Shots" resume database. This will work well for companies employing "internet recruiters", who can spare the time to post themselves or, have worked out appropriate outsourcing to post their openings. Unfortunately, this kind of labor intensive activity is not for everyone. Especially since the annual cost for subscription is $6000 (includes full access and 20 concurrent jobs posted, profile, links etc.). The smart move at Hotjobs is that they guarantee results and offer in writing to refund your money if you haven't made a hire in the first 6 months of use. Good move. We also like their "Statistics" feature which allows subscribers to track activity. Hotjobs is planning new sites for marketing/sales/accounting jobs and has recently announced related software products to support their web products.

Houston Chronicle Interactive

(Publisher/Newspaper)
Houston Chronicle
801 Texas Avenue, Houston, TX 77002
713-224-6868 e-mail: classifieds@chron.com

Jobs? Yes
- Cost to post jobs: Fee
- Cost to see jobs: Free
- Specialty: All
- Industry: N/A
- Location: US/SW/TX/Houston

Resumes? No
- Cost to post resumes: N/A
- Cost to see resumes: N/A

Feature(s)? N/A

Career Advice? No

On the Houston Chronicle web pages visitors will find help wanted ads from the current day's newspaper as well as the prior Sunday. They participate in CareerPath.

HRWorld

www.hrworld.com

(Commercial)
David Mahal, DGM Associates
P.O. Box 10639, Marina del Rey, CA 90295-6639
e-mail: dgm@hrworld.com

Jobs? Yes
- Cost to post jobs: Free
- Cost to see jobs: Free
- Specialty: Human Resources
- Industry: N/A
- Location: US

Resumes? Yes
- Cost to post resumes: Free
- Cost to see resumes: Free

Feature(s)? N/A

Career Advice? No

You have to register to gain access but that is a small price to pay when you can see job openings & resumes for human resource professionals across the country. Positions at all levels broken out by discipline. Jobs are listed in the order they are received. (Yes, just like newsgroups). A guest columnist writes articles about current subjects related to the profession. Check it out.

HRCOMM

www.hrcomm.com

(Association)
The Human Resource Community Network
P.O. Box 23412, Pleasant Hill, CA 94523
Fax: 510-944-5012 e-mail: support@hrcomm.com

Jobs? Yes
- Cost to post jobs: Fee
- Cost to see jobs: Free
- Specialty: Human Resources
- Industry: All
- Location: US

Resumes? No
- Cost to post resumes: N/A
- Cost to see resumes: N/A

Feature(s)? Search by State

Career Advice? No

Registration is free, jobs are posted by state and, while most were on the West coast, HRCOMM is looking to expand from its bulletin board roots. Salary surveys are provided and the cost of acquiring them is included in a 12 month membership ($249). Lots of information on conferences and associations for the HR professional.

HRIM Mall

www.hrimmall.com

(Commercial)
Jim Morrone, PeoplePros, Inc.
5603-B W. Friendly Ave. #269, Greensboro, NC 27410
800-296-3254 Fax: 910-643-9519 e-mail: jim_morrone@hrimmall.com

Jobs? Yes
• Cost to post jobs: Free
• Cost to see jobs: Free
• Specialty: Human Resources/HRIS
• Industry: All
• Location: US

Resumes? No
• Cost to post resumes: N/A
• Cost to see resumes: N/A

Feature(s)? Push to Applicant

Career Advice? Yes

HRIM Mall specializes in information for the Human Resource community. Register your e-mail and the owners will send you updates when new jobs are posted. Site has placed a hot button (new) on the most recent jobs that come in to get job seekers' attention. All jobs have posting dates which is a great help and our only issue with this site is that the jobs are posted in alpha title order rather then by location. The owners indicate that the search engine is coming.

(Commercial)
John Reese, Interactive Search
5959 West Century Blvd. #1122, Los Angeles, CA 90045
800-459-4747 Fax: 310-641-1676 e-mail: info@isearch.com

Jobs? No
- Cost to post jobs: N/A
- Cost to see jobs: N/A
- Specialty: N/A
- Industry: N/A
- Location: US

Resumes? No
- Cost to post resumes: N/A
- Cost to see resumes: N/A

Feature(s)? RT & JSK/Private Database

Career Advice? No

For recruiters inundated with resumes and looking to take some of the paper pushing out of staffing, I-Search might be the answer. A private online database, resumes are sent (via fax, e-mail, snail mail) directly to I-Search and quickly scanned into their system so each company's recruiters can access their "private reserve" from anywhere.

I-Search promises 48 hour turnaround and their security is very tight. Companies do not share resumes. Costs begin at $5,000 for set up. Additional costs for processing and storage are added. I-Search's rates and services compare favorably to high end optical scanning software without the internal operational hassles. They generate simple applicant tracking reports but nothing as sophisticated as their high end competitors... at this date. Recently, I-Search added links to their major clients. Employers reviewing technology options as part of their overall staffing strategy need to factor in the business pros and cons of outsourcing the management and maintenance of their applicant database.

IEEE

www.ieee.org

(Association)
William R. Anderson, Institute of Electrical and Electronic Eng.
445 Hoes Lane, P.O. Box 1331, Piscataway, NJ 08855-1331
202-785-0017 e-mail: rossr@ix.netcom.com

Jobs? Yes
- Cost to post jobs: Fee
- Cost to see jobs: Free
- Specialty: Engineering/Electrical/Electronic
- Industry: All
- Location: US

Resumes? No
- Cost to post resumes: N/A
- Cost to see resumes: N/A

Feature(s)? Push to Applicant

Career Advice? Yes

315,000 electrical/electronic engineers belong to the IEEE. This site has openings categorized on a regional basis. Members can request future job postings be forwarded by e-mail. Employer cost is $15-25 per posting.

IFEBP Online

www.ifebp.org/jobs

(Association)
Barb Pamperin, Int'l Foundation of Employee Benefit Plans
Job Posting Service, P.O. Box 69, Brookfield, WI 53008-0069
414-786-6710 Fax: 414-786-8780 e-mail: infocntr@ifebp.org

Jobs? Yes
- Cost to post jobs: Fee
- Cost to see jobs: Free
- Specialty: Human Resources/Benefits
- Industry: All
- Location: US

Resumes? No
- Cost to post resumes: N/A
- Cost to see resumes: N/A

Feature(s)? N/A

Career Advice? No

The Int'l Foundation of Employee Benefit Plans posts jobs to its site within two business days. Specializing in positions in employee benefits, HR and compensation, these positions can be searched by position title, location and posting date. Limited to 500 words and a single position, rates are $150 for 60 days. Discounts for members.

IICS NY Job Listings

www.iicsny.org/jobs

(Association)
Thiery Sansaricq, International Interactive Comm. Soc. of NY
NY
212-736-4427 e-mail: theory@walrus.com

Jobs? Yes
- Cost to post jobs: Free
- Cost to see jobs: Free
- Specialty: IT/Graphics/Communications
- Industry: All
- Location: US/NE/NY

Resumes? No
- Cost to post resumes: N/A
- Cost to see resumes: N/A

Feature(s)? Newsletter

Career Advice? Yes

The International Interactive Communications Society (IICS) is the nation's oldest professional organization for interactive arts and technology professionals. Positions are posted for free and run the gamut from art directors to web designers. Direct contact information is available. Unfortunately, there were only 6 positions posted on our visit. For recruiters, jobs are free to post. With over 30 chapters and 3,000+ members, this could develop into a useful source of contacts. An email newsletter is also available.

Imcor Provides Top-Level Executives

kiwi.futuris.net/ct/imcor

(Placement Agency)
Laura Copeland
100 Prospect Street, North Tower, Stamford, CT 06901
203-975-8000 Fax: 203-975-8199 e-mail: info@imcor.com

Jobs? Yes
- Cost to post jobs: Fee
- Cost to see jobs: Free
- Specialty: All
- Industry: N/A
- Location: Int'l/US

Resumes? Yes
- Cost to post resumes: Free
- Cost to see resumes: Fee

Feature(s)? N/A

Career Advice? No

Imcor is one of the original firms that specializes in temporary assignments for senior & middle management executives. Many positions that are posted are temporary and could become permanent positions. We live in an age of "try it, you may like it" and many of Imcor's clients prefer to run their recruiting efforts this way. Applicants send their resume via snail mail or fax and Imcor attempts to match them to their openings. Dozens of open positions in the US. Several international. Employer fee only.

Impact Online

www.impactonline.org

(Non-Profit)
Jayne Cravens
715 Colorado Avenue. Ste. 4, Palo Alto, CA 94303
415-327-2389 Fax: 415-327-1395 e-mail: jayne@impactonline.com

Jobs? Yes
- Cost to post jobs: Free
- Cost to see jobs: Free
- Specialty: All
- Industry: Non-Profit
- Location: Int'l/US

Resumes? No
- Cost to post resumes: N/A
- Cost to see resumes: N/A

Feature(s)? N/A

Career Advice? Yes

Impact Online seeks to foster involvement by informing potential volunteers about nonprofit organizations and how to get involved with them. If you are looking to give back and want to take part in something special, here's a place where you can find it.. Volunteer positions are International not just US.

Info Louisiana

www.state.la.us/

(Government)
State of Louisiana
e-mail: webmaster@doc.state.la.us

Jobs? Yes
- Cost to post jobs: Free
- Cost to see jobs: Free
- Specialty: All
- Industry: All
- Location: US/S/LA

Resumes? No
- Cost to post resumes: N/A
- Cost to see resumes: N/A

Feature(s)? N/A

Career Advice? No

This is one State Government developing new online experience but still struggling with old habits. Jobs are posted with limited information but not what you need most- the contact information. Job seekers have to physically go to the state employment office to get the hiring company's name and address. A map of the US allows you to access links to all 50 State's employment openings. As we noted at America's Job Bank, each state provides different contact information. Some provide more online help than others.

infoworks USA

www.infoworksusa.com

(Commercial)
Robert Mulcahy, Infoworks USA
750 Broad Street, Shrewsbury, NJ 07702
800-288-5153 Fax: 888-653-8145 e-mail: info@infoworksusa.com

Jobs? Yes
- Cost to post jobs: Fee
- Cost to see jobs: Free
- Specialty: IT
- Industry: All
- Location: US/NE/SE

Resumes? Yes
- Cost to post resumes: Free
- Cost to see resumes: Fee

Feature(s)? N/A

Career Advice? No

New site that has recently come on board that looks to provide resumes and jobs for the IT marketplace. We were advised that they have 2,000 resumes in their database and get 1,000 to 2,000 new ones a month. They keep them for only 60 days. Corporations pay $9,000 to become members to search the resumes and there is an additional charge of $1,500 per quarter to post up to 25 jobs. Resumes can be posted for free by the job seeker and all contact information is available. On our visit only 1 recruitment firm had posted several jobs and, as this is a new site, you need to give them time to get established. Pricey but, only the employer can determine if the value-added is worth the investment.

Infoworld

www.infoworld.com

(Publisher/Trade)
Janice Crowley
P.O. Box 1172, Skokie, IL 60076
800-227-8365 Fax: 415-312-0607 e-mail: electric@infoworld.com

Jobs? No
- Cost to post jobs: N/A
- Cost to see jobs: N/A
- Specialty: IT/Client Server
- Industry: All
- Location: Int'l./US

Resumes? No
- Cost to post resumes: N/A
- Cost to see resumes: N/A

Feature(s)? N/A

Career Advice? No

Online version of InfoWorld magazine, the "Voice of Client/Server in the Enterprise".

Ingram Recruiting Solutions

www.netaxs.com/people/ying1/

(Placement Agency)
Yvette Ingram, Ingram Recruiting Solutions, Inc.
48 Eden Rock Lane, Wilingboro, NJ 08046
609-871-2165 Fax: 609-871-5307 e-mail: yingl@netaxs.com

Jobs? Yes
- Cost to post jobs: Fee
- Cost to see jobs: Free
- Specialty: IT
- Industry: All
- Location: US

Resumes? Yes
- Cost to post resumes: Free
- Cost to see resumes: N/A

Feature(s)? Push to Applicant

Career Advice? Yes

A well thought through model for placement firms considering the impact of emerging technology on their industry. This is the electronic recruiter of the future in action. A wide range of services are offered to employers. Job seekers can register for e-mail listings or drop off their resume. A referral program offers $$$ to anyone who knows a qualified candidate. We included virtually (no pun intended) no placement firms in CAREERXROADS except those few innovators we've stumbled on in our cyber travels. There is more out there every day.

InJersey

www.injersey.com

(Publisher/Newspaper)
Asbury Park Press
3601 Highway 66, Neptune, NJ 07754
800-232-8884 e-mail: sales@injersey.com

Jobs? Yes
- Cost to post jobs: Fee
- Cost to see jobs: Free
- Specialty: All
- Industry: N/A
- Location: US/E/NJ

Resumes? No
- Cost to post resumes: N/A
- Cost to see resumes: N/A

Feature(s)? N/A

Career Advice? No

Web site for the Home News and the Asbury Park Press newspapers of central NJ. In column classifieds are here but were not sure about the display ads. If you pay for an ad in the paper you get the web component for free. Participates in CareerPath.

InstaMatch Resume Database

www.instamatch.com

(Commercial)
David Andrews, ProsperTech Group, Inc.
2900 W. Anderson Ln #20-181, Austin, TX 78757
e-mail: dandrews@instamatch.om

Jobs? No
- Cost to post jobs: N/A
- Cost to see jobs: N/A
- Specialty: Resume Database
- Industry: All
- Location: US

Resumes? Yes
- Cost to post resumes: Free
- Cost to see resumes: Fee

Feature(s)? N/A

Career Advice? No

Resume database that you can access from the web. Free for job seekers to post their resume and recruiters pay from $14 per week or $48 per month with other packages available. InstaMatch requires a code for access. The site claims 8,000 resumes. Not a niche: truck drivers, nurses, lawyers...and even a few technical people are here. For recruiters, this could be an adventure but, for $14, what have you got to lose?

Insurance Career Center

www.insjobs.com

(Recruiting Related Agency)
Jeffrey Hodes, Bernard Hodes Advertising
555 Madison Avenue, New York, NY 10022
410-266-3970 e-mail: sales@careermosaic.com

Jobs? Yes
- Cost to post jobs: Fee
- Cost to see jobs: Free
- Specialty: Insurance
- Industry: Insurance
- Location: US

Resumes? Yes
- Cost to post resumes: Free
- Cost to see resumes: Fee

Feature(s)? Yes

Career Advice? Yes

Insurance Career Center provides the job seeker free access to post their resume and see opportunities with direct contact information. Recruiters are charged $150 to post a position and, you must be a "member company" to search their resume database.

IntelliMatch

www.intellimatch.com

(Commercial)
Ron Miller, IntelliMatch
10 Alamaden Blvd., San Jose, CA 95128
408-494-7200 Fax: 408-535-2794 e-mail: info@Intellimatch.com

Jobs? Yes
- Cost to post jobs: Fee
- Cost to see jobs: Free
- Specialty: All
- Industry: N/A
- Location: US

Resumes? Yes
- Cost to post resumes: Free
- Cost to see resumes: Fee

Feature(s)? Push to Applicant, Push to Employer

Career Advice? Yes

A matching service with experience, a growing number of partnerships and a very sophisticated technology. IntelliMatch has raised the bar with the release of it's 2.0 program. This newly designed web site includes advanced enhancements that include push, a "personal job agent", and full-text search capability. Job seekers use a structured approach to matching specific job criteria. Resumes can be posted for free and job openings have direct contact information. Job seekers can e-mail their resume directly to the employer from the website. "Candidate Connection", IntelliMatch's service for employers, includes many options priced from a the reasonable range to the .... Keep an eye on this site, it is always creative and innovative.

Inter Links

www.alabanza.com/kabacoff/Inter-Links/employment.html

(Commercial)
Rob Kabacoff

Jobs? No
- Cost to post jobs: N/A
- Cost to see jobs: N/A
- Specialty: All
- Industry: All
- Location: US

Resumes? No
- Cost to post resumes: N/A
- Cost to see resumes: N/A

Feature(s)? JSK/links

Career Advice? Yes

Inter Links provides the connection to major sites for jobs and career information. Owner used to accept new sites but has been overwhelmed and cannot handle the volume any more. Lots of general info and we love to play the games and puzzles here when we get web burn-out.

Interesting Web Sites

Www.usbol.com/wjmackey/weblinks.html

(Company)
W. J. Mackey
e-mail: wjmackey@netcom.com

Jobs? No
- Cost to post jobs: N/A
- Cost to see jobs: N/A
- Specialty: All
- Industry: All
- Location: US

Resumes? No
- Cost to post resumes: N/A
- Cost to see resumes: N/A

Feature(s)? Diversity/Links

Career Advice? No

This site has 65 links to diversity web sites. Great service and, in the future owners may provide articles, internet tools and newslists of interest to African Americans.

International Human Resource Information Mgmt.

www.ihrim.org

(Association)
Kevin Miles, IHRIM
P.O. Box 21345, Seattle, Washington 98111-3345
972-661-3727 e-mail: david@ihrim.org

Jobs? Yes
• Cost to post jobs: Free
• Cost to see jobs: Free
• Specialty: Human Resources/HRIS
• Industry: All
• Location: US

Resumes? No
• Cost to post resumes: N/A
• Cost to see resumes: N/A

Feature(s)? N/A

Career Advice? Yes

Site is under a three phase construction and we have just seen phase one. Lots of HRIS content with a long list of links. Job listings have direct contact but it is a short list. White papers and other features are on the horizon.

International Pharmajobs

www.pharmajobs.com

(Placement/Search/Temp)
Neeto da Silva, R.S.V.P. Personnel Agency
Reuterweg 74, 60323 Frankfurt am Main, Germany
496-995-96660 Fax: 496-995-966611 e-mail: personnel@rsvp-consult.com

Jobs? Yes
• Cost to post jobs: Fee
• Cost to see jobs: Free
• Specialty: All
• Industry: Biotechnology/Pharmaceutical
• Location: Int'l./Asia/Europe

Resumes? Yes
• Cost to post resumes: Free
• Cost to see resumes: Fee

Feature(s)? N/A

Career Advice? No

International Pharmajobs works with companies that have recruitment needs in Asia and Europe. Positions cost 500DM to post and if you need confidentiality, resumes can be sent to the site and forwarded to the recruiter. Corporations can also have jobs posted with their e-mail address and links to their home page. There were dozens of jobs posted in as many categories in this field. Resumes can be purchased if you obtain membership on this site. Check for costs as site is owned by an executive recruitment firm.

International Seafarers Exchange

www.jobxchange.com/xisetoc.htm

(Commercial)
Jack Reynolds, BlueSeas International Inc.
19370 Collins Avenue, Miami Beach, FL 33160
305-705-0264 e-mail: webmaster@jobxchange.com

Jobs? No
- Cost to post jobs: No
- Cost to see jobs: No
- Specialty: All
- Industry: Maritime
- Location: US

Resumes? Yes
- Cost to post resumes: Fee
- Cost to see resumes: Free

Feature(s)? N/A

Career Advice? Yes

If you are looking for a position on a ship that sails the 7 seas...or some of the seaways in between, ISE has lots of information on the different types of openings that this line of trade may have and several links to employers. Applicants pay $30 for 6 months to post their resume. We are advised by the owners that ships get hundreds of resumes all the time and that is why jobs are not presently posted on the site. For now, employers they can see the resumes for free.

Internet Business Network

www.interbiznet.com/

(Commercial)
John Sumser, Internet Business Network
346 Starling Road, Mill Valley, CA 94914
415-380-8244 Fax: 415-383-8676 e-mail: staff@interbiznet.com

Jobs? No
- Cost to post jobs: N/A
- Cost to see jobs: N/A
- Specialty: All
- Industry: All
- Location: US

Resumes? No
- Cost to post resumes: N/A
- Cost to see resumes: N/A

Feature(s)? RT/Links

Career Advice? No

Lot's of links to dozens of sites with a rating system that is hard to fathom. IBN also publishes a web directory that sells for $997. A comprehensive weekly newsletter is available for those who register. Many of this site's top picks also have banners on the site. John Sumser, the site's owner, has developed quite a following and is providing several other services as well.

Internet Career Interest Assessment

www-personal.ksu.edu/~dangle/icia/

(Commercial)
Dennis Angle, Kansas Careers
2323 Anderson Ave., Manhattan, KS 66502
913-532-6540 Fax: 913-532-7732 e-mail: dangle@ksu.edu

Jobs? No
- Cost to post jobs: N/A
- Cost to see jobs: N/A
- Specialty: All
- Industry: All
- Location: US

Resumes? No
- Cost to post resumes: N/A
- Cost to see resumes: N/A

Feature(s)? Career Mgm't.

Career Advice? Yes

Career information is arrayed in 12 categories and 246 individual job choices. Lots of information regarding each individual job outlook. Salary data is included along with links to sites that will provide more specific data. Good information for someone who is exploring their first job or a career change. Split screen makes it all easy to navigate.

Internet Fashion Exchange

www.fashionexch.com

(Commercial)
Gilbert Career Resources Ltd.
275 Madison Avenue, NY, NY 10016
800-967-3846 e-mail: career@tiac.net

Jobs? Yes
- Cost to post jobs: Free
- Cost to see jobs: Free
- Specialty: All
- Industry: Retail/Fashion
- Location: US/E/NY

Resumes? Yes
- Cost to post resumes: Free
- Cost to see resumes: Free

Feature(s)? Yes

Career Advice? Yes

Internet Fashion Exchange was under construction when we went to press, but from their past performance we did not want to leave them out. In the past, site provided resumes and job postings for free for the fashion and retail industry. Unique niche. Look for this site in our monthly reviews.

The Internet Job Locator

www.joblocator.com

(Commercial)
Brett Tabin, Travelers Online
Sherman Oaks, CA
407-672-1669 e-mail: support@joblocator.com

Jobs? Yes
- Cost to post jobs: Fee
- Cost to see jobs: Free
- Specialty: All
- Industry: All
- Location: US

Resumes? Yes
- Cost to post resumes: Free
- Cost to see resumes: Free

Feature(s)? Push to Applicant, Push to Employer

Career Advice? No

Pricing structure may have changed somewhat from last year's model but Job Locator remains a great value. Employers receive credits (a credit is $1 with minimum purchase of $25) and with a 4 month membership each credit represents 1 job posting and one resume search for 21 days. Pretty specific. This site does the searching for employers and e-mails the basic info on matching resumes along with a direct e-mail link to the applicant. Site searches its resume database daily. Jobs will also be posted to newsgroups. For job seekers, direct contact information is provided and the Job Locator will push new, matching jobs via e-mail for free. Positive results could encourage this well designed winner.

Internet Job Surfer

www.rpi.edu/dept/cdc/jobsurfer/jobw.html

(College/University)
Jasmit Singh Kochhar, Rensselaer Polytechnic Institute
Department of Decision Science, and Engineering Systems, Troy, NY 12180
518-276-2952 e-mail: kochhj@rpi.edu

Jobs? No
- Cost to post jobs: N/A
- Cost to see jobs: N/A
- Specialty: All
- Industry: N/A
- Location: US

Resumes? No
- Cost to post resumes: N/A
- Cost to see resumes: N/A

Feature(s)? JSK/Links

Career Advice? No

Jasmit keeps churning out new links for the job seeker and recruiters all over the world. From general job sites to corporations to recruiters, you will find hundreds of links listed in alphabetical order. Dedicated surfer.

Internet Pilot to Physics

www.tp.umu.se/TIPTOP/

(College/University)
Kenneth Holmlund, Umea University
Dept. Theoretical Physics, S-901 87 Umea, Sweden
460-901-67717 e-mail: tiptop-user@tph.tuwien.ac.at

Jobs? Yes
- Cost to post jobs: Free
- Cost to see jobs: Free
- Specialty: Science, Physics/Academic
- Industry: Education
- Location: Int'l/US

Resumes? No
- Cost to post resumes: N/A
- Cost to see resumes: N/A

Feature(s)? No

Career Advice? No

If physics is your interest then the renamed "Internet Pilot" is your world wide stop for opportunities. Information on conferences and technical updates abound for the science minded. Many positions are posted. Most are in the academic world. Contact information is available and job listings are free. Site used to post resumes but that service is no longer available.

Internet.com

www.iworld.com

(Publisher/Trade Magazine)
Tom Emanuel, Mecklermedia
20 Ketchum Street, Westport, CT 06880
203-226-6967 Fax: 203-454-5840 e-mail: feedback@internet.com

Jobs? No
- Cost to post jobs: N/A
- Cost to see jobs: N/A
- Specialty: IT/Internet
- Industry: High Technology
- Location: Int'l/US

Resumes? No
- Cost to post resumes: N/A
- Cost to see resumes: N/A

Feature(s)? RT/Events

Career Advice? No

We list this site as it has information about Internet conferences and exhibitions all around the world. At some of these they tie in job fairs. Lots of product information about the latest gadgets on the web. Great tool for recruiters looking for the places where candidates flock.

IPMA HR Job Pool

www.ipma-hr.org

(Association)
Eleanor Trice, International Personnel Mgmt. Assoc.
1617 Duke Street, Alexandria, VA 22314
703-549-7100 Fax: 703-684-0948 e-mail: ipma@ipma-hr.org

Jobs? Yes
- Cost to post jobs: Fee
- Cost to see jobs: Free
- Specialty: Human Resources
- Industry: Government
- Location: US

Resumes? No
- Cost to post resumes: N/A
- Cost to see resumes: N/A

Feature(s)? Yes

Career Advice? No

Site lists human resource positions for the public sector. Jobs are at all levels and for all locations throughout the US. Rates range from $100 to $150. Direct contact information and salary range is available for each position posted. Neat seeing how much everyone is paid.

Irish Jobs

(Commercial)
John Feeley, Software Expressions
84A Mount Albany, Blackrock Co., Dublin, Ireland
353-128-83732 Fax: 353-128-83732 e-mail: john@exp.ie

Jobs? Yes
- Cost to post jobs: Fee
- Cost to see jobs: Free
- Specialty: IT
- Industry: All
- Location: Int'l/Ireland

Resumes? Yes
- Cost to post resumes: Free
- Cost to see resumes: Fee

Feature(s)? Push to Applicant

Career Advice? No

Irish Jobs has grown since our last visit and continues to supply numerous services. Job seekers can post resumes for free and if they give their e-mail address will be sent a monthly listing of opportunities that match their interests. Recruiters can search the resume database for free but must return to the site as contact information is coded. If you hire a candidate you are charged 950 pounds. Jobs can be posted for 140 pounds and stay on the web for 1 month with resumes going directly to the employer. Site also has an education jobs page (www.exp.ie/edjobs.htm), an engineering jobs page (www.exp.ie/eng.htm), and an Australian jobs page (www.exp.lelaus.htm).

ISA Classifieds

(Association)
Rayann Burnham, Instrument Society of America
67 Alexander Drive, P.O. 12277, Research Triangle Park, NC 27709
919-990-9216 Fax: 919-549-8288 e-mail: rburnham@isa.org

Jobs? Yes
- Cost to post jobs: Fee
- Cost to see jobs: Free
- Specialty: Engineering/Instrumentation & Control
- Industry: All
- Location: Int'l./US

Resumes? Yes
- Cost to post resumes: Fee
- Cost to see resumes: Free

Feature(s)? N/A

Career Advice? Yes

Connected with InTech, the Instrumentation Journal for Measurement and Control, ads placed in the Journal can be added to the net for an additional cost or direct for approximately $65 (50 word limit). Resume posting has a similar charge. On our last visit, there were only a few jobs and no resumes posted. A small niche but a great resource if you happen to be interested in this specialty.

Jaeger's Interactive Career Center

www.jaegerinc.com/jaeger2.html

(Recruiting Related Agency)
Phil Brindley, Jaeger Advertising
Cleveland, OH
216-243-8700 Fax: 216-243-1888 e-mail: info@jaegerinc.com

Jobs? Yes
- Cost to post jobs: Fee
- Cost to see jobs: Free
- Specialty: All
- Industry: All
- Location: US

Resumes? No
- Cost to post resumes: N/A
- Cost to see resumes: N/A

Feature(s)? N/A

Career Advice? No

Recruitment advertising firm that posts positions for it's clients. Long list of openings in all specialties. Each ad includes direct contact information.

JAMA

www.ama-assn.org

(Publisher/Trade Magazine)
American Medical Association
515 North State Street, Chicago, IL 60610
800-262-2260 Fax: 312-464-5871 e-mail: placement@ama-assn.org

Jobs? Yes
- Cost to post jobs: Fee
- Cost to see jobs: Free
- Specialty: Health Care/MD
- Industry: Health Care
- Location: US

Resumes? Yes
- Cost to post resumes: Free
- Cost to see resumes: Fee

Feature(s)? Yes

Career Advice? No

All Physician recruitment ads in JAMA appear at this site. Lots of articles on the profession from their latest publication. They now accept resumes.

Java World

www.javaworld.com

(Publisher/Magazine)
Tony Hunt, Web Publishing Inc.
415-974-7443 Fax: 415-974-4570 e-mail: tony.hunt@javaworld.com

Jobs? Yes
• Cost to post jobs: Fee
• Cost to see jobs: Free
• Specialty: IT/JAVA
• Industry: All
• Location: US

Resumes? No
• Cost to post resumes: N/A
• Cost to see resumes: N/A

Feature(s)? N/A

Career Advice? N/A

Ads placed in Java World Magazine are also placed on their web site. Lots of IT jobs from big name companies were posted on our last visit. Recruiters pay $1,000 per advertisement depending on the amount of copy. Job seekers can get here directly by going to http://supersite.net/JavaWorldJobBank. Jobs are posted to the left. Employers can point and click on"career opportunities" to get an explanation of advertising options on this site. If you want to get here via www.javaworld.com scroll to the "Job Bank SuperSite" button about half way down the page.

Job Accommodation Network (JAN)

janweb.icdi.wuv.edu

(Government)
Dale Brown, Job Accommodation Network
West Virginia University, P.O. Box 6080, Morgantown, WV 26506
800-526-7234 Fax: 304-293-5407 e-mail: dbrown@pcepd.gov

Jobs? No
• Cost to post jobs: N/A
• Cost to see jobs: N/A
• Specialty: All
• Industry: All
• Location: US

Resumes? No
• Cost to post resumes: N/A
• Cost to see resumes: N/A

Feature(s)? RT, Diversity

Career Advice? Yes

JAN is a toll-free information and referral service on job accommodation for people with disabilities and covers the employment provisions of the Americans with Disabilities Act (ADA). Resources for technical assistance, funding, education, and services related to the employment of people with disabilities are here and, in addition, JAN analyzes trends and statistical data related to the technical assistance it provides. JAN can be accessed by phone at 1-800-ADA-WORK (1-800-232-9675) or by Internet.

Jobank

(Commercial)
Jobank
8033 Sunset Blvd., Suite 269, Los Angeles, CA 90046
888-690-562265 Fax: 818-785-6794 e-mail: jobank@jobank.com

Jobs? Yes
- Cost to post jobs: Fee
- Cost to see jobs: Free
- Specialty: All
- Industry: All
- Location: US/W/CA

Resumes? Yes
- Cost to post resumes: Free
- Cost to see resumes: Free

Feature(s)? N/A

Career Advice? No

Jobank seems to be primarily a California based site attempting to move eastward. Employers can see candidate info by salary desired-we don't believe that this is a good idea. Resumes are coded so employers must advise the site's owner which candidates are of interest before contact information is released. Currently, Job seekers post their resume for free but the site advises there will be a $10 charge in the future. Hundreds of resumes are posted. Companies pay $49 to post a position for 30 days. The site charges extra to list positions in additional states.

JobAssistant.com

www.jobassistant.com

(Commercial)
Bill Reilly, JobAssistant.com
781 Creek Road, Bellmawr, NJ 08031
609-933-3942 Fax: 609-933-1042 e-mail: info@jobassistant.com

Jobs? Yes
- Cost to post jobs: Fee
- Cost to see jobs: Free
- Specialty: All
- Industry: All
- Location: US

Resumes? Yes
- Cost to post resumes: Free
- Cost to see resumes: Free

Feature(s)? N/A

Career Advice? No

The cost to post jobs on Job Assistant is $50 per listing for one month. Multiple job listings can be posted for 3 months at a cost of $300 for 10 jobs. Other packages are available. This new site is trying to find it's way. Check back for improvements.

Job, Resume & Career Management Sites on the World Wide Web
• The 1998 Directory •

- 207 -

JobBank USA

www.jobbankusa.com

(Commercial)
Brett Warner, JobBank USA
3232 Cobb Parkway, Suite 611, Atlanta, GA 30339
770-971-1971 Fax: 770-971-7788 e-mail: webmaster@jobbankusa.com

Jobs? Yes
- Cost to post jobs: Fee
- Cost to see jobs: Free
- Specialty: All
- Industry: All
- Location: US

Resumes? Yes
- Cost to post resumes: Fee
- Cost to see resumes: Fee

Feature(s)? Push to Applicant

Career Advice? Yes

Job Bank USA still has a lot of career content but it could use a new format. Jobs can be seen but all contact information goes back through the site. Job seekers have to pay to place their resume in Job Bank's database. Then, when a position matches your criteria, you do receive contact information from the site to see if you have an interest. Recruiters pay $125 to post a job for 60 days. Many other packages are offered. Employers have to register before receiving (via e-mail) additional information about the site. We have no problem with asking for the registration information, but holding back costs and other data related to decision making, does more to raise questions and dampen interest than anything else. There are too many crisp, clean alternatives where all the employer needs to do is point and click to get in.

Job Center

www.jobcenter.com/

(Commercial)
Christopher McQueeney, Job Center Employment Services, Inc.
2 Fennell Street, P.O. Box 125, Skaneateles, NY 13152
800-562-2368 Fax: 315-673-1820 e-mail: service@jobcenter.com

Jobs? Yes
- Cost to post jobs: Fee
- Cost to see jobs: Free
- Specialty: All
- Industry: N/A
- Location: Int'l./US

Resumes? Yes
- Cost to post resumes: Fee
- Cost to see resumes: Free

Feature(s)? Push to Applicant

Career Advice? Yes

Job Center has an agent that matches resumes against listed positions for both the job seeker and the employer. On our last visit the site was running a "sale" and you could post your resume for $5 (total) for six months of service. The usual price is $25/6 for a month listing. Resumes are also posted to various newsgroups which is included in the price of admission. Recruiters can post a job for $20 and it runs for two weeks. Positions/candidate profiles are posted with e-mail responses.

JobDirect

(Commercial/College)
Rachel Bell, JobDirect
5 Greenwich Office Park, Greenwich, CT 06831
203-629-2201 Fax: 203-629-2261 e-mail: sales@jobdirect.com

Jobs? Yes
- Cost to post jobs: Fee
- Cost to see jobs: Free
- Specialty: College
- Industry: All
- Location: US

Resumes? Yes
- Cost to post resumes: Free
- Cost to see resumes: Fee

Feature(s)? Push to Applicant

Career Advice? No

This is a matching service not a listing service. Students can only see jobs after putting their resume in the database. This rapidly growing model was founded by two women who dropped out of college to pursue the development of JobDirect. They traveled across the country in a specially equipped van bringing their "mobile internet" to college after college and collecting resumes. Students get the advantage of "Push" technology as they receive e-mail newsletters of job leads each month. Simple fee schedules to place ads are in the hundreds of dollars rather than thousands. Smart marketing, a unique access to the campus, growing operational savvy (multiple vans) and opportunities to sponsor make this a contender.

JobFest

www.jobfest.com

(Recruiting Related Agency)
Shaker Advertising Agency, Inc.
Shaker Bldg., 1100 Lake Street, Oak Park, IL 60301
800-323-5170 Fax: 708-848-2740 e-mail: info@shaker.com

Jobs? Yes
• Cost to post jobs: N/A
• Cost to see jobs: N/A
• Specialty: IT
• Industry: All
• Location: US

Resumes? No
• Cost to post resumes: N/A
• Cost to see resumes: N/A

Feature(s)? JSK/Links

Career Advice? Yes

Unique approach driving candidates directly to company home pages linked from the JobFest site. Potential candidates are made aware of and given access to JobFest through Computer trade shows. Additional services for 1998 may make this two way communication.

JobHunt: On-Line Job Meta-List

www.job-hunt.org

(College/University)
Dane Spearing, Stanford University
e-mail: dave@job-hunt.org

Jobs? No
• Cost to post jobs: N/A
• Cost to see jobs: N/A
• Specialty: All
• Industry: All
• Location: US

Resumes? No
• Cost to post resumes: N/A
• Cost to see resumes: N/A

Feature(s)? JSK/Links

Career Advice? No

This is the definition of "meta-list". Links are categorized by academia, general, science/engineering/medicine, classified ads, recruiting agencies, companies and newsgroups. You can also see resume banks, reference, commercial and university career centers. All in alpha order- with a short explanation of each. New sites are marked as such and those with a "smile " are those that Dane feels are outstanding job resources. Job Hunt is an Icon on the 'net. Increasingly it will be hard to maintain this list for free without some outside support.

JOBlynx

joblynx.com

(Commercial)
Andrea Hoover, JobLynx
2797 Candle Lane, Green Bay, WI 54304
920-496-2266 Fax: 920-499-2001 e-mail: success@joblynx.com

Jobs? No
- Cost to post jobs: N/A
- Cost to see jobs: N/A
- Specialty: IT
- Industry: N/A
- Location: US

Resumes? Yes
- Cost to post resumes: Fee
- Cost to see resumes: Fee

Feature(s)? JSK/Links

Career Advice? No

Claims to have 4,500 headhunters, 1,200 employment resources and 6 job databases. Job seekers have their resume shopped (confidentially) for $19.95 for one month.   Other packages available for longer periods of time.   While this site states it keeps resumes confidential, we still wonder how 4,500 recruiters can keep a top IT prospect confidential. Interesting idea bringing recruiters together for free to share resumes.

JobNavigator

www.jobs.co.za

(Commercial)
Vanessa Wallace, Systems Publishers
Private Bag X8, Craighall 2024, South Africa
027-117-891808 Fax: 027-117-894725 e-mail: vanessaw@systems.co.za

Jobs? Yes
- Cost to post jobs: Fee
- Cost to see jobs: Free
- Specialty: IT
- Industry: All
- Location: Int'l/South Africa

Resumes? Yes
- Cost to post resumes: Free
- Cost to see resumes: N/A

Feature(s)? N/A

Career Advice? No

Mostly IT positions are posted but other categories are growing. Free to post resumes. Positions are listed with direct contact information. Cost to employer is $800 per month for a minimum of 3 months. Employers have the ability to load as many jobs as they wish and to see the complete resumes of the prospects who have responded. A split screen and search engine make it easier to connect. Site makes a point to ask each employer if this is an affirmative action position. At first we thought it silly as who would say no, then we realized where we were. Cyberspace is an eyeopener.

Job Net.com & Online Opportunities

www.jobnet.com

(Commercial)
Ward Christman, Online Opportunities
64 E Uwchlan Avenue, Suite 254, Exton, PA 19341
610-873-6811 e-mail: sysop@jobnet.com

Jobs? Yes
- Cost to post jobs: Fee
- Cost to see jobs: Free
- Specialty: All
- Industry: All
- Location: US/E/PA

Resumes? Yes
- Cost to post resumes: Free
- Cost to see resumes: Fee

Feature(s)? N/A

Career Advice? No

The owner, Ward Christman has given his site a new look and, with it he has improved access to one of the best regional sites. Positions are posted with direct contact information. Job seekers can post their resume to JobNet for free and, If you want additional coverage, you can have it posted to 400 databases for $49.95. Recruiters can post a job for $50 a month. Site owner will also assist you with placing your openings on other sites... for a fee. Packages include help with a dozen other possibilities...all carefully thought out to enhance this site's overall service. Training, hands-on support, a monthly newsletter, periodic special announcements and a local resume database claimed to include 26,000+ resumes. Contact Ward for a full set of rates and services. If you are thinking of recruiting in the Delaware Valley, Online Opportunities should be part of your strategy.

The Job Resource

www.solimar1.stanford.edu

(College/University)
Stanford University, CA
e-mail: comments@solimar.stanford.edu

Jobs? Yes
• Cost to post jobs: Free
• Cost to see jobs: Free
• Specialty: College
• Industry: All
• Location: US

Resumes? Yes
• Cost to post resumes: Free
• Cost to see resumes: Free

Feature(s)? N/A

Career Advice? No

The Job Resource is provided by students of Stanford University. This totally free site provides resumes from students from across a wide range of universities and colleges. All are coded for confidentiality and recruiters must e-mail information about their openings and await the students reply. (Sure will give headhunters a fit as site only wants jobs from companies). Hundreds of jobs posted and search engine gives easy access. Well designed and the price is right.

Job Resources by US Region

www.wm.edu/csrv/career/stualum/jregion.html#toporcrsv

(College/University)
College of William & Mary
Williamsburg, VA 23187
757-221-3240 Fax: 757-221-3329 e-mail: career@facstaff.wm.edu

Jobs? No
• Cost to post jobs: N/A
• Cost to see jobs: N/A
• Specialty: All
• Industry: All
• Location: US

Resumes? No
• Cost to post resumes: N/A
• Cost to see resumes: N/A

Feature(s)? JSK/Links, Search by State

Career Advice? No

A long list of links to job resources. Sort by region and states, national sites, short term (Summer, Post-Grad, Internships) and Directories. A one line description gives you just enough to get your interest.

Job Search Academic Links

www.bgssu.edu/departments/english/GSC_MLA/JobSearch.html

(College/University)
Alan Rea, Modern Language Assoc. of America Student Caucus
e-mail: alan@bgne.bgsu.edu

Jobs? Yes
• Cost to post jobs: Free
• Cost to see jobs: Free
• Specialty: Teaching
• Industry: Education
• Location: US/W/CA

Resumes? No
• Cost to post resumes: N/A
• Cost to see resumes: N/A

Feature(s)? JSK/Links

Career Advice? No

A listing of links to positions in the academic world. A "current positions being filled" link shows jobs in the LA California area schools.

Job Search

www.ventura.com/jsearch/jshome1.html

(Commercial)
Peter H. Wolf
137 East Thousand Oaks Blvd., Suite 203, Thousand Oaks, CA 91360
805-496-9908 Fax: 805-496-5512 e-mail: jobsearch@adnetsol.com

Jobs? Yes
• Cost to post jobs: Fee
• Cost to see jobs: Free
• Specialty: All
• Industry: All
• Location: US/W/CA

Resumes? Yes
• Cost to post resumes: Fee
• Cost to see resumes: Fee

Feature(s)? N/A

Career Advice? Yes

Job Search claims it has access to 40,000 companies and over 100,000 news stories, 1,000 resumes and 500 active job openings throughout Southern California. For the recruiter, a long list of resumes is available but you must pay a fee to see the contact information. For the job seeker, positions are posted with direct contact information.

Job Search Strategies

www.vjf.com/pub/docs/jobsearch.html

(Commercial)
Cynthia Chin-Lee, Westech
4701 Patrick Henry Drive, #1901, Santa Clara, CA 95054
408-970-8800 e-mail: cchinlee@aol.com

Jobs? No
- Cost to post jobs: N/A
- Cost to see jobs: N/A
- Specialty: N/A
- Industry: N/A
- Location: US

Resumes? No
- Cost to post resumes: N/A
- Cost to see resumes: N/A

Feature(s)? JSK/Links, Diversity

Career Advice? Yes

Cynthia Chin-Lee, JSS's owner, continues to provide a good list of links to minority sites for jobs and career guidance. This site is part of Westech Career Expo.

Jobs for Programmers

www.prgjobs.com

(Recruiting Related Agency)
JFP Resources
1085 South 124th Street, Brookfield, WI 53005
414-782-0072 e-mail: info@ifpresources.com

Jobs? Yes
- Cost to post jobs: Fee
- Cost to see jobs: Free
- Specialty: IT
- Industry: High Technology
- Location: Int'l/US

Resumes? Yes
- Cost to post resumes: Fee
- Cost to see resumes: Fee

Feature(s)? N/A

Career Advice? No

Job for Programmers provides IT candidates. Recruiters can have a 30 day free test drive to check out the service and see if it fits their needs. "Note Pad" concept with brief description of positions, company or name of recruiting agency and relocation information make this an easy site to navigate. Site claims 3,500 resumes in their database. Resumes can be seen but contact information is coded. Interesting way of displaying resume information that is a good model for all to follow. Site will e-mail new resumes to recruiters. Well planned design and at $1,000 for a 7 month run is worth a visit.

CAREERXROADS©
Job, Resume & Career Management Sites on the World Wide Web
• The 1998 Directory •

- 215 -

JobSecurity

www.jobsecurity.com

(Commercial)
Steve Litt, American Troublebusters
18405 Valerio St. #1, Reseda, CA 91335
e-mail: slitt@jobsecurity.com

Jobs? No
• Cost to post jobs: N/A
• Cost to see jobs: N/A
• Specialty: All
• Industry: All
• Location: Int'l/US

Resumes? No
• Cost to post resumes: N/A
• Cost to see resumes: N/A

Feature(s)? Career Mgm't.

Career Advice? Yes

Interesting articles and tips from the author of "Job Seeker's Guide" are free here. Practical information on what you need to know about computer buzz words caught our eye.

JobServe: IT Vacancies in the UK

www.jobserve.com

(Commercial)
Dave Smith, JobServe Ltd.
Haland House, 66 York Road, Weybridge, Surrey, England KT139DY
016-218-17335 Fax: 441-932-829527 e-mail: dave@jobserve.com

Jobs? Yes
• Cost to post jobs: Fee
• Cost to see jobs: Free
• Specialty: IT
• Industry: All
• Location: Int'l/UK

Resumes? Yes
• Cost to post resumes: Free
• Cost to see resumes: Fee

Feature(s)? Push to Applicant

Career Advice? No

Job Serve claims over 33,000 e-mails daily to IT professionals in the UK. We believe it. If you get their daily blurb, you'll understand. Employers post openings and Job Serve pushes them out. Candidates interested in subscribing should send a blank e-mail message to: subscribe@jobserve.com. This site has had a successful run for awhile and it continues to grow. Job Serve also publishes a list of freelance IT professionals that is sent to over 700 recruitment agencies (UK & Europe).

JobSmart California Job Search Guide

(Government)
Brent Fraser, Bay Area Library & Information System
KPIX
415-765-8737 e-mail: fraserb@kpix.groupw.wec.com

Jobs? No
- Cost to post jobs: N/A
- Cost to see jobs: N/A
- Specialty: All
- Industry: All
- Location: US/W/CA

Resumes? No
- Cost to post resumes: N/A
- Cost to see resumes: N/A

Feature(s)? N/A

Career Advice? Yes

If you are in California (Bay Area) and need information on where the jobs are or who to go to for help, the local library is on the web and doing a great job. Tons of career information on different regions of CA are present with links to numerous sites. A salary calculator is built in (this site has also received accolades as having the largest number of links to salary surveys on the web). If you want to contact the library system directly to find out more information: electra@jobsmart.org (the other e-mail is the promotional agency for the banner advertising).

JobSource Careers for College Grads

www.jobsource.com/

(Commercial)
George McGrady, Market Source Corporation
2 Commerce Drive, Cranbury, NJ 08512
609-860-5341 e-mail: mcgrady@marketsource.com

Jobs? Yes
- Cost to post jobs: Fee
- Cost to see jobs: Free
- Specialty: College
- Industry: All
- Location: US

Resumes? Yes
- Cost to post resumes: Free
- Cost to see resumes: Fee

Feature(s)? N/A

Career Advice? Yes

Split screen design makes it easy to view this site emphasizing jobs for the recent college graduate. Search engine does a nice job by first showing you the name of the employer and the location. When you click again you see a brief job description, direct contact information and link to the company. For recruiters the cost to post a job is $150 and internship listings are $100 each for 60 days. Other packages are available. Site claims to provide an "Agent." However, once you set the criteria for your job search, the agent sends the matching openings to a "mailbox" for you to retrieve on your next visit. Convenient, still, this is another site unwilling to go all the way to your desktop in an attempt to keep the traffic high.

CAREERXROADS©
Job, Resume & Career Management Sites on the World Wide Web
• The 1998 Directory •
- 217 -

JOBTRAK

www.jobtrak.com

(Commercial)
Ken Ramberg, Jobtrak Corporation
1964 Westwood Blvd, 3rd Floor, Los Angeles, CA 90025
800-999-8725 Fax: 310-475-7912 e-mail: kramberg@jobtrak.com

Jobs? Yes
- Cost to post jobs: Fee
- Cost to see jobs: Free
- Specialty: College
- Industry: N/A
- Location: US

Resumes? Yes
- Cost to post resumes: Free
- Cost to see resumes: Fee

Feature(s)? Yes

Career Advice? Yes

JOBTRAK advertises extensively in college newspapers to attract students to use their service. In addition, the site has agreements with 600+ colleges who provide students and alumni with a password and then offer companies the ability to reach just their target schools' students and alumni. This makes eminent sense if the students are graduates of programs that a company wants to target but begins to lose its appeal if the company is merely trying to reduce its overall response (there are better solutions to this "problem"). JOBTRAK has done an outstanding marketing job and has garnered a tremendous amount of visibility which keeps student traffic and advertisers active. In addition to the cost of job postings which range from $15 for 1 college to $395 for all colleges (the most popular is a 6 pack of colleges for $75), JOBTRACK offers banners and links that range as high as $10,000. In the Fall of 1997, employers were able to search a resume database to find students and alumni.

Job Vault

www.lafayette.edu/careers

(College/University)
Deborah Jones, Lafayette College
Career Services, 201 Hogg Hall, Easton, PA 18042
610-250-5118 e-mail: jonesd@lafayette.edu

Jobs? Yes
- Cost to post jobs: Free
- Cost to see jobs: Free
- Specialty: All
- Industry: All
- Location: US/E/PA

Resumes? Yes
- Cost to post resumes: Free
- Cost to see resumes: Free

Feature(s)? N/A

Career Advice? Yes

Lafayette could be taking college recruiting one rung higher by loading all of their students and alumni resumes into an optically scanned resume system to make it easier for recruiters interested their graduates. At present, this database cannot be accessed from the web but, if it could...   The Career Planning and Placement professionals go into their resume database and conduct searches for employers. Anyone can see direct contact information on the jobs posted and employers must register and get a password to post jobs and see resumes. These services are free.

CAREERXROADS©
Job, Resume & Career Management Sites on the World Wide Web
• The 1998 Directory •
- 218 -

JobWeb

www.jobweb.org/

(Association/College)
National Association of Colleges and Employers
62 Highland Avenue, Bethlehem, PA 18017
800-544-5272 Fax: 610-868-0208 e-mail: sandy@jobweb.org

Jobs? Yes
- Cost to post jobs: Fee
- Cost to see jobs: Free
- Specialty: College
- Industry: N/A
- Location: US

Resumes? No
- Cost to post resumes: N/A
- Cost to see resumes: N/A

Feature(s)? Search by State, Diversity, Career Mgm't.

Career Advice? Yes

JobWeb is still a great value on the net. A creation of the National Association of Colleges and Employers (NACE), JobWeb provides enormous content to compliment its efficient, self-service postings and searchable profiles. Banners and links are also available and at reasonable prices (a link from your profile goes for just $100/month added to the annual profile cost of $300). Recruiters pay $80 to post a job for a month and direct contact information is available on all jobs posted. JobWeb's search engine categorizes jobs by region of the US and title to make it easier for the job seeker. Also check out Catapult which is on the JobWeb site for additional information about the college career market, diversity and much more.

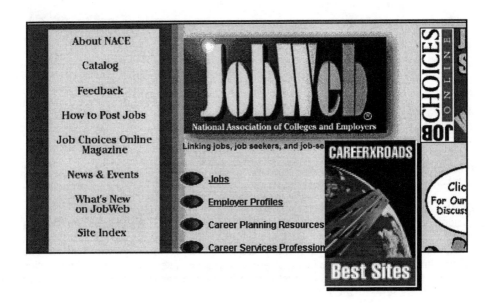

JobXChange Coolest Jobs on the Planet

www.jobxchange.com

(Commercial)
Jack Reynolds, BlueSeas International Inc.
19370 Collins Avenue, Suite 1412C, Miami Beach, FL 33160
305-705-0264 e-mail: webmaster@jobxchange.com

Jobs? Yes
- Cost to post jobs: Fee
- Cost to see jobs: Free
- Specialty: All
- Industry: Entertainment
- Location: US

Resumes? No
- Cost to post resumes: N/A
- Cost to see resumes: N/A

Feature(s)? N/A

Career Advice? Yes

"Jobs in Adventurous Fields" is the best way to characterize one part of this site that specializes in opportunities that are little "off center". Recruiters pay $30 per month with a $30 one time set up fee. What job seekers will find isn't your usual techie fare. Instead, these adventurers can choose to make a living in everything from Ballooning to Skydiving. It's sister site, "Cool Careers", serves up links to jobs like Jeopardy Contestant and Dallas Cowboy Cheerleaders. We've always liked unique niche sites and this one is definitely a one-of-a-kind.

Jobs in Higher Education

volvo.gslis.utexas.edu~acadres/jobs/index.html

(University)
Dan Knauft, National Academic Advising Association
University of Texas, Austin, TX
e-mail: dknauft@fiat.gslis.utexas.edu

Jobs? Yes
- Cost to post jobs: Free
- Cost to see jobs: Free
- Specialty: Teaching
- Industry: Education
- Location: Int'l./US

Resumes? No
- Cost to post resumes: N/A
- Cost to see resumes: N/A

Feature(s)? Search by State

Career Advice? Yes

Jobs in Higher Ed continues to improve. Maintained by the University of Texas, positions in the academic world are posted. Formerly known as "Job listings in Academia" the search engine emphasizes openings by state. Positions can also be found for Canada/Australia and the UK. Links to numerous college sites for open jobs, online publications and associations make this a practical site to visit for all kinds of information.

JOBS jobs Jobs

www.jobsjobsjobs.com

(Commercial)
Margaret Cooley
1330 Harker, Palo Alto, CA 94301
415-322-4722 Fax: 415-326-2479 e-mail: jobsjobsjobs@coolware.com

Jobs? Yes
• Cost to post jobs: Fee
• Cost to see jobs: Free
• Specialty: IT
• Industry: All
• Location: US/W/CA/San Francisco

Resumes? No
• Cost to post resumes: N/A
• Cost to see resumes: N/A

Feature(s)? N/A

Career Advice? No

As if there weren't enough Bay area job sites. We think they breed here. Nice site. Anywhere else it would be highly visible. Lists jobs for the Bay area. Click on their map of local cities and the openings appear by date of posting. Employers pay $49 per posting per month or they can have a banner ad for $150 with free listings. Jobs are primarily in the IT/IS area.

Jobs Mathematics

www.cs.dartmouth.edu/~gdavis/policy/jobmarket.html

(College/University)
Geoff Davis, Dartmouth College
210 Sudikoff Lab, Math Depart. Bradley Hall, Hanover, NH 03755
603-646-1618 Fax: 603-646-1672 e-mail: gdavis@cs.dartmouth.edu

Jobs? No
• Cost to post jobs: N/A
• Cost to see jobs: N/A
• Specialty: Science/Mathematics
• Industry: All
• Location: Int'l./US

Resumes? No
• Cost to post resumes: N/A
• Cost to see resumes: N/A

Feature(s)? JSK/Links

Career Advice? No

Information on the field of mathematics and what employers are looking for from people with these skills. Lots of links to various web sites that could assist you in finding a position.

Journalism-Related Jobs

(College/University)
Paul Grabowicz, Louisiana Tech
e-mail: grab@ix.netcom.com

Jobs? Yes
• Cost to post jobs: Free
• Cost to see jobs: Free
• Specialty: Journalism
• Industry: Journalism
• Location: US

Resumes? No
• Cost to post resumes: N/A
• Cost to see resumes: N/A

Feature(s)? N/A

Career Advice? No

Not much has changed since our last review. This site continues to link with the Boston Globe, California Journalism Job Bank and other newspapers/magazines for journalism positions. The owner, Paul Grabowicz is amazing in that he obviously works hard to maintain this free site and keep the job openings updated by week. You can check all the back "issues". Simple site that gets the job done. No muss, no fuss.

JWT Specialized Communications

www.jwtworks.com

(Recruiting Related Agency)
Chuck Robbins, JWT Specialized Communications
466 Lexington Ave., 4th Floor, NY, NY 10017
212-856-0045 Fax: 212-210-1097 e-mail: questions@jwtworks.com

Jobs? Yes
• Cost to post jobs: Fee
• Cost to see jobs: Free
• Specialty: All
• Industry: All
• Location: US

Resumes? Yes
• Cost to post resumes: Free
• Cost to see resumes: N/A

Feature(s)? N/A

Career Advice? Yes

JWT Specialized Communications is the recruitment advertising division of J. Walter Thompson. Their "HR live" section has interesting information for recruiters. Site posts reports on the latest layoffs, job fairs, internet demographic links, hot HR issues, and the results of the last Employment Management Association survey of cost per hire. Also on our visit we viewed a "virtual job fair" (really JWT clients posting jobs on this site).

Kansas Careers

www-personal.ksu.edu/~dangle/

(College/Diversity)
Kansas State University
Kansas Careers, 2323 Anderson Avenue Ste.248, Manhattan, KS 66502
913-532-2912 Fax: 913-532-7732 e-mail: dangle@ksu.ksu.edu

Jobs? No
- Cost to post jobs: N/A
- Cost to see jobs: N/A
- Specialty: All
- Industry: N/A
- Location: US/MW/KS

Resumes? No
- Cost to post resumes: N/A
- Cost to see resumes: N/A

Feature(s)? Yes

Career Advice? Yes

Site features an internet assessment for women and maintains gender and diversity links for career and job information. A focused site that should be visited.

Kansas City Star

www.kccareers.com/

(Publisher/Newspaper)
Kansas City Star
1729 Grand Boulevard, Kansas City, MO 54108
816-234-4000

Jobs? Yes
- Cost to post jobs: Fee
- Cost to see jobs: Free
- Specialty: All
- Industry: N/A
- Location: US/MW/MO/KC

Resumes? Yes
- Cost to post resumes: Free
- Cost to see resumes: N/A

Feature(s)? N/A

Career Advice? No

Sunday and daily classified employment advertisements are posted on this site. Has a new career management section with some interesting articles. Search engine needs help as "blue lights" were "on" for links to each job that we typed in but it did not work. Employers pay for space in the newspaper and the web site is added for free. You can place your resume online but you are not advised about what happens to it (candidates supposedly can send it from this site via e-mail to whomever they wish). We wonder what this newspaper are intending to do with all of the resumes they are collecting.

Kelly Services

www.kellyservices.com

(Recruiting Related Agency)
Kelly
999 West Big Beaver Road, Troy, MI 48084
248-269-2920 Fax: 810-522-9819 e-mail: staffing@kellyservices.com

Jobs? No
- Cost to post jobs: N/A
- Cost to see jobs: N/A
- Specialty: G/S
- Industry: All
- Location: US

Resumes? Yes
- Cost to post resumes: Free
- Cost to see resumes: N/A

Feature(s)? N/A

Career Advice? No

Kelly Services is one of the largest temporary corporations in the world. Job seekers can post their resume on this site and find the local Kelly office near you. Temporary agencies place numerous professionals as well as clerical help and should not be overlooked.

Knoxville News-Sentinel Online

www.knoxnews.com/

(Publisher/Newspaper)
208 W. Church Avenue, Knoxville, TN 59038
423-523-3131 e-mail: webmaster@knownews.com

Jobs? Yes
- Cost to post jobs: Fee
- Cost to see jobs: Free
- Specialty: All
- Industry: All
- Location: US/S/TN/Knoxville

Resumes? Yes
- Cost to post resumes: Yes
- Cost to see resumes: N/A

Feature(s)? Push to Applicant

Career Advice? No

The Knoxville News-Sentinel has come a long way. This online classified uses "AdRover" to push information to the job seeker. This site conducts daily job searches for registrants and e-mail the results to them.

LatinoWeb

(Commercial)
P.O. Box 3852, Montebello, CA 90640
818-300-8445 e-mail: support@latinoweb.com

Jobs? Yes
• Cost to post jobs: Free
• Cost to see jobs: Free
• Specialty: All
• Industry: All
• Location: US/W/CA

Resumes? No
• Cost to post resumes: N/A
• Cost to see resumes: N/A

Feature(s)? Diversity

Career Advice? Yes

A much longer list of job postings was found on this visit. Recruiters can still post positions for free as the site makes its money elsewhere. Good content on Latino communities and their organizations. LatinoWebChat has been added for visitors to interact.

Law Employment Center

(Publisher/Trade)
Frank Fitts, New York Law Publishing Company
345 Park Avenue South, New York, NY 10010
800-888-8300 Fax: 212-481-8110 e-mail: feedback@lfextra.com

Jobs? Yes
• Cost to post jobs: Fee
• Cost to see jobs: Free
• Specialty: Law
• Industry: Legal
• Location: US/E/NY

Resumes? No
• Cost to post resumes: N/A
• Cost to see resumes: N/A

Feature(s)? N/A

Career Advice? Yes

The National Law Journal has it's legal classified ads on the web and recruiters can place positions in print as well for $9.45 per line. Listings of recruiters who deal in placing lawyers are available. Open positions that have been listed with direct contact information can also be seen. A comprehensive salary survey helps attract traffic.

Layover

(Commercial)
Bruce Martin, Layover.com
872 East Main Street, Ephrata, PA 17522
717-859-4546 Fax: 717-859-1524 e-mail: layover@ptd.net

Jobs? Yes
- Cost to post jobs: Fee
- Cost to see jobs: Free
- Specialty: Driver
- Industry: Trucking
- Location: US

Resumes? Yes
- Cost to post resumes: Fee
- Cost to see resumes: Fee

Feature(s)? N/A

Career Advice? Yes

Who said blue collar jobs were not on the web. Numerous jobs are posted and tons of links to corporations looking for truck drivers. Lots of information on this industry including diesel prices, how to work with your family while you are on the road and other interesting items which make this site more then just a quick layover. You can post messages in layover's lounge and make them available to your family or whomever you choose.

Learning@Living

www.living-icic.com

(Commercial)
Mike Bourcier, 413-1027 Davie Street
Vancouver, BC, Canada V6E 4L2
604-869-3863 Fax: 604-869-3864 e-mail: learning@living-icic.com

Jobs? No
- Cost to post jobs: N/A
- Cost to see jobs: N/A
- Specialty: All
- Industry: N/A
- Location: Int'l/Canada/US

Resumes? No
- Cost to post resumes: N/A
- Cost to see resumes: N/A

Feature(s)? Push to Applicant, Career Mgm't.

Career Advice? Yes

This career management site combines a book, a web site and one-on-one coaching. Subscribers get a workbook, hundreds of links, updates and coaching from the authors Mike Bourcier and Michele Levesque (for 90 days via e-mail) to help them navigate a course toward the modern work world. Books sells for $19.95.

Lee Hecht Harrison

www.careerlhh.com

(Recruiting Related Agency)
Lee Hecht Harrison
50 Tice Boulevard, Woodcliff Lake, NJ 07675
800-611-4544 Fax: 201-505-1439 e-mail: webmaster@careerlhh.com

Jobs? No
- Cost to post jobs: N/A
- Cost to see jobs: N/A
- Specialty: All
- Industry: ALL
- Location: US

Resumes? Yes
- Cost to post resumes: Free (See Note)
- Cost to see resumes: Free

Feature(s)? N/A

Career Advice? Yes

At the HR Info Center employers can review resumes (after registering) of their clients and see some interesting articles. A national severance policy survey caught our eye. Jobs were posted in the past but apparently they've been discontinued.

Lendman's Recruiting Resources Gateway

www.lendman.com

(Job Fair)
The Lendman Group
141 Business Park Drive, Virginia Beach, VA 23462
804-473-2450 e-mail: micahel@nolinet.com

Jobs? Yes
- Cost to post jobs: Fee
- Cost to see jobs: Free
- Specialty: All
- Industry: All
- Location: US

Resumes? Yes
- Cost to post resumes: Free
- Cost to see resumes: Fee

Feature(s)? N/A

Career Advice? Yes

If you need to participate in a job fair, this is one of the biggest players in this sector of the staffing industry. Lendman's site has a schedule of future events and invites job seekers to post their resume for free. If you are an employer and you participate in Lendman job fairs, you can also search their on-line resume database. Jobs are posted but, you have to go back to the home page and register to see the contact information. Check out the "Lendman Top 10" on their career resources magazine page. It's a hoot.

Lexonline's Legal Employment Marketplace

www.lexonline.com

(Commercial)
11500 Ladera Vista, Austin, TX 78759
e-mail: kpaxne@io.com

Jobs? Yes
- Cost to post jobs: Fee
- Cost to see jobs: Free
- Specialty: Law
- Industry: All
- Location: US/MW/TX

Resumes? Yes
- Cost to post resumes: Fee
- Cost to see resumes: Free

Feature(s)? N/A

Career Advice? Yes

Lexonline's Legal Employment Marketplace deals with positions primarily in the Texas area. (attorney, part time law students, paralegal/legal assistants/secretary) You can search by several major cities to make your visit easier for you. Recruiters pay $30 to post a job while candidates pay $20 to post a resume. Both are posted for one month. Check out the "lawyer jokes" as we all need a laugh once in a while.

Links on the Web

www.cob.ohio-state.edu/other/other.html#jobs

(College/University)
Ohio State Univ. Fisher College of Business
Ohio

Jobs? No
- Cost to post jobs: N/A
- Cost to see jobs: N/A
- Specialty: All
- Industry: All
- Location: US

Resumes? No
- Cost to post resumes: N/A
- Cost to see resumes: N/A

Feature(s)? JSK/Links

Career Advice? No

An interesting list of links to get you started in your job search. All fields are represented here with some corporations and general interest sites listed as well.

Loading Zone

www.loadingzone.com

(Commercial)
Ryan Langhus
S2669 County Road V, Hillsboro, WI 54634
800-492-6857 e-mail: rsm@loadingzone.com

Jobs? Yes
- Cost to post jobs: Fee
- Cost to see jobs: Fee
- Specialty: Hauling Loads
- Industry: Trucking
- Location: US

Resumes? Yes
- Cost to post resumes: Fee
- Cost to see resumes: Fee

Feature(s)? N/A

Career Advice? No

Truck drivers have several places to go on the web to find jobs for long and short haul loads and, this is one of them. Loading Zone has only been up since May of 1997 but backers have over 30 years in the trucking business and know what they are doing. You can have a 10 day free trial to "cyber road" this site. Cost to post your resume is $19.95 for six months and $10 to see job opportunities (where to pick up the next load). Employers pay $10 to post and $10 to see resumes. Families and employers can go online in their chat room to discuss issues as well. Simple, easy to understand. We wish them the best of luck.

Los Angeles Times

www.latimes.com

(Publisher/Newspaper)
Nancy Massa, Los Angeles Times
145 S. Spring Street, Los Angeles, CA 90012
Fax: 213-237-3181 e-mail: classifieds@@latimes.com

Jobs? Yes
- Cost to post jobs: Fee
- Cost to see jobs: Free
- Specialty: All
- Industry: N/A
- Location: US/W/CA/LA

Resumes? No
- Cost to post resumes: N/A
- Cost to see resumes: N/A

Feature(s)? N/A

Career Advice? Yes

LA Times has created a new home page with the classified button right at the top for ease of access. Search engine makes it easy to view either Sunday or daily advertisements. Paper also participates in CareerPath (See CareerPath).

Macintosh Employment Registry

www.mactalent.com

(Commercial)
Doug Noble, Go! SouthFlorida Inc.
780 Palm Bay Lane, Suite 1709, Miami, FL 33138
305-754-0222 Fax: 305-757-2448 e-mail: doug@mactalent.com

Jobs? Yes
• Cost to post jobs: Fee
• Cost to see jobs: Free
• Specialty: IT/Macintosh
• Industry: All
• Location: US

Resumes? Yes
• Cost to post resumes: Fee
• Cost to see resumes: Free

Feature(s)? Push to Employer

Career Advice? No

If you are a Mac afficionado and seeking employment this site is a niche home for you. MER is promoted through links to career/recruiting sites and postings on listserves and newsgroups. Job seekers can post their resume for $49 for a month. If you need privacy it will cost you $9 extra. Job seekers can select a code name so their employers cannot see who they are. Recruiters can search to their hearts content for resumes. it's all free. Site claims over 900 Mac users are on board. Now that the sign up has recently changed from free to fee, we'll see whether the growth continues as rapidly. Job postings cost $50 for a 4 week run and the site will e-mail the opening to all who have signed up. 30 day no-quibble money back guarantee. Detailed search engine for ease of access. Good job and worth a visit if Mac is your thing.

Main Quad

www.mainquad.com

(Commercial)
Kevin Watters, Main Quad Global Comm for Coll Stud
1770 Union Street, San Francisco, CA 94123
415-346-4242 Fax: 415-353-0685 e-mail: kevin@mainquad.com

Jobs? No
• Cost to post jobs: N/A
• Cost to see jobs: N/A
• Specialty: College
• Industry: All
• Location: US

Resumes? Yes
• Cost to post resumes: Free
• Cost to see resumes: Fee

Feature(s)? N/A

Career Advice? No

Main Quad is for college students who want to send their resume off to potentially 200+ corporations that have links here. Neat idea. Unfortunately, we can't understand why cost information isn't available on the site and no response to repeated e-mails suggests we take a pass here until they get it together.

Malaysia Online

www.mol.com.

(Commercial)
Mark Chang, #1 Ground Floor Office
Equatorial Penang, 1 Jalan bukit Jambul, 11900 Penang, Malaysia
603-642-8653 Fax: 604-642-8653 e-mail: info@mol-usa.com

Jobs? Yes
• Cost to post jobs: Fee
• Cost to see jobs: Free
• Specialty: All
• Industry: All
• Location: Int'l./Malaysia/Singapore

Resumes? Yes
• Cost to post resumes: Free
• Cost to see resumes: Fee

Feature(s)? Push to Employer

Career Advice? Yes

If you want to work in Malaysia/Singapore this site has positions posted and also provides employers with an "Agent" that surfs through a resume database to find candidates. Mark Chang claims he has over 30,000 resumes in his database. He believes confidentiality is the key to success as only the "agent" can do a resume search.

Manpower

www.manpower.com

(Placement/Search/Temp)
Manpower, Inc.
Milwaukee, WI

Jobs? Yes
• Cost to post jobs: Fee
• Cost to see jobs: Free
• Specialty: All
• Industry: All
• Location: Int'l/US

Resumes? Yes
• Cost to post resumes: Yes
• Cost to see resumes: N/A

Feature(s)? Search by State

Career Advice? Yes

Manpower employs over 500,000 people in temporary positions. Their search engine will direct you to hundreds of jobs but they are all coded. You can submit your resume to the company directly from this site or visit your local Manpower office.

Manufacturing Job Search

www.manufacturing.net/resources/jobs/default.htm

(Publisher/Trade)
Reed Elsevier, Inc.
25 Victoria Street, London, UK SW1HOEX,UK
440-171-2228420 Fax: 440-171-2275799 e-mail: feedback@manufacturing.net

Jobs? Yes
- Cost to post jobs: Fee
- Cost to see jobs: Free
- Specialty: All
- Industry: All
- Location: Int'l/UK/US

Resumes? Yes
- Cost to post resumes: Free
- Cost to see resumes: Fee

Feature(s)? N/A

Career Advice? No

Manufacturing Job Search is an international publisher who has incorporated media information at this site. Magazines include: Control Engineering, Design News, Logistics Management and many others. This site is a"point of entry" for the "Monster Board". This means that job seekers hoping to find positions posted here will click on the jobs button and, "powered by the MonsterBoard", will be linked to the career hub. Nice marketing idea. May have a few problems when the job seekers realize they've left the niche. Rates are $150 per job posting. Manufacturing Job search does have links to relevant newsgroups & discussion forums. Good site design. Business models using different "points of entry" to the same central job site may catch on. We think its growth is limited.

Marketing Classifieds

www.marketingjobs.com

(Commercial)
Woody Haskins, Marketing Classifieds
4132 E. 17-36, Pinckney, MI 48169
810-231-6990 Fax: 810-271-6743 e-mail: whaskins@ismi.net

Jobs?
- Cost to post jobs: Fee
- Cost to see jobs: Free
- Specialty: Marketing
- Industry: All
- Location: US

Resumes? Yes
- Cost to post resumes: Free
- Cost to see resumes: Fee

Feature(s)? N/A

Career Advice? No

Marketing positions and resumes are posted with direct contact information. Resumes can be posted for free while jobs cost $25 per month per posting. Resume database can be searched for a monthly fee of $30.

MBA Central

(Commercial)
Jeffrey Hyman, 399 Sherman Avenue
Suite 1, Palo Alto, CA 94306
800-932-4670 Fax: 415-327-8089 e-mail: info@mbacentral.com

Jobs? Yes
- Cost to post jobs: Fee
- Cost to see jobs: Free
- Specialty: College/MBA
- Industry: All
- Location: US

Resumes? Yes
- Cost to post resumes: Free
- Cost to see resumes: Fee

Feature(s)? Push to Applicant

Career Advice? No

Interesting niche for MBA graduates/students. E-mail for free software to create a portfolio which applicants submit to the site. Employers post their requirements and job seekers are then sent an e-mail when there is a match. If the candidate is interested he/she can then send their resume via e-mail (or snail mail) to MBA Central where it will be printed out and forwarded to the hiring manager. They do not store resumes but have collected thousands of e-mails. Smart marketing and a clearly defined niche make this a site to watch. The skill based software makes sense as it narrows down the search criteria and allowing the recruiter to be very specific. Recruiters pay $1,995 for an initial search of graduates and $995 for second year graduating students. Volume packages are available. Candidates are presented in 4 days.

MBA Employment Connection Assoc.

www.mbanetwork.com/meca

(Association)
Brian Chase, MBA Employment Connection Association
P.O. Box 415, Palmyra, CA 22963
804-286-3866 Fax: 804-286-3866 e-mail: meca@MBAnetwork.com

Jobs? Yes
- Cost to post jobs: Fee
- Cost to see jobs: Free
- Specialty: College/MBA
- Industry: All
- Location: US

Resumes? Yes
- Cost to post resumes: Free
- Cost to see resumes: Free

Feature(s)? N/A

Career Advice? No

MBA graduates have a number of specific sites to gravitate to and the "employment connection" provides a free service with value. Recruiters can view candidates with contact information for free. An interesting search engine allows an employer to point and click or use keyword search. Jobs can be posted for $65 per month per posting. On our last visit over 650 MBA profiles in the database.

MBA Job

(Commercial)
MBAJOB, Inc.
P.O. Box 15861, Nashville, TN 37215-8681
615-298-4369 Fax: 615-298-4369 e-mail: mba@mbajob.com

Jobs? Yes
- Cost to post jobs: Free
- Cost to see jobs: Free
- Specialty: MBA
- Industry: All
- Location: US

Resumes? Yes
- Cost to post resumes: Fee
- Cost to see resumes: Free

Feature(s)? N/A

Career Advice? No

MBAJob was created by students to provide access to employers while having resumes online. Job seekers pay $15-$25 to post their resume while recruiters can post jobs for free. We saw dozens of large corporations with links to their home pages so we would recommend recruiters contact the site as there must be some additional charges. Many schools are represented and the resumes are in a simple format and easy to read. All have e-mail links back to the students. Amazing how times have changed.

MedConnect

(Commercial)
Medical Network, Inc.
Princeton, NJ
e-mail: reply@medconnect.com

Jobs? Yes
- Cost to post jobs: Fee ,
- Cost to see jobs: Free
- Specialty: Health Care/MD
- Industry: Health Care
- Location: US

Resumes? Yes
- Cost to post resumes: Free
- Cost to see resumes: Fee

Feature(s)? N/A

Career Advice? Yes

Medical positions are posted to this site by specialty or by contract group. Employer contact information can be seen and, job seekers who register with the site, can then e-mail directly.

Med Hunters

www.medhunters.com

(Placement Agency)
Robin Kerr, 180 Dundas St. West, Suite 2403
Toronto, Ontario, Canada M5G 1Z8
800-664-0278 Fax: 416-977-6128 e-mail: robin@medhunters.com

Jobs? Yes
- Cost to post jobs: Fee
- Cost to see jobs: Free
- Specialty: Health Care
- Industry: Health Care
- Location: Int'l/Canada/US

Resumes? Yes
- Cost to post resumes: Free
- Cost to see resumes: Fee

Feature(s)? N/A

Career Advice? No

Site is in transition and looking to provide additional services to the hospital/medical market. At present, it allows corporations to search their database and rates are based on their expectation of hires. You gain access for $3,000 and can hire 5 people and then the price drops from there. Med Hunters will be adding job postings and allowing employers many more tools to play with.   Owners are in the recruiting business and specialize in Canada/US and the Far East markets.

MedSearch

www.medsearch.com

(Commercial)
Larry Bouchard, Monster Board
2 Kendall Street, Suite 301 P.O. Box 586, Framingham, MA 01701
508-429-6805 Fax: 508-879-4651 e-mail: office@medsearch.com

Jobs? Yes
- Cost to post jobs: Fee
- Cost to see jobs: Free
- Specialty: Science/Biomedical
- Industry: Health Care
- Location: US

Resumes? Yes
- Cost to post resumes: Free
- Cost to see resumes: Fee

Feature(s)? N/A

Career Advice? Yes

MedSearch broke a few hearts when they were acquired by Monster Board. What used to be an $800 entry fee to search this site's resume database has now been placed along side the other Monster services at $1,900 a quarter or $6,900 a year. Individual job postings-mostly biomedical, biotechnology, research and other scientific openings cost $150 to post. Many other packages are available. MedSearch now has an international side where positions can be posted and job seekers can obtain direct contact information for free. Career information is available. Recruiters have access to the site's agent who will search resumes for posted positions.

Medical Device Link

www.devicelink.com

(Publisher/Trade)
Rebecca Bermudez, Canon Communications, Inc.
3340 Ocean Park Blvd., Suite 1000, Santa Monica, CA 90405
310-392-8839 Fax: 310-392-4920 e-mail: feedback@canon.com

Jobs? Yes
• Cost to post jobs: Fee
• Cost to see jobs: Free
• Specialty: Science/Medical Device
• Industry: Health Care
• Location: US

Resumes? No
• Cost to post resumes: N/A
• Cost to see resumes: N/A

Feature(s)? N/A

Career Advice? Yes

Interesting information on the medical device field with several jobs posted. All include direct contact information. Articles are posted from the Medical Device & Information Industry Magazine. A salary "estimator" is also available but with the way the questions are asked, the value of this information leaves us in doubt.

MedicalJobs

www.MEDJOB.com

(Commercial)
Impact Publications
e-mail: info@medjob.com

Jobs? Yes
• Cost to post jobs: Fee
• Cost to see jobs: Free
• Specialty: Health Care/MD
• Industry: Health Care
• Location: US/SE

Resumes? No
• Cost to post resumes: N/A
• Cost to see resumes: N/A

Feature(s)? N/A

Career Advice? No

Positions are posted in the medical and health care fields from doctors, office administrators and other health care professionals. Site is still concentrated in the southeast US and has not expanded out of that area. Medical jobs has not grown since our last review.

MedZilla

(Placement Agency)
Frank Heasley, Ph.D., Franklin Search Group
4522 54th Place West, Redmonds, WA 98026-3811
206-742-4292 Fax: 206-742-2172 e-mail: fheasley@chemistry.com

Jobs? Yes
- Cost to post jobs: Fee
- Cost to see jobs: Free
- Specialty: Science/Chemistry/Pharmaceutical/Health care
- Industry: Biotechnology/Pharmaceutical
- Location: US

Resumes? Yes
- Cost to post resumes: Free
- Cost to see resumes: Fee

Feature(s)? N/A

Career Advice? Yes

MedZilla (Franklin Search Group) Online is designed for biotechnology, medicine, healthcare and pharmaceutical candidates and employers. Job listings and an extensive highly focused database of current resumes are available. All candidate services are free, including posting resumes to the databank and searching and applying for advertised jobs. Employers may query the candidate database at no charge, but there is a fee to obtain contact information. Posting jobs costs $100. Academic postings for postdocs and faculty are free for employers to list.

Mercury Center Web

(Publisher/Newspaper/Agent)
Janet Huebner, San Jose Mercury News
750 Ridder Park Drive, San Jose, CA 95190
408-920-5585 e-mail: jehuebner@sjmercury.com

Jobs? Yes
- Cost to post jobs: Fee
- Cost to see jobs: Free
- Specialty: All
- Industry: N/A
- Location: US/W/CA/San Jose

Resumes? No
- Cost to post resumes: Free
- Cost to see resumes: N/A

Feature(s)? Push to Applicant

Career Advice? No

Mercury Center, the pioneering internet laboratory of the San Jose Mercury News, has relaunched TALENT SCOUT (www.sjmercury.com/talentscout) with a range of new features including Voices of Women in Technology, a regular column on women and workplace issues sponsored by Women in Technology International. Additional features for job seekers include: tips, FREE AGENT- a tool to help post resumes; online registration for job fairs sponsored by the paper; a national job fair organization; and, a weekly job forecast for the silicon valley area. Publisher also participates in CareerPath (see CarerPath)

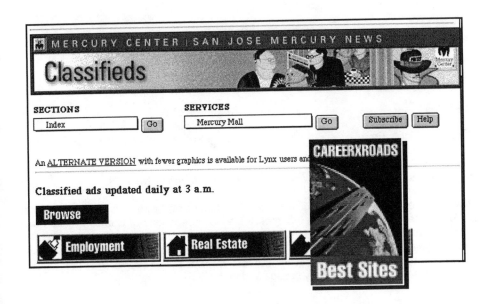

Milwaukee Journal Sentinel

www.onwis.com

(Publisher/Newspaper)
Milwaukee Journal
333 W. State Street, Milwaukee, WI 53203
888-886-6947 e-mail: onwis@onwis.com

Jobs? Yes
• Cost to post jobs: Fee
• Cost to see jobs: Free
• Specialty: All
• Industry: N/A
• Location: US/MW/WI/Milwaukee

Resumes? No
• Cost to post resumes: N/A
• Cost to see resumes: N/A

Feature(s)? N/A

Career Advice? No

Newspaper help-wanted classified advertisements are posted on this site. Currently, their Display help wanted ads are not posted to the Web. Paper participates in CareerPath.

Ministry Connect

www.ministry.connect.org

(Non-Profit)
Bernadette Dougherty, Ministry Resource Center
1600 Martine Avenue, Scotch Plains, NJ 07076
908-889-6425 Fax: 908-889-7867 e-mail: ministrc@webspan.net

Jobs? Yes
• Cost to post jobs: Fee
• Cost to see jobs: Free
• Specialty: Ministry
• Industry: Religion
• Location: US

Resumes? Yes
• Cost to post resumes: Fee
• Cost to see resumes: Free

Feature(s)? Search by State

Career Advice? No

Ministry Connection was founded as a collaborative venture by the Ministry Resource Center for Women Religious. This group incorporates 14 congregations of Catholic Sisters and provides career services for people interested in the ministry. Site provides jobs in administration, education, health care, parish/pastoral/spiritual as well as social service and volunteer groups. Fee to post jobs is $4 and resumes are $25. They will also provide pro-bono services. Jobs are posted by groups and by state.

Minneapolis Star Tribune

www.startribune.com

(Publisher/Newspaper)
425 Portland Avenue
Minneapolis, MN 55488
800-827-8742 e-mail: oswalrs@gw.startribune.com

Jobs? Yes
• Cost to post jobs: Fee
• Cost to see jobs: Free
• Specialty: All
• Industry: N/A
• Location: US/MW/MN/Minnesota

Resumes? No
• Cost to post resumes: N/A
• Cost to see resumes: N/A

Feature(s)? N/A

Career Advice? No

Help wanted classified advertisements from Sunday's newspaper can be seen on this site. Search engine shows you a short synopsis of the position you have selected and then you can see full details by taking one more step. Publisher also participates in CareerPath (see CareerPath). Help wanted display ads are not included on this Internet site.

MINORITIES' JOB BANK

www.minorities-jb.com

(Publisher)
Penny Francis, Black Collegian Online
140 Carondelet Street, New Orleans, LA 70130
504-523-0154 e-mail: penny@black-collegian.com

Jobs? Yes
• Cost to post jobs: Fee
• Cost to see jobs: Free
• Specialty: All
• Industry: All
• Location: US

Resumes? Yes
• Cost to post resumes: Free
• Cost to see resumes: Fee

Feature(s)? Diversity

Career Advice? Yes

The Black Collegian has recently launched this site to provide career opportunities specifically for people of color. There were dozens of job openings on our last visit. A search engine has been added for ease of access. Direct contact information on employers is available. Information "Villages" have been created for African, Asian, Hispanic, Native-American and other global minorities. In these content areas, there are interesting articles on career management and other topics affecting minorities. Resumes can be posted for free if you are a student with better then a 3.0 GPA or have 2 or more years of professional experience (we'll bet the owners would appreciate your opinions about this last feature).

Mississippi Careers Online

www.whipcomm.com/whipcomm/mscareer/index.html

(Commercial)
Whippoorwill Communications
P.O. Box 4870, University, Mississippi 38677
800-662-5621 Fax: 601-234-9980 e-mail: bafitts@sunset.backbone.olemis

Jobs? Yes
- Cost to post jobs: Fee
- Cost to see jobs: Free
- Specialty: All
- Industry: N/A
- Location: US/S/MS

Resumes? Yes
- Cost to post resumes: Fee
- Cost to see resumes: Free

Feature(s)? N/A

Career Advice? Yes

The Mississippi talent bank will post your resume for $14.95 for a full year. Jobs are posted with direct contact information. We only saw 4 on our last visit.

MMWire Online

www.mmwire.com

(Publisher/Trade)
Scott Nance, Phillips Business Information
1201 Seven Locks Road, Suite 300, Potomac, MD 20854
301-340-7788 Fax: 301-309-3847 e-mail: snance@phillips.com

Jobs? Yes
- Cost to post jobs: Fee
- Cost to see jobs: Free
- Specialty: IT/Multimedia
- Industry: All
- Location: US

Resumes? Yes
- Cost to post resumes: Free
- Cost to see resumes: Free

Feature(s)? N/A

Career Advice? No

Job postings at MMWire are available for $49.95 each and are posted for one month. An online form will make it easy for candidates to apply. Resumes were also posted on our visit but we only saw two listed. Jobs were posted in alpha order for all areas of multimedia.

The Monster Board

www.monster.com

(Recruiting Related Agency)
2 Kendall Street, Suite 301 P.O. Box 586, Framingham, MA 01701
508-879-4641 Fax: 508-879-4651

Jobs? Yes
• Cost to post jobs: Fee
• Cost to see jobs: Free
• Specialty: All
• Industry: All
• Location: Int'l/US

Resumes? Yes
• Cost to post resumes: Free
• Cost to see resumes: Fee

Feature(s)? Push to Employer

Career Advice? Yes

The Monster Board has a search agent to help job seekers match their interests with posted positions. The resulting openings are then placed in an private inbox, to await your return. Why not push the openings all the way to the job seeker's desktop rather then making them return? Need traffic? Recruiters can view resumes for $6,900 a year or $1,900 a quarter. The Monster vows to have over 70,000 in it's database. Recruiters can plug in their job criteria and the "monster 'cruiter" will do the rest of the work for you. This push tool searches for new resumes as they come in and sends them to you. Job Fair schedules are available. Joyce Lain Kennedy's articles on career advice are a great resource. Employers pay $150 to post each job and many other packages are available. International areas have also been added and include: Australia, Canada and the UK. Truly a Monster site with many features that have made it a successful career hub. Site is owned by TMP, a recruitment advertising firm.

Montgomery Newspapers

metroworld.com

(Publisher/Newspaper)
Montgomery Newspapers
290 Commerce Drive, Fort Washington, PA 19034
215-542-0200 Fax: 215-283-2555 e-mail: psehelp@lyonesse.membrane.com

Jobs? Yes
- Cost to post jobs: Fee
- Cost to see jobs: Free
- Specialty: All
- Industry: All
- Location: US/E/PA

Resumes? No
- Cost to post resumes: N/A
- Cost to see resumes: N/A

Feature(s)? N/A

Career Advice? Yes

In column classified advertisements are available here at this online service for local Montgomery County (PA) newspaper.

MTS Group

www.mtsboston.com

(Recruiting Related Agency)
Dave Crowley. MTS Group
235 Bear Hill Road, Waltham, MA 02154
617-890-9880 Fax: 617-890-4888 e-mail: dave@mtsboston.com

Jobs?
- Cost to post jobs: Fee
- Cost to see jobs: Free
- Specialty: IT
- Industry: All
- Location: US

Resumes?
- Cost to post resumes: Free
- Cost to see resumes: Fee

Feature(s)? N/A

Career Advice? No

MTS specializes in providing IT resumes to their clients. Recruiters pay $8,000 to post jobs while advising the site their criterion for resumes they wish to review. Internal "resume miners" go through the database to provide candidates on a weekly basis. Site claims 18,000 technical resumes and over 200 corporations as clients. Jobs are posted with some direct contact information but best if you send your resume to MTS. Search engine for jobs was difficult to operate on our visits. Site also has locations in SF, Carolinas and Washington DC. We like the weekly resume updates and that they do the searching for you. Price will be an issue to some.

Multimedia Jobs (UI-Design Jobs)

www.io.tudelft.nl/uidesign/jobs.html

(College/University)
Raghu Kolli, Meru Research
Kluyverweg 2a, 2629 HT Delft, The Netherlands
311-526-82564 Fax: 311-526-82530 e-mail: editor@meru.nl

Jobs? Yes
- Cost to post jobs: Free
- Cost to see jobs: Free
- Specialty: IT
- Industry: All
- Location: Int'l./US

Resumes? No
- Cost to post resumes: N/A
- Cost to see resumes: N/A

Feature(s)? N/A

Career Advice? No

This is a collaborative site between a web design firm and several universities in The Netherlands to promote jobs & information about multimedia and interaction design. Half a dozen jobs were posted with direct contact information from all over the world. Very specific niche that is a free service for both the recruiter and the job seeker.

Music Pages

www.musicpages.com/index.htm

(Commercial)
Fax: 817-685-9536 e-mail: bobm1@musicpages.com

Jobs? Yes
- Cost to post jobs: Free
- Cost to see jobs: Free
- Specialty: All
- Industry: Music
- Location: US

Resumes? No
- Cost to post resumes: N/A
- Cost to see resumes: N/A

Feature(s)? N/A

Career Advice? No

From technical jobs to music teachers, all can be found here... and all can be seen for free. Contact information with direct links to music corporations are available. A site search engine is under construction.

My Future

www.myfuture.com

(Commercial)
e-mail: thebrains@myfuture.com

Jobs? No
- Cost to post jobs: N/A
- Cost to see jobs: N/A
- Specialty: College/High School
- Industry: All
- Location: US

Resumes? No
- Cost to post resumes: N/A
- Cost to see resumes: N/A

Feature(s)? Career Mgm't.

Career Advice? Yes

My Future is geared for high school graduates who are not sure what they want to do with the rest of their lives. The site includes: a resume work sheet to help you put your best foot forward; a cover letter; financial aid info with links to directories; and, a money game that takes you through actual career situations and scores your answers. Nice site for parents as well as students.

NAACB Job Board and Resume Bank

computerwork.com

(Association)
Peggy Smith, National Association of Computer Consulting Bus.
800-313-1920 e-mail: naccb@resourcecenter.com

Jobs? Yes
- Cost to post jobs: Fee
- Cost to see jobs: Free
- Specialty: IT
- Industry: Computer
- Location: US

Resumes? Yes
- Cost to post resumes: Free
- Cost to see resumes: Fee

Feature(s)? N/A

Career Advice? Yes

The National Association of Computer Consulting Businesses posts company positions with direct contact information. A resume bank that is free for job seekers but employers, must become a member of the organization in order to regularly post jobs and search the resume bank. In addition, there is a monthly charge of $195. Site continues to have technical problems and is not set up with the greatest format. Over 250 members.

NACUBO

www.nacubo.org

(Association)
Pierce McManus, Nat. Assoc. of College & U. Business Officers
2501 M Street NW, Suite 400, Washington, DC 20037
202-861-2514 Fax: 202-861-2583 e-mail: pmcmanus@nacubo.nche.edu

Jobs? Yes
• Cost to post jobs: Fee
• Cost to see jobs: Free
• Specialty: Education/Executive
• Industry: Education
• Location: US

Resumes? No
• Cost to post resumes: N/A
• Cost to see resumes: N/A

Feature(s)? Yes

Career Advice? No

Employment opportunities in higher education administration are posted here for this association of chief business officers. You will need to go into the "resource directory" and then to "employment opportunities" to find them. Positions are listed with direct contact information and are in many different areas. Employers place ads in the association's monthly magazine. The web is an added value component of the print.

Nando Times

www.nando.net

(Publisher/Newspaper)
Raleigh News & Observer
127 West Hargett Street, Suite 406, Raleigh, NC 27601
919-829-4610 e-mail: mchoate@nando.net

Jobs? Yes
• Cost to post jobs: Fee
• Cost to see jobs: Free
• Specialty: All
• Industry: N/A
• Location: US/E/NC/Raleigh

Resumes? No
• Cost to post resumes: N/A
• Cost to see resumes: N/A

Feature(s)? N/A

Career Advice? No

Classified advertising for jobs can be seen in The Raleigh News & Observer. You can link here to sister publications: The News Tribune (Tacoma Washington), The Sacramento Bee (Sacramento CA), The Modesto Bee (Modesto CA), The Fresno Bee(Fresno CA), The Anchorage Daily News(Anchorage Alaska) and the Tri-City Herald (Richland Washington)

The National (Int'l) Home Workers Association

www.homeworkers.com

(Association)
The International Homeworkers Assoc.
1925 Pine Avenue, Suite No. 9035, Niagara Falls, NY 14301
716-284-6387 Fax: 905-572-6164 e-mail: iha@homeworkers.com

Jobs? Yes
- Cost to post jobs: Fee
- Cost to see jobs: Fee
- Specialty: All
- Industry: All
- Location: US

Resumes? Yes
- Cost to post resumes: Fee
- Cost to see resumes: Free

Feature(s)? Career Mgm't./HomeWork

Career Advice? Yes

Site has been under construction on our most recent visits but is making improvements. Hundreds of resumes have been added for people who work out of their homes and like it. Membership is $99.90 per year and brings subscribers reading material about working from home and a directory to employers. Other packages are available. Job seekers must become members to view open positions. We wonder what members think of this site and especially about those "lifetime" memberships.

National Business Employment Weekly

www.nbew.com

(Publication/Trade)
Mary LaMagna, Dow Jones & Company, Inc.
US Rte. 1 at Ridge Road, South Brunswick, NJ 08852
800-323-6239 Fax: 609-520-7315

Jobs? No
- Cost to post jobs: N/A
- Cost to see jobs: N/A
- Specialty: N/A
- Industry: N/A
- Location: US

Resumes? No
- Cost to post resumes: N/A
- Cost to see resumes: N/A

Feature(s)? Career Mgm't.

Career Advice? Yes

If you buy this weekly publication, you will see all of the classified ads from the NBEW which include all of the Wall Street Journal's 4 editions. On The NBEW's site you can see the career management articles published in this weekly tabloid. Recruiters can purchase banners for $3,600 per quarter.

National Diversity Journalism Job Bank

www.newsjobs.com

(Publisher/Newspaper)
Jody Kestler, Florida Times-Union
One Riverside Ave., Jacksonville, FL 32202
904-359-4079 Fax: 904-359-4478 e-mail: newsjobs@newsjobs.com

Jobs? Yes
- Cost to post jobs: Free
- Cost to see jobs: Free
- Specialty: Journalism
- Industry: Publishing
- Location: US

Resumes? No
- Cost to post resumes: N/A
- Cost to see resumes: N/A

Feature(s)? Diversity

Career Advice? Yes

Why do people make something so simple so complicated. Employers can post jobs to this site for free. A great service but then the resumes are coded and the job seeker has to send their resume to the web site with the job/code. The site then sends the contact information back to the job seeker. Lots of jobs are posted in many different newspaper occupations. The site's owners have indicated that they are satisfied with this cumbersome model and feel their process works well as they are getting a lot of resumes. Who are we to argue with success. Nice effort is made here by the Florida Times-Union to support the profession.

National Educators Employment Review

www.teacherjobs.com/

(Publisher/Trade)
P.O. Box 60309, Colorado Springs, CO 80960
719-632-5877 Fax: 800-377-1146 e-mail: info@netgraftx.ocm

Jobs? Yes
- Cost to post jobs: Free
- Cost to see jobs: Fee
- Specialty: Teaching
- Industry: Teaching
- Location: US

Resumes? Yes
- Cost to post resumes: Free
- Cost to see resumes: Free

Feature(s)? Search by State

Career Advice? Yes

The National Educators Employment Review is a monthly publication and the intent of this site is to get you to spend $52 to subscribe. They allow you to post positions and see resumes for free but job seekers can only see a few samples of job openings. To see the bulk of the free postings you have to subscribe to the publication. Search engine helps job seekers to find resumes by state and some articles about finding your next teaching position are worth a read.

National Paralegal Reporter

www.paralegals.org

(Association)
National Federation of Paralegal Association
P.O. Box 33108, Kansas City, MO 64114
816-941-4000 Fax: 816-941-2725 e-mail: info@paralegals.com

Jobs? Yes
- Cost to post jobs: Fee
- Cost to see jobs: Free
- Specialty: Law/Paralegal
- Industry: Legal
- Location: US

Resumes? No
- Cost to post resumes: N/A
- Cost to see resumes: N/A

Feature(s)? Search by State

Career Advice? Yes

Another niche that excels. Jobs can be posted and direct contact information is available for the job seeker. Click on a map of the US and select the state of your choosing. Jobs are listed in alpha order- no search engine exists. Employers post jobs for $50 per opening for a six month listing. Too long. Articles on professional advancement and career guidance are also available.

The National Society of Black Engineers

www.nsbe.org

(Association)
NSBE
1454 Duke Street, Alexandria, VA 22314
703-549-2207 Fax: 703-683-5312

Jobs?
- Cost to post jobs: Fee
- Cost to see jobs: Free
- Specialty: Engineering
- Industry: All
- Location: US

Resumes?
- Cost to post resumes: N/A
- Cost to see resumes: N/A

Feature(s)? Diversity

Career Advice? Yes

Provides classifieds from NSBE, a monthly publication for minority engineers. Primarily college oriented. Career Fair information is also available.

National Society of Professional Engineering HP

www.nspe.org

(Association)
NSPE
1420 King Street, Alexandria, VA 22314
703-684-4811 e-mail: customer.service@nspe.org

Jobs? Yes
• Cost to post jobs: Fee
• Cost to see jobs: Free
• Specialty: Engineering/PE
• Industry: Construction
• Location: US

Resumes? No
• Cost to post resumes: N/A
• Cost to see resumes: N/A

Feature(s)? Search by State

Career Advice? Yes

Engineers are represented here in all technical areas. Recruiters pay $50 to post a position on the web but if you place an ad in their publication "Engineering Times" the online can be had for only $15 extra. Nice thing about their job listings is that the states that have positions posted are highlighted so you do not waste your time. No search engine so you will have to scroll down the lines. (they get it but...) Information also available on scholarships and other industry related topics. Some of the info is only available to members of the association.

NationJob Network

www.nationjob.com

(Commercial)
Bob Levinstein, NationJob, Inc.
2010 S. Ankeny Blvd., Ankeny, IA 50021
800-292-7731 Fax: 515-965-6737 e-mail: njsales@nationjob.com

Jobs?
- Cost to post jobs: Fee
- Cost to see jobs: Free
- Specialty: All
- Industry: All
- Location: US/MW

Resumes?
- Cost to post resumes: Free
- Cost to see resumes: N/A

Feature(s)? Push to Applicant

Career Advice? Yes

NationJob Network is primarily a national site with Midwest strength that has a lower profile than it should. This site's agent, "PJ Scout", can "push" job info matching the interests of 150,000 registered job seekers right to their desktop. NationJob will post a job description for 30 days for $75 or $100 with a one-page company profile. Thousands of jobs were listed on our visit.

NationJob has developed dozens of specialty pages from Aeronautical Engineering to Sales and Marketing. Even an HR page with a great selection of openings can be found here. In the near future opportunities listed at NationJob will automatically be posted to America's Job Bank and Yahoo as added value. Site design is simple so you can get in and out fast with no problems. A top value by any standard.

Nature Biotechnology

www.biotech.nature.com

(Publisher/Trade)
Nature America
345 Park Avenue South, 10th Fl, NY, NY 10010
212-726-9254 Fax: 212-696-9482 e-mail: classifed@natureny.com

Jobs?
- Cost to post jobs: Fee
- Cost to see jobs: Free
- Specialty: Science/BioTech
- Industry: All
- Location: Int'l./US

Resumes?
- Cost to post resumes: N/A
- Cost to see resumes: N/A

Feature(s)? Yes

Career Advice? No

Nature Magazine publishes their job listings on the web. When you place a print ad in their publication, you receive one week of web advertising for free. All direct contact information is available on all job postings. You can list technical and general life science meetings for free here also.

NatureMedicine

www.medicine.nature.com

(Publisher/Newspaper)
Nature America
345 Park Avenue South, 10th Fl, NY, NY 10010
212-726-9254 Fax: 212-696-9482 e-mail: classifed@natureny.com

Jobs?
- Cost to post jobs: Fee
- Cost to see jobs: Free
- Specialty: Science/Medicine
- Industry: All
- Location: Int'l./US

Resumes?
- Cost to post resumes: N/A
- Cost to see resumes: N/A

Feature(s)? Yes

Career Advice? No

Nature Magazine publishes their job listings on the web. When you place a print ad in their publication, you receive one week of web advertising for free. All direct contact information is available on all job postings.

Navy

www.navyjobs.com

(Government)
800-872-6289 e-mail: 857_at_fmso.navy.mil

Jobs? Yes
- Cost to post jobs: N/A (See Note)
- Cost to see jobs: Free
- Specialty: All
- Industry: Military
- Location: US

Resumes? No
- Cost to post resumes: Free
- Cost to see resumes: N/A (See Note)

Feature(s)? N/A

Career Advice? Yes

From enlisted opportunities to officer's careers, from nuclear engineer to chaplain, the Navy is riding its own wave to the future. They even have a classy online application. The Navy site is clean, easy to understand and contains career information that is straight forward. Solid technical job. Great concept. Navy rules.

NCWorld Magazine

supersite.net/NCWorldJobBank

(Publisher/Trade)
SuperSite.Net
10228 N. Stelling Road, Bldg 2, Cupertino, CA 95014
408-343-0300 Fax: 408-252-3081 e-mail: sales@supersite.net

Jobs? Yes
- Cost to post jobs: Fee
- Cost to see jobs: Free
- Specialty: IT
- Industry: Computer
- Location: Int'l/US

Resumes? No
- Cost to post resumes: N/A
- Cost to see resumes: N/A

Feature(s)? N/A

Career Advice? No

Funny, when you start to review a site you only see a technical magazine. Then you continue to scroll and up pops the jobs page. Network centric computing has jobs posted with direct contact information. A separate listing of hot jobs and hot companies has been farmed out to SuperSite.Net which we will review also. NCWorld will sell you a banner while SuperSite sells the job postings. Rates to post range from $250 for 5 jobs to $750 a month to list 100. Jobs may be changed (exchanged) at any time for no additional charge. So, if you fill an opening quickly, just replace it with another. Good idea.

NCTM Jobs Online

www.nctm.org/

(Association)
Nat. Council of Teachers of Mathematics
attn: Jobs Online, 1906 Association Drive, Reston, VA 20191
703-620-9840 Fax: 703-476-2970 e-mail: jobs@nctm.org

Jobs? Yes
- Cost to post jobs: Fee
- Cost to see jobs: Free
- Specialty: Science/Mathematics/Teaching
- Industry: Education
- Location: US

Resumes? Yes
- Cost to post resumes: N/A
- Cost to see resumes: N/A

Feature(s)? N/A

Career Advice? No

The NCTM has 117,000 members devoted to mathematics, the teaching of mathematics and the discovery of new approaches to improve the teaching of mathematics. Grades Pre-K through 12 and post secondary are represented. Costs range $100-$250 for job postings depending on the number of words (30 day listing). Members can list positions wanted for free.

Needle In Cyberstack

home.revealed.net/albee

(College/University)
John Albee, Davenport Community Schools
736 Westfield Road, Davenport, IA 52806
319-386-2171 e-mail: albee@revealed.net

Jobs? No
- Cost to post jobs: Free
- Cost to see jobs: Free
- Specialty: All
- Industry: All
- Location: US

Resumes? No
- Cost to post resumes: N/A
- Cost to see resumes: N/A

Feature(s)? N/A

Career Advice? Yes

John Albee, this site's owner, is a teacher with an interest in providing a directory and guides to help make the internet easier for students, faculty, staff and library patrons. Nice efforts like this make the internet work for everyone. Positions are listed by the above categories to help folks in this Midwest community. From multi-search tools to John's " best on the web" choices, you will learn a lot from a visit.

Nerd World

www.nerdworld.com

(Commercial)
e-mail: webguru@nerdworld.com

Jobs? No
- Cost to post jobs: N/A
- Cost to see jobs: N/A
- Specialty: All
- Industry: All
- Location: US

Resumes? No
- Cost to post resumes: N/A
- Cost to see resumes: N/A

Feature(s)? RT

Career Advice? No

Nerd World has hundreds of annotated links to jobs. It also has a unique list of technical user groups and information on when they meet throughout the US. If you want to press the flesh with "techies" this is the place to do find out where and when.

NetJobs Information Services

www.netjobs.com

(Commercial)
6695 Millcreek Drive, Unit 1, Mississauga, Canada L5N5R8
905-542-9484 Fax: 905-542-9479 e-mail: info@netjobs.com

Jobs? Yes
- Cost to post jobs: Fee
- Cost to see jobs: Free
- Specialty: All
- Industry: All
- Location: Int'l/Canada

Resumes? Yes
- Cost to post resumes: Fee
- Cost to see resumes: Free

Feature(s)? N/A

Career Advice? Yes

Canadian based site that charges recruiters $100 to post a position. Jobs can be searched by title, company and location or, simply check what has come in during the last 10 days. Job seekers pay $30 to post their resume for six months.

Net-Temps

(Recruiting Related Agency)
Net-Temps Inc.
130 Middlesex Road, Tyngsboro, MA 01879
e-mail: sales@net-temps.com

Jobs? Yes
- Cost to post jobs: Fee
- Cost to see jobs: Free
- Specialty: IT
- Industry: Computer
- Location: US

Resumes? Yes
- Cost to post resumes: Free
- Cost to see resumes: Fee

Feature(s)? N/A

Career Advice? No

Net-Temps is touted as one of the best on the net. To be sure, NetTemps has developed an amazing following in the placement/staffing community. Job openings are automatically posted to over 200 locations on the web and resumes acquired from dozens of sources. The site backs up its confidence with a 30 day free trial period. Great concept. Works well for the Staffing/placement community.

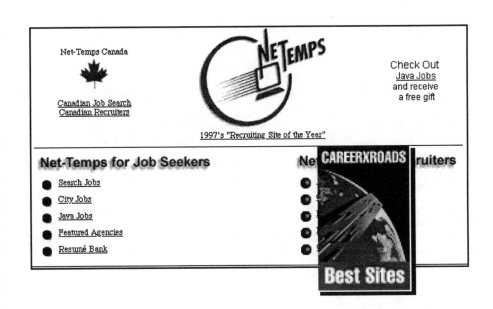

Netshare

www.netshare.com

(Commercial)
Kathy Simmons, Netshare, Inc.
2 Commercial Boulevard, Ste. 200, Novato, CA 94949
800-241-5642 Fax: 415-883-1799 e-mail: netshare@netshare.com

Jobs? Yes
- Cost to post jobs: Free
- Cost to see jobs: Fee
- Specialty: All
- Industry: All
- Location: Int'l/US

Resumes? Yes
- Cost to post resumes: Fee
- Cost to see resumes: Fee

Feature(s)? Push to Applicant

Career Advice? Yes

Netshare is one of the original players in the job lead generation business. Job seekers and employers- particularly on the west coast- need to be aware of this service. Job seekers pay $110 for 3 months, $175 for six or $300 for 12 months depending on the level of report desired. Netshare sends leads via e-mail or snail mail twice a month. Senior positions from $70k to 500K are listed. Sample positions can be viewed at this site. Companies can post openings at no cost . Employers can search their database of candidates for $495. Jobs are not online at this date.

Network World Fusion

www.nwfusion.com

(Publisher/Trade)
Ann Roskey, Network World
The Meadows, 161 Worcester Rd., Framingham, MA 01701
800-622-1108 Fax: 508-820-1283 e-mail: aroskey@nww.com

Jobs? Yes
- Cost to post jobs: Fee
- Cost to see jobs: Free
- Specialty: IT/Network
- Industry: High Technology
- Location: US

Resumes? No
- Cost to post resumes: N/A
- Cost to see resumes: N/A

Feature(s)? N/A

Career Advice? Yes

Weekly publication focusing on Network IS management issues, analysis, and news. A Help Desk forum offers Network IS managers advice. Editors link to resources and articles across the Web. Positions from the publication's classified section are listed online. You have to register to be able to see the open positions.

New England Journal of Medicine

www.nejm.org/

(Publisher/Trade)
New England Journal of Medicine
1440 Main Street, Waltham, MA 02154
617-893-3800 Fax: 617-893-7729 e-mail: nejmads@massmed.org

Jobs? Yes
- Cost to post jobs: Fee
- Cost to see jobs: Free
- Specialty: Health Care/MD
- Industry: Health Care
- Location: US

Resumes? No
- Cost to post resumes: N/A
- Cost to see resumes: N/A

Feature(s)? N/A

Career Advice? No

Help wanted advertisements that have been placed in the journal are posted to their web site for no additional charge. Search engine has great detail(maybe too much) but a valiant effort. All positions have direct contact information and there were over 550 posted on our last visit.

New Haven Register Online

www.ctcentral.com

(Publisher/Newspaper)
Jeryl Parade, New Haven Register
40 Sargent Drive, New Haven, CT 06511
203-789-5484

Jobs? Yes
- Cost to post jobs: Fee
- Cost to see jobs: Free
- Specialty: All
- Industry: All
- Location: US/E/CT

Resumes? No
- Cost to post resumes: N/A
- Cost to see resumes: N/A

Feature(s)? N/A

Career Advice? No

Connecticut newspapers have gotten together (New Haven Register, The Herald, The Middletown Press, The Bristol Press and The Register Citizen) to form this web site. Search engine makes the job easy to go through their classified sections and another feature is that you can click on a job and it will add it to a notepad for you so that when you are done they are saved just for you. No more having to scramble for a pen and keep searching. When you run your ad in the New Haven Register on Sunday it will cost you an additional $1 to run on their web site.

New Jersey Online

www.nj.com

(Publisher/Newspaper)
Madhavi Saifee, Advance Internet
Star Ledger, 30 Journal Square, Jersey City, NJ 07306
201-459-2871 e-mail: webmaster@nj.com

Jobs? Yes
- Cost to post jobs: Fee
- Cost to see jobs: Free
- Specialty: All
- Industry: All
- Location: US/E/NJ

Resumes? No
- Cost to post resumes: N/A
- Cost to see resumes: N/A

Feature(s)? N/A

Career Advice? No

Search the classified advertisements for the last 7 days or the day you enter this site for the Newark Star Ledger and Trenton Times. Also available is a listing of the top 100 corporations of NJ broken down in numerous ways. This is an excellent tool for the job seeker or the recruiter and we highly recommend you check it out. Search engine for jobs and also for the top 100 list. Note pad is available (click on the job that you are interested in and the site saves it for you to a personal file). Nice first effort.

New Media Assoc. of NJ

www.nmanj.com

(Association)
Clara Stricchiola, Trien Rosenberg
177 Madison Ave, Morristown, NJ 07962
201-267-4200 e-mail: newmedia@nmanj.com

Jobs? Yes
- Cost to post jobs: Free
- Cost to see jobs: Free
- Specialty: IT/Multimedia
- Industry: All
- Location: US/E/NJ

Resumes? No
- Cost to post resumes: N/A
- Cost to see resumes: N/A

Feature(s)? N/A

Career Advice? No

New media association that encompasses all of the disciplines that utilize electronic communication tools for business, cultural and/or educational purposes. They are looking for sponsors and at this time you can post jobs on this site for free. A NJ niche that corporations will support.

New York Times

www.nytimes.com

(Publisher/Newspaper)
Kerrie Gillis, New York Times
229 W. 43rd Street, New York, NY 10036
212-237-3181 e-mail: kerrie@nytimes

Jobs? Yes
- Cost to post jobs: Fee
- Cost to see jobs: Free
- Specialty: All
- Industry: N/A
- Location: US/E/NY/NYC

Resumes? No
- Cost to post resumes: N/A
- Cost to see resumes: N/A

Feature(s)? N/A

Career Advice? No

Sunday classified advertisements are posted on this site for all to see. Also has a note pad feature to save jobs to a personal file. With their search engine it seems you are better off selecting all of the positions in the category you wish. The NYT announced that they will be posting daily classified ads but, on our visit, these were not present.

News Page

www.newspage.com

(Commercial)
Individual, Inc.
8 New England, Executive Park West, Burlington, MA 01803
800-766-4224 Fax: 617-273-6060

Jobs? No
- Cost to post jobs: N/A
- Cost to see jobs: N/A
- Specialty: All
- Industry: All
- Location: US

Resumes? No
- Cost to post resumes: N/A
- Cost to see resumes: N/A

Feature(s)? Push to Applicant, RT & JSK/Research

Career Advice? No

Would you like to be able to search 65,000 corporations for their individual profiles. Find out who is hiring, who is laying? E-mails are sent to subscribers on a daily basis for $6.95 a month. We were members of this site when it was called "Heads Up" and you received the information by the topic you selected via fax. Now, with the web, you can obtain a lot of information for free and, if you want more specific data, you can then subscribe to additional levels of service. Some articles have an extra charge per item. For recruiters who want to stay ahead of the curve, or job seekers who want to know what's hot, this is a service that you should definitely look into.

News Rover

(Commercial)
S&H Computer Systems
1027 17th Avenue South, Nashville, TN 37212
615-327-3670 Fax: 615-321-5929 e-mail: info@sandh.com

Jobs? No
- Cost to post jobs: N/A
- Cost to see jobs: N/A
- Specialty: All
- Industry: All
- Location: US

Resumes? No
- Cost to post resumes: N/A
- Cost to see resumes: N/A

Feature(s)? RT & JSK/Newsgroups

Career Advice? No

News Rover will allow you to extract information from Usenet newsgroups (not available for MAC). Download a demonstration copy for Windows 95 or NT to check it out. For recruiters or job seekers this could enable you to find thousands of contacts. This may be an interesting alternative to DejaNews, a web-based search engine that drills into news groups.

NJ JOBS

(Commercial)
Robert Peters, Advanced Interactive Communications
908-303-9333 Fax: 908-303-8614 e-mail: info@njjobs.com

Jobs? Yes
- Cost to post jobs: Fee
- Cost to see jobs: Free
- Specialty: All
- Industry: All
- Location: US/E/NJ

Resumes? Yes
- Cost to post resumes: Fee
- Cost to see resumes: Free

Feature(s)? Yes

Career Advice? No

Simple and to the point, NJ Jobs will post opportunities for recruiters for $25 per week and if you want your resume on their site it will cost you $20 for the first month or $40 for 90 days. Site has a fair number of positions posted from all disciplines. Direct contact information is available for all job seekers. Biggest value is the site's address.

NJ Job Search

(Government)
Fred Cantwell, State of New Jersey
609-530-3481

Jobs? Yes
• Cost to post jobs: Free
• Cost to see jobs: Free
• Specialty: All
• Industry: All
• Location: US/NJ

Resumes? No
• Cost to post resumes: N/A
• Cost to see resumes: N/A

Feature(s)? N/A

Career Advice? No

A state employment service that finally gets it and it happens to be our home state. NJ Job Search allows employers to post positions for free. When the applicant clicks on the job of their choice they get "direct contact with the employer" either through e-mail which they go directly to from the site or a phone, address or fax. Simple, easy to use and numerous professional and non-technical positions were posted on our visit.

The Nonprofit/Fundraising Jobnet

www.philanthropy-journal.org

(Non-Profit)
Sean Bailey, 2 W Hargett Street.
Suite 805, Raleigh, NC 27601
919-832-3747 Fax: 919-832-2369 e-mail: seanbailey@mindspring.com

Jobs? Yes
• Cost to post jobs: Fee
• Cost to see jobs: Free
• Specialty: All
• Industry: Non-Profit
• Location: US

Resumes? No
• Cost to post resumes: N/A
• Cost to see resumes: N/A

Feature(s)? N/A

Career Advice? Yes

If you are interested in a position in the non-profit world the Philanthropy Journal Online is an online digital effort that you may want to look into. Numerous jobs at all levels are posted with direct contact information. From directors to fund raisers you will find it here. Awkward pricing policy to post jobs as they charge $1 per day and $.50 per word.

Norfolk Virginian-Pilot Online

www.infi.net/pilot

(Publisher/Newspaper)
Norfolk Virginian-Pilot
150 W. Brambleton Ave., Norfolk, VA 23510
800-446-2004 e-mail: pilot@infi.net

Jobs? Yes
• Cost to post jobs: Fee
• Cost to see jobs: Free
• Specialty: All
• Industry: N/A
• Location: US/E/VA/Norfolk

Resumes? No
• Cost to post resumes: N/A
• Cost to see resumes: N/A

Feature(s)? N/A

Career Advice? No

If you want to know more about opportunities in this area of Virginia, Pilot Online is the place to find the newspaper's help wanted classified listings. Recruiters need to place an ad in the newspaper to get the online component.

The NYC Headhunter's Mall

jobs-nyc.com

(Placement Agency)
Kevin McIntyre
175 West 4th Street, New York, NY 10014
212-242-2191 e-mail: kevin@jobs-nyc.com

Jobs? Yes
• Cost to post jobs: Free (See Note)
• Cost to see jobs: Free
• Specialty: All
• Industry: All
• Location: US

Resumes? Yes
• Cost to post resumes: Free
• Cost to see resumes: Fee

Feature(s)? N/A

Career Advice? No

This site is a group of New York staffing companies who have joined together. The site's split screen lets you easily find each agency as well as look at job postings. Employer's pay fees for hires. A list of links to career related sites is also available. Quick and easy. Posting positions is restricted to the members of this group.

O Hayo Sensei

(Publisher/Newspaper)
1032 Irving Street
Suite 508, San Francisco, CA 94122
800-367-5457 e-mail: editor@ohayosensei.com

Jobs?
- Cost to post jobs: Fee
- Cost to see jobs: Free
- Specialty: Teaching
- Industry: Education
- Location: Int'l./US

Resumes?
- Cost to post resumes: Free
- Cost to see resumes: Free

Feature(s)? N/A

Career Advice? No

This bi-weekly newsletter lists teaching positions in Japan for public schools, colleges and universities. Employer cost to post a job is $50 for 2 issues. Resume profile can be posted for free. Direct contact information for all postings is available. Ads are in English. If you want to know more about working in Japan there are some interesting people on this site to help you out.

Oasys Network

www.oasysnet.com/home.html

(Commercial)
800-367-5457 e-mail: info@oasysnet.com

Jobs?
- Cost to post jobs: N/A
- Cost to see jobs: N/A
- Specialty: Advertising/Graphic Arts
- Industry: Advertising
- Location: US

Resumes?
- Cost to post resumes: Free
- Cost to see resumes: Fee

Feature(s)? N/A

Career Advice? No

Freelance artists can post their resume and portfolio here for free. Companies pay $200 per month to view the potential candidates. There are no jobs posted, the recruiters simply view the job seekers' resumes and work samples. Ask for a free trial.

Omicron Personal Career Center

www.omicronet.com/career/resume.htm#top

(Association)
e-mail: resumes@omicronet.com

Jobs?
- Cost to post jobs: N/A
- Cost to see jobs: N/A
- Specialty: IT
- Industry: High Technology
- Location: US

Resumes?
- Cost to post resumes: Free
- Cost to see resumes: Free

Feature(s)? N/A

Career Advice? Yes

Site has not changed since our last review. This association will post IT resumes for free for 90 days. Directory of events for this group is also posted.

One Net

w3.one.net/~denek/Employ/emp496.htm

(Commercial)
e-mail: denek@one.net

Jobs?
- Cost to post jobs: N/A
- Cost to see jobs: N/A
- Specialty: All
- Industry: All
- Location: US

Resumes?
- Cost to post resumes: N/A
- Cost to see resumes: N/A

Feature(s)? JSK/Links

Career Advice? No

Links to 20 major job boards. Other links to a salary calculator, relocation cost analysis and a corporate yellow pages so you can scope out companies. Long and short- not much here.

Online Career Center

www.occ.com

(Commercial)
Gina Gioe, Online Career Center
2780 Waterfront Pkwy. E. Dr., Suite 100, Indianapolis, IN 46214
317-293-6499 Fax: 317-293-6692 e-mail: occ@occ.com

Jobs?
- Cost to post jobs: Fee
- Cost to see jobs: Free
- Specialty: All
- Industry: N/A
- Location: US

Resumes?
- Cost to post resumes: Free
- Cost to see resumes: Fee

Feature(s)? Search by State, Career Mgm't.

Career Advice? Yes

OCC will always be known as a pioneer in the online recruiting field. Uniquely positioned as a member sponsored association of 400+ companies, OCC in 1997 charged new members an annual subscription of $3,900 for unlimited posting and access to the resume database. Other packages were also available as were banners, profiles and hosting services. Well designed and executed, this site offers job applicants an outstanding array of information about job fairs, conferences, links to 800 colleges, and career related articles from well known authors. Career and College Forums allow the job seeker to ask questions and get answers from people all over the world. Joyce Lain Kennedy publishes career info and tips on this site. All in all, OCC site is still solid but some content has become dated and it could use a new look and needs to adopt newer technology to compete with its career hub sisters. Agent did not work on our visit and several of the diversity links were months out of date.

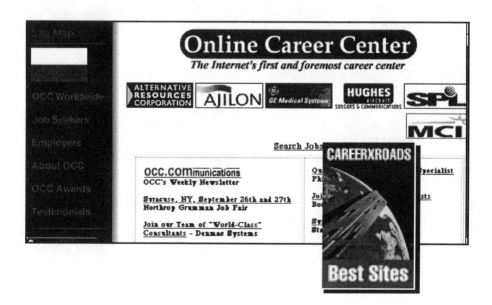

Online Directory of Internships in Youth Dev.

www.nassembly.org

(Association)
David Holmes, The National Assembly
1319 F Street, NW Suite 601, Washington, DC 20004
202-347-2080 e-mail: david@nassembly.org

Jobs?
- Cost to post jobs: Free
- Cost to see jobs: Free
- Specialty: College
- Industry: Non-Profit
- Location: US

Resumes?
- Cost to post resumes: N/A
- Cost to see resumes: N/A

Feature(s)? Search by State

Career Advice? Yes

The National Assembly of The National Voluntary Health and Social Welfare Organizations is continually updated and contains over 2000 internship and career opportunities available through youth development agencies across the US. It can be searched by state, city or the type of internship that matches an individual's particular interest or skill.

Online Sports Career Center

www.onlinesports.com:80/pages/careercenter.html

(Placement/Search/Temp)
Online Sports
9070 Rotherham Avenue, San Diego, CA 92129
800-856-2638 Fax: 800-856-2632 e-mail: comments@onlinesports.com

Jobs?
- Cost to post jobs: Fee
- Cost to see jobs: Free
- Specialty: Sports
- Industry: Retail/Recreation
- Location: US

Resumes?
- Cost to post resumes: N/A
- Cost to see resumes: N/A

Feature(s)? N/A

Career Advice? No

Site is owned by a recruiting company which shows profiles of professionals involved in anything related to the sports field: coaches, sales people, sporting goods, recreation etc. For fun, point and click on your favorite team or player and see what your old baseball cards are worth today. Nothing extra here. Cost to post ads is the fee you'll pay if you get a candidate.

Orlando Sentinel

www.orlandosentinel.com

(Publisher/Newspaper)
Orlando Sentinel Online
633 N. Orange Avenue, Orlando, FL 32801
407-420-5179

Jobs?
- Cost to post jobs: Fee
- Cost to see jobs: Free
- Specialty: All
- Industry: N/A
- Location: US/SE/FL/Orlando

Resumes?
- Cost to post resumes: N/A
- Cost to see resumes: N/A

Feature(s)? No

Career Advice? No

There are some good newspaper classified sites and then.... This site needs help so here it is. Rule #1: Make it easy on the job seeker. The search engine on this site runs you through a maze that would leave the smartest mouse two turns short of the cheese. We had to go through 7 screens to find an engineering opening. If you have the time, you will surely get there, but we recommend you pack your lunch. Rule 2: See Rule 1.

Parksville/Qualicum Career Center

qb.island.net/~careers/

(Commercial)
Career Center
154 Memorial Avenue, Parksville, Canada
250-248-3205 e-mail: careerx@qb.island.net

Jobs?
- Cost to post jobs: N/A
- Cost to see jobs: N/A
- Specialty: All
- Industry: All
- Location: Int'l/Canada

Resumes?
- Cost to post resumes: N/A
- Cost to see resumes: N/A

Feature(s)? Career Mgm't.

Career Advice? Yes

Strictly a career management site with articles and a "center" for career assistance. Dozens of links to Canadian sites for jobs.

PassportAccess

(Commercial)
John Malone, Passport Access
3470 Mt. Diablo Blvd., Ste. 150, Lafayette, CA 94549
510-552-1000 Fax: 510-552-1010 e-mail: webboy@passportaccess.com

Jobs?
- Cost to post jobs: Fee
- Cost to see jobs: Free
- Specialty: All
- Industry: All
- Location: US

Resumes?
- Cost to post resumes: Free
- Cost to see resumes: Fee

Feature(s)? N/A

Career Advice? No

Passport Access' owner claims that over 80,000 resumes are in their database. Their search engine makes it is easy to find what you want (recruiters can get in and out in short order). Employers search resumes for $600 per year. An unlimited number of jobs can be posted for 3 months for $400. Technical openings in sales, marketing, finance or IT are listed. Job seekers use this site for free.

Penton Publishing's Career Link

(Publisher/Trade)
Penton Classifieds
1100 Superior Ave., 6th Floor, Cleveland, OH 44114
216-696-7000 Fax: 216-696-8207 e-mail: careerlink@penton.com

Jobs?
- Cost to post jobs: Fee
- Cost to see jobs: Free
- Specialty: Hospitality, Aviation
- Industry: All
- Location: US

Resumes?
- Cost to post resumes: N/A
- Cost to see resumes: N/A

Feature(s)? N/A

Career Advice? No

Publisher posts a all of its classified ads posts from 14 technical niche publications in engineering, management, manufacturing, hospitality, airline/aviation, sales and electronics industries. Recruiters pay $100 per month to post direct to the web site.

Perioperative Online Employment Opportunities

www.aorn.org

(Publisher)
Deb Smith, Association of Operating Room Nurses
2170 South Parker Road, Suite 300, Denver, CO 80231
800-755-2676 Fax: 303-750-3212 e-mail: custsvc@aorn.org

Jobs?
- Cost to post jobs: Fee
- Cost to see jobs: Free
- Specialty: Health Care/Nursing/OR
- Industry: Health Care
- Location: US

Resumes?
- Cost to post resumes: Fee
- Cost to see resumes: Fee

Feature(s)? Search by State

Career Advice? No

With 41,000 nurses in 350 chapters in all 50 states, this is an organization that recruiters should know about and job seekers belong to. Association has added a job referral service that retains your resume and, when recruiters post positions, they conduct a database search for you. Cost to job seekers is $25 for members.

Peterson's Education Center

www.petersons.com

(Commercial)
Cris Maloney, Peterson's
202 Carnegie Center, Princeton, NJ 08540
609-243-9111 Fax: 609-243-9150 e-mail: info@petersons.com

Jobs?
- Cost to post jobs: Fee
- Cost to see jobs: Free
- Specialty: College/Internship
- Industry: All
- Location: US

Resumes?
- Cost to post resumes: N/A
- Cost to see resumes: N/A

Feature(s)? Career Mgm't.

Career Advice? Yes

Peterson's is a major source for career information and not just for college students. Go to the "Careers & Jobs" button and drill down to one of the most comprehensive listings of employers we have seen. Excellent articles on career management draw from Peterson's many publications. If you are thinking of going to school, going back to school or just don't want to ever leave school, this is the place to look. Internship positions listed here are well hidden. Let us know when you find them.

Pharmaceuticals Jobs Today

pharma.mond.org/jobs.html

(Association)
Society of Chemical Industry
14/15 Belgrave Square, London, UK SW1X 8PS
441-712-353681 Fax: 441-718-231698 e-mail: (See Notes)

Jobs?
- Cost to post jobs: Free
- Cost to see jobs: Free
- Specialty: Science/Pharmaceuticals
- Industry: All
- Location: Int'l./US

Resumes?
- Cost to post resumes: Free
- Cost to see resumes: Free

Feature(s)? Push to Applicant

Career Advice? No

Pharmaceuticals Jobs Today is part of the Society of the Chemical Industry which has over 6,000 members and is an organization based in England. This site's opportunities are primarily corporate research and development. Employers can e-mail their openings directly to the site. (advertising@chemind.demon.co.uk) Job Seeker register and are e-mailed "alerts" of new jobs that fit their criteria. The price is right. Only 85 jobs were posted on our last visit. Looks underutilized. Give it a try.

PHRC Job Opps

www.perc.net/hr.html

(Association)
Doug Kalish, Positive Employee Relations Council
e-mail: dkalish@perc.net

Jobs?
- Cost to post jobs: Free
- Cost to see jobs: Free
- Specialty: Human Resources
- Industry: All
- Location: US

Resumes?
- Cost to post resumes: Free
- Cost to see resumes: Free

Feature(s)? No

Career Advice? N/A

Several resumes and jobs for human resource professionals are listed. Send opportunities for posting via e-mail in as follows: title, requirements, duties, contact info. That's all there is. That's all you need.

Physician RecruitNet

www.physiciannet.com/index.html

(Publisher/Trade)
Transcontinental Publishing
P.O. Box 45454, Phoenix, AZ 85064-5454
602-331-8448 Fax: 602-331-8448 e-mail: trans@pub@physiciannet.com

Jobs?
- Cost to post jobs: Fee
- Cost to see jobs: Free
- Specialty: Health Care/MD
- Industry: Health Care
- Location: Int'l./US

Resumes?
- Cost to post resumes: N/A
- Cost to see resumes: N/A

Feature(s)? N/A

Career Advice? No

Is there a doctor in the house? You can find all kinds of opportunities listed by region at this site. All jobs are coded. Emphasis is on Physician openings in most disciplines in both domestic and international markets.

Physicians Employment

www.physemp.com/physician

(Commercial)
Cass Greene
58 ½ Main Street 200, Fairfield, IA 52556
515-472-0998 Fax: 515-472-3007 e-mail: physemp@lisco.com

Jobs?
- Cost to post jobs: Fee
- Cost to see jobs: Free
- Specialty: Health Care/MD
- Industry: Health Care
- Location: US

Resumes?
- Cost to post resumes: N/A
- Cost to see resumes: N/A

Feature(s)? Search by State

Career Advice? Yes

You have to register to see a physician but after that is done you enter a split screen world that makes it easy to see all the listed opportunities in the medical field: physician, nursing and allied health. Direct contact information is posted by occupation and location (state). Recruiters pay $255 per quarter to post up to 15 different positions. Ask for a trial job. Site claimed to have over 4,000 physicians in their database. Easy, simple to understand.

Pioneer Press

(Publisher/Newspaper)
Pioneer Press
Chicago, IL
847-998-3400 Fax: 708-251-7606

Jobs?
• Cost to post jobs: Fee
• Cost to see jobs: Free
• Specialty: All
• Industry: N/A
• Location: US/MW/IL

Resumes?
• Cost to post resumes: N/A
• Cost to see resumes: N/A

Feature(s)? N/A

Career Advice? No

Help wanted advertising for 48 newspapers serving this suburban Chicago market.

Philadelphia On-Line Classifieds

(Publisher/Newspaper)
Dennis Wichterman, Philadelphia Inquirer
400 N. Broad Street, Philadelphia, PA 19101
215-563-5000 e-mail: online.staff@phillynews.com

Jobs?
• Cost to post jobs: Fee
• Cost to see jobs: Free
• Specialty: All
• Industry: N/A
• Location: US/E/PA/Phil.

Resumes?
• Cost to post resumes: N/A
• Cost to see resumes: N/A

Feature(s)? N/A

Career Advice? No

Help wanted Sunday classifieds of the Philadelphia Inquirer are posted to the web. When you enter your name the site will keep a running list of positions you have selected and will then print a listing for you. This notepad is a growing trend among newspapers.

Plasma Laboratory Wis

(College/University)
Prof Yitzhak Maron
972-893-44055 Fax: 972-893-44106

Jobs?
- Cost to post jobs: Free
- Cost to see jobs: Free
- Specialty: Science/Physics
- Industry: Higher Education/Research
- Location: Int'l/US

Resumes?
- Cost to post resumes: N/A
- Cost to see resumes: N/A

Feature(s)? No

Career Advice? No

International research and post-doc positions can be listed and seen. If atomic & plasma physics is your niche then this is the place you would want to visit. e-mail your openings to: fnmaron@weizmann.weizmann.ac.il. All postings have a date. A number of links to technical topics are also available. Only 4 jobs listed on our last visit. But then, how often do you need a plasma physicist.

PolySort

www.polysort.com

(Commercial)
Janie Campbell
4040 Embassy Parkway, Ste. 180, Akron, OH 44333
800-326-8666 Fax: 330-665-5152 e-mail: icampbel@polysort.com

Jobs?
- Cost to post jobs: Fee
- Cost to see jobs: Free
- Specialty: Science/Chemistry
- Industry: Rubber and Plastics
- Location: US

Resumes?
- Cost to post resumes: N/A
- Cost to see resumes: N/A

Feature(s)? N/A

Career Advice? No

If your are into plastics or rubber (hmmm) then polysort is the place to play. This is strong, well run industry site has a job posting area but, on our visit, only 8 jobs were posted and 1 "position wanted". $100-$250 is a typical cost for posting. Employers will soon discover the potential here. Site also distributes an Industry newsletter. Ads are on the web within 48 hours.

Potpourri Shoppers

www.netview.com/pp/employ/

(Publisher/Newspaper)
Harte-Hanks Communications
e-mail: classifieds@nvcom.net

Jobs?
- Cost to post jobs: Free
- Cost to see jobs: Free
- Specialty: All
- Industry: All
- Location: US/W/CA

Resumes?
- Cost to post resumes: N/A
- Cost to see resumes: N/A

Feature(s)? N/A

Career Advice? No

Site is a conglomeration of help wanted classifieds and positions wanted in no particular order.

Princeton 1Info (US 1); Local Shopper

www.princetoninfo.com

(Publisher/Newspaper)
Barbara Figge Fox, US 1 Newspapers
12 Roszel Road, Princeton, NJ 08540
609-452-0033 Fax: 609-452-0038 e-mail: events@princetoninfo.com

Jobs?
- Cost to post jobs: Fee
- Cost to see jobs: Free
- Specialty: All
- Industry: All
- Location: US/E/NJ

Resumes?
- Cost to post resumes: Free
- Cost to see resumes: Free

Feature(s)? No

Career Advice? Yes

Local, central NJ weekly newspaper that allows the job seeker to post a brief description of their skills for free. Good local information on living in this area of the country. Site has a search engine for jobs under construction. All jobs have direct contact information posted.

Pro/E Job Network

www.pejn.com

(Commercial)
Josh Rothman, Mercury Enterprises
P.O. Box 1983, Tustin, CA 92781
Fax: 404-685-0840 e-mail: pejn@pejn.com

Jobs? Yes
- Cost to post jobs: Fee
- Cost to see jobs: Free
- Specialty: Engineering Design
- Industry: All
- Location: Int'l/US

Resumes? Yes
- Cost to post resumes: Free
- Cost to see resumes: N/A

Feature(s)? Search by State, Push to Applicant

Career Advice? No

Pro/E Job Network posts positions for engineers skilled in Pro/Engineer software. Recruiters pay $100 to post positions for 30 days. Job seekers can send their resume directly to the corporation via snail mail or e-mail. Search engine allows you to find positions throughout the US. Easy access in a unique niche.

Pro Net Search

bisinc.com/pronet/index.html

(Commercial)
Buck Information Systems, Inc.
22 Orchard Hill, Hamilton, Ontario, Canada L8P2V8
800-355-2666 e-mail: psmail@inforamp.net

Jobs?
- Cost to post jobs: Fee
- Cost to see jobs: Free
- Specialty: IT
- Industry: Computer
- Location: Int'l/Canada/US

Resumes?
- Cost to post resumes: Free
- Cost to see resumes: Fee

Feature(s)? Push to Applicant

Career Advice? No

Site concentrates on computer and technology positions around the world, Canada and the US jobs predominate. Employers are given a free trial for their first position and then the cost is $85 Canadian or $65 US. The job seeker can post their resume for free but if you want the information to be confidential there is a $25 additional charge. Site also will push new listings to you on a weekly basis for free.

Project Connect

career.soemadison.wisc.edu/projcon.htm

(Non-Profit)
Steve Head, University of Wisconsin-Madison
608-262-1755 e-mail: (See notes)

Jobs? Yes
• Cost to post jobs: Free
• Cost to see jobs: Free
• Specialty: Teaching
• Industry: Education
• Location: US

Resumes? No
• Cost to post resumes: N/A
• Cost to see resumes: N/A

Feature(s)? N/A

Career Advice? No

Project Connect is a national cooperative between school districts and universities to get educational staffing on the Internet. This program began in 1992 to set standards for vacancy and candidate information. Job openings are transmitted via an online database that teachers can search. You can send your openings to: E-mail to:

project connect@uw-epcs.soemadison.wisc.edu .

You will need to register at this site to see open jobs.

Purchasing NAPM

catalog.com/napmsv/jobs.htm

(Association)
Nat'l Assoc. of Purchasing Mgmt.
P.O. Box 32156, San Jose, CA 95152-2156
408-929-6276 Fax: 408-929-6277 e-mail: info@napmsv.com

Jobs?
• Cost to post jobs: Free
• Cost to see jobs: Free
• Specialty: Purchasing
• Industry: All
• Location: US/W/CA

Resumes?
• Cost to post resumes: N/A
• Cost to see resumes: N/A

Feature(s)? N/A

Career Advice? No

Silicon Valley purchasing association posts open positions in purchasing on the web for all to see and it is free. Simple site that lists jobs in alpha order.

Purdue's Job List

www.ups.purdue.edu/student/jobsites.htm

(College/University)
Purdue University
West Lafayette, IN
e-mail: ups@www.purdue.edu

Jobs?
- Cost to post jobs: N/A
- Cost to see jobs: N/A
- Specialty: All
- Industry: All
- Location: US

Resumes?
- Cost to post resumes: N/A
- Cost to see resumes: N/A

Feature(s)? JSK/Links

Career Advice? No

More than a few sites provide links but no one maintains them better than Purdue. Over 1,000 sites are listed. Categories include: job searching sites, job listings by geography, federal government, international, classifieds, resume services, corporations, professional recruiters and other university placement and career services. They rank sites and give special markings for new sites. Recruiter take note: If you are looking for entry level engineers, there are several gems at Purdue that will make a visit here worthwhile. Think of it as a treasure hunt.

Pyramus Online

www.pbgi.com/resucom/search.htm

(Commercial)
Pyramus Online
P.O. Box 82836, Portland, OR 97282
800-327-5101 Fax: 503-231-0474 e-mail: sales@pyramus.com

Jobs?
- Cost to post jobs: Free
- Cost to see jobs: Free
- Specialty: All
- Industry: All
- Location: US

Resumes?
- Cost to post resumes: Fee
- Cost to see resumes: Free

Feature(s)? Push to Employer

Career Advice? No

Owners make their living as web site designers. As an added business venture they have created this interesting site that will send recruiters. Employers post jobs for free. Agency recruiters (site claims over 690 have registered) can post positions or candidates and split the search fees. Applicants are charged $39.00 to post their resume. Very well designed.

QuestMatch

www.decisivequest.com

(Commercial)
Rick Donnelli, Decisive Quest, Inc.
735 N. Plano Road, Richardson, TX 75081
972-480-9070 e-mail: webmaster@questmatch.com

Jobs?
- Cost to post jobs: Fee
- Cost to see jobs: Free
- Specialty:College/IT/Engineering/Accounting
- Industry: All
- Location: US

Resumes?
- Cost to post resumes: Free
- Cost to see resumes: Fee

Feature(s)? Push to Applicant

Career Advice? No

Candidates who visit QuestMatch fill out a skills profile. Corporations are then given access and if there is an interest an e-mail is sent to the candidate with the company name, location and a brief job description. Interesting twist in pricing is that the employer pays $100 to search the resume database and, if they hire someone, they pay $500 for a college student or $2,000 for a professional. Company concentrates on entry level college graduates, IT/IS, Accounting and Electrical Engineering professionals. The job seeker has to download software to gain access. Site claims your skill based profile will only be sent to those companies you OK.

Quintessential Career & Job Hunting Guide

www.stetson.edu/~rhansen/careers.html

(College/University)
Randall Hansen, Stetson University
Deland, FL 32720-3771
800-688-0101 e-mail: randall.hansen@stetson.edu

Jobs?
- Cost to post jobs: N/A
- Cost to see jobs: N/A
- Specialty: All
- Industry: All
- Location: US

Resumes?
- Cost to post resumes: N/A
- Cost to see resumes: N/A

Feature(s)? JSK/Links

Career Advice? Yes

Great list of links and information for the job seeker. The owner will critique your cover letter for free. Links are divided into several logical categories like "resumes", "jobs", "recruiters", etc. with a brief explanation. A real time saver. Particularly good for the recent college graduate, but anyone can and should visit this site.

RadioFrame

www.mindspring.com/~coleman/radioframe.html

(Commercial)
David Coleman, 4180 Triple Creek Court
Atlanta, GA 30319
770-936-9131

Jobs?
- Cost to post jobs: N/A
- Cost to see jobs: N/A
- Specialty: Radio
- Industry: Entertainment
- Location: US

Resumes?
- Cost to post resumes: N/A
- Cost to see resumes: N/A

Feature(s)? JSK/Links

Career Advice? Yes

Owner lists for fun hundreds of links to other radio web sites and their career opportunities. Site also maintains helpful content on the music business. There is a problem with the site's graphics getting in the way as you surf.

Raleigh Classifieds On-line

www.news-observer.com/classads

(Publisher/Newspaper)
Raleigh News & Observer
215 S. McDowell St., Raleigh, NC 27602
919-836-5719 Fax: 919-836-2897 e-mail: sbrown@nando.com

Jobs?
- Cost to post jobs: Fee
- Cost to see jobs: Free
- Specialty: All
- Industry: All
- Location: US/E/NC/Raleigh

Resumes?
- Cost to post resumes: N/A
- Cost to see resumes: N/A

Feature(s)? N/A

Career Advice? No

Daily or Sunday classified advertisements are here for all to see.

Real Bank

www.realbank.com

(Commercial)
Fran Grossman, RealBank
295 Greenwich Street, Suite 149, New York, NY 10007
212-344-2118 Fax: 212-344-2539 e-mail: jobs@realbank.com

Jobs?
• Cost to post jobs: Fee
• Cost to see jobs: Free
• Specialty: Real Estate
• Industry: Real Estate
• Location: US

Resumes?
• Cost to post resumes: Fee
• Cost to see resumes: Free

Feature(s)? N/A

Career Advice? No

Pricing has changed at Real Bank and now recruiters pay $95 to post a position. All resumes are coded. You can see some contact information on candidates (e-mail, phone) but candidates are charged $99 to place their resume on this site. Confidentiality has a price. Niche site that charges on both ends.

Real Jobs

www.real-jobs.com

(University)
Dr. Norm Miller, University of Cincinnati
513-556-7088 e-mail: norm.miller@uc.edu

Jobs?
• Cost to post jobs: Free
• Cost to see jobs: Free
• Specialty: Real Estate Agent
• Industry: Real Estate
• Location: Int'l./US

Resumes?
• Cost to post resumes: Free
• Cost to see resumes: Free

Feature(s)? N/A

Career Advice? No

At Real Jobs, real estate agents can post their resume. For now, all companies can search the database without cost. Positions are listed for US/Canada/Europe and Asia. This site was initially developed by a professor to support college placement activities but quickly expanded to assist Alumni, professional and trade associations as well.

Recruit '97

www.recruit97.com

(Recruiting Related Agency)
Miller Freeman, Inc.
One Penn Plaza, NY, NY 10119
800-820-3076 e-mail: resume@recruit97.com

Jobs?
- Cost to post jobs: N/A
- Cost to see jobs: N/A
- Specialty: IT
- Industry: All
- Location: US

Resumes?
- Cost to post resumes: Free
- Cost to see resumes: Fee

Feature(s)? N/A

Career Advice? Yes

Job Fair information includes upcoming dates and show locations. Links to sponsoring companies are here. Job seekers and recruiters can learn where to go and who is hiring. Job seekers can post their resume for the next show. Pretty basic.

RecruitNet

recruitnet.guardian.co.uk/

(Publisher/Newspaper)
The Guardian Media Group
e-mail: feedback@guardian.co.uk

Jobs?
- Cost to post jobs: Fee
- Cost to see jobs: Free
- Specialty: All
- Industry: All
- Location: Int'l/UK

Resumes?
- Cost to post resumes: N/A
- Cost to see resumes: N/A

Feature(s)? Push to Applicant

Career Advice? No

This publication is doing a great job. Browse the Guardian newspaper's help-wanted or post your particular job interests. This UK site will then "push" matching jobs to your desktop. If you want additional job info, click on the "brief" and you'll receive the full text.

Recruiters Online Network

www.ipa.com

(Recruiting Related Agency)
Bill Vick
3325 Landershire Lane, Suite 1001, Plano, TX 75023
972-612-8425 Fax: 972-612-1924 e-mail: ipainfo@ipa.com

Jobs?
- Cost to post jobs: Fee
- Cost to see jobs: Free
- Specialty: All
- Industry: All
- Location: US

Resumes?
- Cost to post resumes: Free
- Cost to see resumes: Fee

Feature(s)? N/A

Career Advice? Yes

Here is where headhunters gather to share information, resumes and client data. Cost to be a member is $395 per year and this allows you to search a large database for resumes. Job seekers can post their resume for free. Career information is available. There are hundreds of jobs posted and, as one would expect, they are the listings of employment agencies. Bill Vick has been out here for awhile.

RecruitEX Technologies

www.recruitex.com/

(Commercial)
Greg Scott, Recruitex Technologies Inc.
1434 Johnston Road, 2nd Floor, White Rock, BC, Canada V4B 3Z5
604-899-2224 Fax: 604-538-4841 e-mail: gregs@recruitex.com

Jobs?
- Cost to post jobs: Free
- Cost to see jobs: Free
- Specialty: All
- Industry: All
- Location: Int'l/Canada/US

Resumes?
- Cost to post resumes: Free
- Cost to see resumes: Free

Feature(s)? N/A

Career Advice? Yes

Recruitex is a one-stop shopping network for recruiters and job seekers. Recruiters can see profiles of candidates and then notify the site of their interest to receive the contact information. Job seekers must first submit their resume to one of the agency members of this site before they can search the jobs database. This site makes you work a little more than necessary. All services are free to job seekers. Placement agencies should take a look.

Recruiting Links.com

www.recruiting-links.com/

(Commercial)
Al Spencer, Skillsearch Corporation
3354 Perimeter Hill Drive, Suite 235, Nashville, TN 37211-4129
800-252-5665 Fax: 615-843-2638 e-mail: moreinfo@recruiting-links.com

Jobs?
- Cost to post jobs: N/A
- Cost to see jobs: N/A
- Specialty: All
- Industry: All
- Location: US

Resumes?
- Cost to post resumes: N/A
- Cost to see resumes: N/A

Feature(s)? JSK/Links

Career Advice? No

Technically, recruiting-links is neither a job database nor a resume databank. Using push technology, job seekers search against many of the general skill requirements provided by the employer and then link to the employers' jobs page directly. Site claims to have more than 700 employer links at this site. Employers pay $250 per month or $1900 for an annual subscription. Completely redesigned in 1997, recruiting-links is also providing monthly reports on the site's activity. Measurement is our Rule # 3.

Recruitment Extra

www.recruitmentextra.com

(Commercial)
Madeline Krazit
201-750-0521 e-mail: jkraz@aol.com

Jobs?
- Cost to post jobs: N/A
- Cost to see jobs: N/A
- Specialty: All
- Industry: All
- Location: US

Resumes?
- Cost to post resumes: N/A
- Cost to see resumes: N/A

Feature(s)? RT/Research

Career Advice? Yes

New site that provides industry information for the savvy recruiter. From salary surveys to layoffs. This site, which represents publisher products and services has taken an interesting slant on helping recruiters do their job. Recruitment Extra makes "extra" money by selling links to vendors like job fairs and recruitment advertising agencies.

Red Guide to Temporary Agencies

www.panix.com/~grvsmth/redguide/

(Commercial)
Angus B. Grieve-Smith, Angus B. Grieve-Smith
794 President Street, Apt. 1-L, Brooklyn, NY 11215
718-398-8794 e-mail: grvsmth@panix.com

Jobs?
- Cost to post jobs: N/A
- Cost to see jobs: N/A
- Specialty: All
- Industry: All
- Location: US/E/NY/NYC

Resumes?
- Cost to post resumes: N/A
- Cost to see resumes: N/A

Feature(s)? JSK/Links

Career Advice? Yes

This site's owner, Angus, provides a directory of New York temporary employment agencies. Done in alpha order with contact info, it is plain vanilla but a great reference. Great story about why he does this.

Rehab Options

www.rehaboptions.com

(Commercial)
Rehab Options USA
6617 W. Boynton Beach Blvd, Suite 202, Boynton, FL 33437
800-863-8314 Fax: 800-357-8684 e-mail: ken@ehaboptions.com

Jobs?
- Cost to post jobs: N/A
- Cost to see jobs: N/A
- Specialty: Health Care/Rehab, PT/OT, Speech
- Industry: Health Care
- Location: US

Resumes?
- Cost to post resumes: Free
- Cost to see resumes: Fee

Feature(s)? Push to Employer

Career Advice? No

Site for Physical Therapists, PTs, OTs, COTAs and Speech Language Pathologists. Employers pay from $24.04 to $43.27 per week to see resumes. Is this with tax included or what? Resumes can be posted for free and they are then e-mailed to the subscribing employers. Claims to have jobs but you have to call to get them and we assume that's after posting your resume. Hmmm.

Restrac

(Recruiting Related Agency)
Hank Howie, Restrac, inc.
91 Hartwell Avenue, Lexington, MA 02173-3125
617-869-5000 Fax: 617-869-5050 e-mail: wwrequest@restrac.com

Jobs?
• Cost to post jobs: N/A
• Cost to see jobs: N/A
• Specialty: N/A
• Industry: All
• Location: US

Resumes?
• Cost to post resumes: N/A
• Cost to see resumes: N/A

Feature(s)? RT/Resume Database

Career Advice? No

We list Restrac and sites like it so that recruiters and job seekers will know where to go to learn more about optical scanning and applicant tracking systems. Worth a look just to see their growing partnerships. Expect a web component...someday.

Resumania On-line

(College/University)
Eric Schnell, University of Minnesota
Employee Career Program, 1313 5th St. SE STE 220, Minneapolis, MN 55414
e-mail: schne050@tc.umn.edu

Jobs?
• Cost to post jobs: N/A
• Cost to see jobs: N/A
• Specialty: All
• Industry: All
• Location: US

Resumes?
• Cost to post resumes: N/A
• Cost to see resumes: N/A

Feature(s)? Career Mgm't.

Career Advice? Yes

Resumania On-line gives you six steps to perfect your resume. We feel they do one of the best jobs in keeping it simple and focused for the job seeker. A valuable check sheet is provided so you can critique your work. Review samples of different styles of resumes. Wish they gave their recommendations on resumes in regards to optical scanning systems. This is not discussed and, in our opinion, should be a top priority if you want to work in a company using emerging technology. Great effort. Kudos.

Resumatch, Inc.

resumatch.com

(Commercial)
P.O. Box 434, Gainesville, FL 32602
e-mail: david@resumatch.com

Jobs?
- Cost to post jobs: N/A
- Cost to see jobs: N/A
- Specialty: All
- Industry: All
- Location: US

Resumes?
- Cost to post resumes: Fee
- Cost to see resumes: Free

Feature(s)? N/A

Career Advice? No

This site makes it easy for the employers to search for resumes that match their job specs. Free for employers. Job seekers pay a fee to post their resume. Direct contact information is available on all resumes, no codes, no hide & seek. Many different disciplines are here.

The Resume Exchange

imagiware.com/resume.cgi

(Commercial)
Thomas Tongue, Imagiware
4833 Sheboygan Avenue #334, Madison, WI 53705
e-mail: ttongue@imagiware.com

Jobs?
- Cost to post jobs: N/A
- Cost to see jobs: N/A
- Specialty: Resume Database
- Industry: All
- Location: US

Resumes?
- Cost to post resumes: Fee
- Cost to see resumes: Free

Feature(s)? N/A

Career Advice? No

Standard resume database. Easy to use. Job seekers pay $25 to have their resume posted for six months.

Resume-Link

(Commercial/Resumes)
Susan Ross
P.O. Box 218, 3960 Brown Park Drive, Hillaird, OH 43026
614-777-4000 Fax: 614-771-5708 e-mail: rtrem@resume-link.com

Jobs?
- Cost to post jobs: N/A
- Cost to see jobs: N/A
- Specialty: All
- Industry: All
- Location: US

Resumes?
- Cost to post resumes: Free
- Cost to see resumes: Fee

Feature(s)? N/A

Career Advice? No

After drilling deep we finally found the answers to our questions but, quite frankly, if a job seeker...or a recruiter doesn't understand what a site is all about, they'll go elsewhere. Employers select the association of their choice and send a job description to the site. Within 3-5 days the recruiter is expected to receive a fax of all matching resumes. If unable to forward six matches, employers are entitled to one free search. Member associations are listed...and there are some great ones that recruiters will want to target. However, we were the recruiting, we would want to do our own searches. Seems to be an awkward online business model. These folks have a great history and we look forward to their next generation. Call for pricing.

Resumes on the Web

(Commercial)
Sharon Das, Resumes on the Web
959 Severin Drive, Bridgewater, NJ 08807
908-429-9141 Fax: 908-828-4700 e-mail: sdas@ifu.net

Jobs?
- Cost to post jobs: Fee
- Cost to see jobs: Free
- Specialty: All
- Industry: All
- Location: US

Resumes?
- Cost to post resumes: Fee
- Cost to see resumes: Free

Feature(s)? N/A

Career Advice? No

Time to change the name of this site as they have both jobs and resumes. If you want your resume posted it will cost you $10.50 (confidential if you wish). Recruiters pay $7.00 to post a job.

Resumix

www.resumix.com

(Recruiting Related Agency)
Resumix Inc.
890 Ross Drive, Sunnyvale, CA 94089
408-744-3800 Fax: 408-744-3888 e-mail: info@resumix.com

Jobs?
- Cost to post jobs: N/A
- Cost to see jobs: N/A
- Specialty: All
- Industry: All
- Location: US

Resumes?
- Cost to post resumes: N/A
- Cost to see resumes: N/A

Feature(s)? N/A

Career Advice? Yes

Why not learn how to prepare an optically scanned resume from one of the companies selling the systems to read, store, search, and communicate and track it. A resume builder will take you step by step through the process. Joyce Lain Kennedy has a link here for her career assistance tips. Some important rules of for responding to leads online are here. Recruiters should be familiar with Resumix products whether they are ready for them or not.

Richmond Times-Dispatch

www.gateway-va.com/pages/classads/online/index.htm

(Publisher/Newspaper)
Richmond Newspapers, Inc.
e-mail: classfeedback@timesdispatch.com

Jobs?
- Cost to post jobs: Fee
- Cost to see jobs: Free
- Specialty: All
- Industry: All
- Location: US/S/Va

Resumes?
- Cost to post resumes: N/A
- Cost to see resumes: N/A

Feature(s)? N/A

Career Advice? No

Richmond Times-Dispatch (Virginia) posts the newspaper classified advertisements on this site. You can send e-mail for more information. Site participates in CareerPath (see CareerPath).

Right Management Consultants, Inc.

www.right.com

(Recruiting Related Agency)
1818 Market Street, Thirty-third floor, Philadelphia, PA 19103
800-237-4448 Fax: 215-988-0081 e-mail: info@right.com

Jobs?
- Cost to post jobs: Free
- Cost to see jobs: Fee
- Specialty: All
- Industry: All
- Location: US

Resumes?
- Cost to post resumes: Fee (See Notes)
- Cost to see resumes: Free

Feature(s)? N/A

Career Advice? Yes

Any company can post positions on Right's web site but only their "client's" (job seekers being outplaced by this firm) can see the openings. Resumes can be obtained by corporate recruiters only (no headhunters need apply here). Employers will need a password to get into the database. An interesting Internet handbook with explanations geared to the novice about what to do and where to go is also available.

The Riley Guide

www.dbm.com/jobguide

(Commercial)
Margaret Riley, Margaret Riley
3726 Nimitz Rd., Kensington, MD 20895
301-946-1917 Fax: 301-933-9529 e-mail: mfriley@erols.com

Jobs?
- Cost to post jobs: N/A
- Cost to see jobs: N/A
- Specialty: All
- Industry: All
- Location: Int'l/US

Resumes?
- Cost to post resumes: N/A
- Cost to see resumes: N/A

Feature(s)? JSK/Links

Career Advice? Yes

Margaret will always be the "Queen of the Links" to us. An "icon" to anyone who has been out on the net more than a couple years, Margaret still maintains a great lists of links categorized every which way you can think of. Interesting career management articles make this a top site in it's niche.

Roanoke Times Online

www.roanoke.com

(Publisher/Newspaper)
Roanoke Times & World News
201-09 W. Campbell Street, Roanoke, VA 24010
800-346-1234 Fax: 540-981-3415 e-mail: lindah@roanoke.com

Jobs?
- Cost to post jobs: Fee
- Cost to see jobs: Free
- Specialty: All
- Industry: All
- Location: US/E/VA/Roanoke

Resumes?
- Cost to post resumes: N/A
- Cost to see resumes: N/A

Feature(s)? N/A

Career Advice? No

The Roanoke Times, the "Gateway to Southwest Virginia", posts their Sunday classifieds on this web site for all to see. A search engine makes the job easier but it is very basic - no advanced options, multiple words etc.

Rocky Mountain News

www.denver-rmn.com

(Publisher/Newspaper)
400 West Colfax Ave., Denver, CO 80204
303-892-2676 e-mail: nilesr@denver-rmn.com

Jobs?
- Cost to post jobs: Fee
- Cost to see jobs: Free
- Specialty: All
- Industry: All
- Location: US/W/CO/Denver

Resumes?
- Cost to post resumes: N/A
- Cost to see resumes: N/A

Feature(s)? N/A

Career Advice? No

Classified advertisements can be seen from this newspaper using their directory and while you are there, check out their "Internet Guide" down the left side of their home page as it has some helpful links and features. If you only stop by to get a good laugh and see the comics, it's worth the trip. CareerPath member.

RPI Career Resource Home Page

www.rpi.edu/dept/cdc/homepage.html

(College/University)
Jasmit Singh Kochhar, Rensselaer Polytechnic Institute
Career Development Center, Troy, NY 12180
518-276-2952 e-mail: kochhj@rpi.edu

Jobs?
- Cost to post jobs: N/A
- Cost to see jobs: N/A
- Specialty: All
- Industry: All
- Location: US

Resumes?
- Cost to post resumes: N/A
- Cost to see resumes: N/A

Feature(s)? JSK/Links

Career Advice? No

Jasmit is just churning out the links to hundreds of career resources. Some parts of this site have not been updated for quite awhile and yet others are freshly minted. Links to employers, professional societies, career services at various colleges as well as human resources and cyber alumni are all worthwhile. Here you also have links to newsgroups and can connect to RPI's Internet Job Surfer- the motherload of links.

The RS/6000 Employment Page

www.s6000.com/job.html

(Commercial)
Donohue Consulting, Inc.
P.O. Box 42046, Washington, DC 20015
202-362-8144 Fax: 202-364-2249 e-mail: dci@s6000.com

Jobs?
- Cost to post jobs: Free
- Cost to see jobs: Free
- Specialty: IT/RS 6000
- Industry: All
- Location: US

Resumes?
- Cost to post resumes: Free
- Cost to see resumes: Free

Feature(s)? N/A

Career Advice? No

Donohue Consulting provides a free service by posting jobs and resumes for people interested in RS/6000 (the world of IT). When you place your resume on the site, Job seekers can add a searchable profile. Company claims to provide this site as a service to the industry.

Sacramento Bee

www.sacbee.com/classads

(Publisher/Newspaper)
2100 Q Street, Sacramento, CA 95816
916-321-1234

Jobs?
- Cost to post jobs: Fee
- Cost to see jobs: Free
- Specialty: All
- Industry: All
- Location: US/W/CA/Sacramento

Resumes?
- Cost to post resumes: N/A
- Cost to see resumes: N/A

Feature(s)? N/A

Career Advice? No

Classified advertisements from the prior Sunday or "today" can be viewed. Search engine makes this site an easy road to travel. Publisher participates in CareerPath (see CareerPath).

Saludos Web

www.saludos.com

(Publisher/Diversity)
Erika Christiansen, Saludos Hispanos
73-121 Fred Waring Drive, Suite 100, Palm Desert, CA 92260
760-776-1206 Fax: 760-776-1229 e-mail: saludos@well.net

Jobs?
- Cost to post jobs: Fee
- Cost to see jobs: Free
- Specialty: All
- Industry: All
- Location: US/W/CA

Resumes?
- Cost to post resumes: Free
- Cost to see resumes: Free

Feature(s)? Search by State, Diversity

Career Advice? Yes

This Hispanic web site is supported by the Saludos Hispanos magazine. Resumes can be posted for free. Job postings cost $59 for one month. Career articles are well written and provide insight into what it really takes to get a job.

San Francisco Chronicle Classified on the Gateway

www.sfgate.com/classifieds/

(Publisher/Newspaper)
Greg DeMaagd, San Francisco Chronicle/Examiner
925 Mission Street, San Francisco, CA 94103
415-777-7021

Jobs?
- Cost to post jobs: Fee
- Cost to see jobs: Free
- Specialty: All
- Industry: All
- Location: US/W/CA/San Francisco

Resumes?
- Cost to post resumes: N/A
- Cost to see resumes: N/A

Feature(s)? Push to Applicant

Career Advice? Yes

Newspaper help wanted classifieds. An agent has been added for job seekers who register their job interests. The Chronicle will send you all the matching ads via e-mail. Career management articles and a column about the companies that are hiring in the bay area round out a progressive site.

Science Global Career Network

www.sciencemag.org

(Publisher/Trade Magazine)
Gabrielle Boguslawaki, Science Magazine
1200 NY Avenue N.W., Washington, DC 20005
202-326-6400 Fax: 202-682-0816 e-mail: gbogusla@aaas.org

Jobs?
- Cost to post jobs: Fee
- Cost to see jobs: Free
- Specialty: Science
- Industry: Science
- Location: Int'l./US

Resumes?
- Cost to post resumes: N/A
- Cost to see resumes: N/A

Feature(s)? N/A

Career Advice? Yes

Science Magazine's help wanted ads can be seen here. Recruiters pay for print and receive the web component free. All contact information is available on the site. Ads are grouped by the date of the publication. These ad groups are then listed by "title" and information about the number of ads in each discipline is then displayed. In addition, you can search by country or, in the case of the US, by location. Career workshops - really bulletin boards, allow the viewer to ask the "expert of the month" questions and receive replies. The Q&A "threads" are posted for everyone. Site also highlights career articles from past issues.

SciWeb - The Life Science Home Page

www.sciweb.com/career.html

(Commercial)
Sci Web, Inc.
e-mail: jobcenter@sciweb.com

Jobs?
- Cost to post jobs: Fee
- Cost to see jobs: Free
- Specialty: Science/Biology
- Industry: All
- Location: US

Resumes?
- Cost to post resumes: Free
- Cost to see resumes: Free

Feature(s)? N/A

Career Advice? Yes

SciWeb is for positions and resumes in the life science area. Biotechnology, pharmaceuticals, medical diagnostics, and health care are the fields that this site caters to. Only had one job posted on our visit but over 60 resumes of technical professionals at all levels were here.

SCWIST Work Pathfinder

www.harbour.sfu.ca/scwist/pathfinder/index.htm.

(Association/Diversity)
Society for Canadian Women in Science & Technology
Canada
e-mail: scwist@sfu.ca

Jobs?
- Cost to post jobs: N/A
- Cost to see jobs: N/A
- Specialty: Science
- Industry: All
- Location: Int'l/Canada

Resumes?
- Cost to post resumes: N/A
- Cost to see resumes: N/A

Feature(s)? Diversity

Career Advice? Yes

Career management site for women interested in technology and the sciences. Links to many Canadian companies that have jobs posted. Interesting stories about six women: how their careers have grown and how their expectations for the future have changed. If you are interested in breaking the glass ceiling, make a few friends here.

SEACnet Southeastern Atlantic Coast Career Network

minerva.acc.Virginia.EDU/~seacnet/

(College/University)
Southeastern Atlantic Coast Univ.
VA
800-843-9638

Jobs?
- Cost to post jobs: Free
- Cost to see jobs: N/A
- Specialty: All
- Industry: All
- Location: US/SE

Resumes?
- Cost to post resumes: N/A
- Cost to see resumes: Free

Feature(s)? Video Conferencing

Career Advice? Yes

Visitors will discover that a consortium of university career centers that have gotten together to provide video conferencing (interviewing) and give recruiters access to 400,000 students. Some major universities are represented and this concept should be taken very seriously by recruiters. Imagine sitting in your company's office and interviewing candidates from 21 schools without ever leaving town. Get the picture? Employer's can also retrieve resumes from these different universities and post job openings. There may be some charges as each university has different rules but this is as close to a one-stop(free)shopping as there is out there. Watch this one. E-mail: seacnet@minerva.acc.virginia.edu. Best site for its vision and teamwork regardless of the outcome.

The Seamless Website

www.seamless.com/jobs/

(Commercial)
Kevin Lee Thomason, TSW Ltd
300 Montgomery Street, 4th Flo, San Francisco, CA 94104
415-732-5600 Fax: 415-732-5606 e-mail: access@seamless.com

Jobs?
- Cost to post jobs: Free
- Cost to see jobs: Free
- Specialty: Law
- Industry: All
- Location: US/W/CA

Resumes?
- Cost to post resumes: Free
- Cost to see resumes: Free

Feature(s)? N/A

Career Advice? Yes

The legal profession can post resumes, link to jobs for free and share Q&As regarding careers and jobs. Well done and easy to access.

Seattle Times

www.seatimes.com/classified/

(Publisher/Newspaper)
Seattle Times
1120 John Street, Seattle, WA 98111
206-464-2994 e-mail: webmaster@webster.seatimes.com

Jobs?
- Cost to post jobs: Fee
- Cost to see jobs: Free
- Specialty: All
- Industry: All
- Location: US/NW/WA/Seattle

Resumes?
- Cost to post resumes: N/A
- Cost to see resumes: N/A

Feature(s)? N/A

Career Advice? No

Seattle Times classified advertisements can be searched but make sure you click on employment and not career directory (we were confused when no "hits" appeared). CareerPath participant.

SenseMedia Job Board

sensemedia.net/getajob/

(Commercial)
SenseMedia
e-mail: info@sensemedia.net

Jobs?
- Cost to post jobs: N/A
- Cost to see jobs: N/A
- Specialty: All
- Industry: All
- Location: US

Resumes?
- Cost to post resumes: N/A
- Cost to see resumes: N/A

Feature(s)? JSK/Links

Career Advice? No

Dozens of links in alpha order to all kinds of employment sites.

The Shaker Edge

www.shaker.com

(Private site)
Mike Temkin, Shaker Advertising Agency, Inc.
Shaker Bldg., 1100 Lake Street, Oak Park, IL 60301
800-323-5170 Fax: 708-848-2740 e-mail: info@shaker.com

Jobs? Yes
• Cost to post jobs: N/A
• Cost to see jobs: N/A
• Specialty: All
• Industry: All
• Location: US

Resumes? No
• Cost to post resumes: N/A
• Cost to see resumes: N/A

Feature(s)? Yes

Career Advice? Yes

Recruitment advertising firm provides job listings in human resources, HR news, links to HR associations and a map of the US linking company layoffs by state. Additional specialized services are password protected for clients.

Shawn's Internet Resume Center

www.inpursuit.com/sirc/

(Commercial)
In Pursuit
6405 Paddington Ct., #304, Centreville, CT 20121
e-mail: shawn@netrail.net

Jobs?
• Cost to post jobs: Fee
• Cost to see jobs: Free
• Specialty: N/A
• Industry: All
• Location: US

Resumes?
• Cost to post resumes: Fee
• Cost to see resumes: Free

Feature(s)? N/A

Career Advice? No

This site's target audience is executives. Owner charges $30 to put job seeker's paper on their site. Employers are charged $5.00 per job. Direct contact information is available on jobs and resumes. We are curious about how many "executives" will choose to post their resume to a public web site.

ShowBizJobs

www.showbizjobs.com

(Commercial)
Paul Buss, Entertainment Recruitment Network
7095 Hollywood Blvd., Suite 711, Hollywood, CA 90028
213-851-6442 e-mail: ern@bluehawk.com

Jobs?
- Cost to post jobs: Fee
- Cost to see jobs: Free
- Specialty: All
- Industry: Entertainment
- Location: US

Resumes?
- Cost to post resumes: Fee
- Cost to see resumes: Fee

Feature(s)? N/A

Career Advice? No

Corporations in the entertainment field from film, television, recording and attraction industries are present. On one of our visits we found jobs posted for America Online, Jim Hensen Productions and many others. Jobs can be seen with direct contact data. Fee to post your resume is $35 for six months. Cost to employers requires an annual membership fee of $250 and then $50 for each job (30 days). Great niche. All disciplines, part time and IT types as well.

SHRM HR Jobs

(Association/Publisher)
Society for Human Resource Management
1800 Duke Street, Alexandria, VA 22314
703-548-3440 Fax: 703-836-0367 e-mail: shrm@shrm.org

Jobs?
- Cost to post jobs: Fee
- Cost to see jobs: Free
- Specialty: Human Resources
- Industry: All
- Location: US

Resumes?
- Cost to post resumes: N/A
- Cost to see resumes: N/A

Feature(s)? Push to Applicant

Career Advice? Yes

The SHRM (Society for Human Resource Management) website has grown enormously this year. It continually improves while providing valuable content for the human resource community. Job Seekers who register on the site's jobs page will receive notification of new positions via e-mail. These listings will eventually see print in the Society's monthly tabloid "HRNews".After promising to post jobs online within 48 hours of receipt, the number of print pages grew from an average of 2 each month to more than a dozen. At $20+ per line, this is a successful business model. Other association publishers might want to take note.

Siam Net

www.siam.net/jobs/

(Commercial)
Mike Carter, Siam Job
Thailand
e-mail: feedback@siam.net

Jobs? Yes
- Cost to post jobs: Free
- Cost to see jobs: Free
- Specialty: All
- Industry: All
- Location: Int'l./Thailand

Resumes? Yes
- Cost to post resumes: Free
- Cost to see resumes: Free

Feature(s)? N/A

Career Advice? No

Siam Net or Siam Job depending on which page you enter from, posts jobs and resumes for Asian countries, in particular, Thailand. A sophisticated search engine has adopted the "note pad" concept so you can select the resumes and jobs you need and then view a summary list when you are. Must be new. Amazing when you think about the power of the web as we are looking at resumes from Thailand and looking for jobs thousands of miles away.

Silicon Valley Technical Employment Agencies

www.sease.com/jobs.html

(Commercial)
Jim Sease, Sease Associates
P.O. Box 390576, Mountain View, CA 94039
415-964-3348 e-mail: jim@sease.com

Jobs? No
- Cost to post jobs: N/A
- Cost to see jobs: N/A
- Specialty: IT
- Industry: High Technology
- Location: US/W/CA

Resumes? No
- Cost to post resumes: N/A
- Cost to see resumes: N/A

Feature(s)? JSK/Links

Career Advice? No

E-mail and contact information for technical employment agencies in California's Silicon Valley. Owner includes a list of recruitment firms with all contact data. We read an interesting article on why employment agencies prefer to receive resumes today via e-mail which supports our own observations. If you are looking for a technical position on the West coast and comfortable working with recruiters, this list may come in handy.

Singapore Online

www.singapore.com

(Commercial)
Richard Goh, Accel Infotech (S) Pte Ltd.
111 North Bridge Road #04-27, Peninsula Plaza, Singapore 17908
653-366-997 Fax: 653-362-833 e-mail: accel@technet.sg

Jobs? Yes
• Cost to post jobs: Fee
• Cost to see jobs: Free
• Specialty: All
• Industry: All
• Location: Int'l./Singapore

Resumes? No
• Cost to post resumes: N/A
• Cost to see resumes: N/A

Feature(s)? N/A

Career Advice? No

Dozens of major companies have posted openings on this site for the Singapore market. You must have an office located in Singapore to post positions. Rates are a flat $200 per job regardless of the number of openings. Site intends provide all information necessary for doing business in this country.

SkillBank

lapis.com/skillbank/index.htm

(Commercial)
Lapis Software Associates, LLC
601 Jefferson Road, Suite 207, Parsippany, NJ 07054
201-844-4006 Fax: 201-884-4233 e-mail: skillinfo@lapis.com

Jobs? No
• Cost to post jobs: N/A
• Cost to see jobs: N/A
• Specialty: All
• Industry: All
• Location: US

Resumes? Yes
• Cost to post resumes: Free
• Cost to see resumes: Free

Feature(s)? Push to Applicant

Career Advice? No

This supplier of software services provides free skill matching for both employers and applicants. The database offers the applicants with skill choices. Employers also select and search for skills they require. Employers can contact applicants who match or, if the applicant chooses to keep their information private, then the employer's interest is forwarded to the applicant.

SkillScape

www.skillscape.com

(Commercial)
Colin Houghton, SkillScape Skills Management Services Ltd.
403-247-0079 Fax: 403-202-2445 e-mail: info@skillscape.com

Jobs? Yes
- Cost to post jobs: Free
- Cost to see jobs: Free
- Specialty: All
- Industry: All
- Location: US

Resumes? Yes
- Cost to post resumes: Free
- Cost to see resumes: Free (See Note)

Feature(s)? Push to Applicant

Career Advice? No

Skill Scape is free for recruiters to post jobs and free for them to review candidate profiles and contact information- but only the profiles and contact information of those applicants that are responding to their posting. It will cost an employer $35 to look at the candidate contact information of those folks who are not responding to the posting (profiles, you can always see for free). Completing the sites skillset questionnaire takes 30 minutes.

Social Service.com

www.socialservice.com

(Non-Profit)
Administrative Technology Services
P.O. Box 7089, Kansas City, MO 64113
e-mail: joblink@socialservice.com

Jobs? Yes
- Cost to post jobs: N/A
- Cost to see jobs: N/A
- Specialty:
- Industry: All
- Location: US

Resumes? No
- Cost to post resumes: N/A (See Notes)
- Cost to see resumes: N/A (See Notes)

Feature(s)? Push to Applicant, JSK Links

Career Advice? No

Social Service.com provides links to social service jobs across the US. Links will take you to current openings in social agencies and on-line classifieds from local newspapers. Did not provide links to all sites but many are represented. Site will also e-mail new links to you as they register.

Society of Women Engineers

www.swe.org

(Association/Diversity)
Society of Women Engineers
120 Wall Street, 11th Floor, New York, NY 10005
212-509-9577 Fax: 212-509-0224 e-mail: vp-special.services@swe.org

Jobs? Yes
- Cost to post jobs: Free
- Cost to see jobs: Free
- Specialty: Engineering
- Industry: All
- Location: US

Resumes? Yes
- Cost to post resumes: N/A (See Notes)
- Cost to see resumes: N/A (See Notes)

Feature(s)? Push to Applicant

Career Advice? No

SWE members registering here are automatically forwarded job information as it is e-mailed by the corporations seeking engineers. It's amazing that this no cost service to a company isn't a used by all employers. SWE recommends that interested members use Resume-link's database to store their resume. Recruiters can subscribe and receive a disc with information about each candidate. We like the use of "push" on the job openings although it would be better if it were more visible on the site. Resume approach is a little behind the curve.

The Software Contractors' Guild

www.scguild.com/

(Association)
David Keeney
P.O. Box 257, Nottingham, NH 03290-0257
e-mail: admn@www.scguild.com

Jobs? No
- Cost to post jobs: N/A
- Cost to see jobs: N/A
- Specialty: IT
- Industry: IT
- Location: US

Resumes? Yes
- Cost to post resumes: Fee
- Cost to see resumes: Free

Feature(s)? Yes

Career Advice? No

The Software Contractor's Guild posts resumes of software contractors and states that it has 476 members (July '97). Job seekers pay to post a resume ($12 per year). For employers, resumes are free to see. This site has added a bulletin board section about what is going on in the recruitment of contractors. Also found at the site was a frequently asked questions section geared to tactical career issues. Makes interesting reading.

Southern Jobs - Job Digest

www.southernjobs.com

(Commercial)
Randy Rose, JobDigest
2110 Hollow Brook Drive, Colorado Springs, CO 80918
719-590-7400 Fax: 719-590-7500 e-mail: rrose@jobdigest.com

Jobs? Yes
- Cost to post jobs: Fee
- Cost to see jobs: Free
- Specialty: All
- Industry: All
- Location: US/S

Resumes? Yes
- Cost to post resumes: Free
- Cost to see resumes: Free

Feature(s)? N/A

Career Advice? No

Southern Jobs concentrates on opportunities in OK, AL, KY, TN, MS, LA and AR. Job seekers and recruiters can search by city. Cost to post jobs is $15 per opening. Resumes can be posted for free. Unfortunately a quick test of this site didn't turn up grits let alone openings or candidates.

Space Jobs

www.spacejobs.om

(Commercial)
Space Jobs Inc.
153 St.-Andrew Street, Suite 100, Ottawa, ON K1N5G3
888-366-6337 Fax: 613-562-1784 e-mail: info@spacejobs.com

Jobs? Yes
- Cost to post jobs: Fee
- Cost to see jobs: Free
- Specialty: Engineering/Aerospace
- Industry: Aerospace
- Location: US

Resumes? Yes
- Cost to post resumes: Free
- Cost to see resumes: N/A

Feature(s)? Push to Applicant

Career Advice? No

Space Jobs is for the aerospace engineers and others who dream about new worlds to conquer. GE, Rockwell and some of the biggest players in space worldwide are here. Job seekers register their skills and receive e-mails when positions match. Recruiters pay $150 to post a position. Opportunities are located all over the world. Beam me up Scotty!

SPIE's Employment Center

optics.org/employment/

(Association)
Mark Mugittroyd, Society of Photo-Optical Instrumentation Engineers
1000 20th Street, Bellingham, WA 98225
360-676-3290 Fax: 360-647-1445 e-mail: advertising@spie.org

Jobs? Yes
• Cost to post jobs: Fee
• Cost to see jobs: Free
• Specialty: Science/Optical Physics
• Industry: All
• Location: US

Resumes? Yes
• Cost to post resumes: Free
• Cost to see resumes: Free

Feature(s)? N/A

Career Advice? No

The International Society for Photo-Optical Instrumentation Engineeringallowsprofessionals to post their resume for free for sixty days (there were over 170 present on our last visit). Recruiters can see resumes for free and post jobs for $300 for a four week run. There were 65 jobs with direct contact information and the date of posting. All transactions can be conducted through the website. Simple and easy to understand. Well done.

St. Louis Area Companies on the Net

www.st-louis.mo.us/st-louis/companies.html

(College/University)
Brian Smith, Washington University
School of Engineering, St. Louis, MO
314-935-4850 e-mail: brians@cait.wustl.edu

Jobs? No
• Cost to post jobs: N/A
• Cost to see jobs: N/A
• Specialty: All
• Industry: All
• Location: US/MW/MO/St. Louis

Resumes? No
• Cost to post resumes: N/A
• Cost to see resumes: N/A

Feature(s)? JSK/Links

Career Advice? No

If you are looking for a job in St. Louis go no further then the list of links on this site. It is one of the longest state lists we have ever seen. Brief description of each may make your journey profitable.

St. Paul Pioneer Planet

www.pioneerplanet.com/classifieds/

(Publisher/Newspaper)
Amy Lindgren, St. Paul Pioneer Press
345 Cedar Street, St. Paul, Minnesota 55101
612-222-5011 e-mail: getajob@pioneerplanet.infi.net

Jobs? Yes
- Cost to post jobs: Fee
- Cost to see jobs: Free
- Specialty: All
- Industry: All
- Location: US/MW/MN/St. Paul

Resumes? No
- Cost to post resumes: N/A
- Cost to see resumes: N/A

Feature(s)? N/A

Career Advice? Yes

Employment advertising for the St. Paul Minnesota Press can be searched at this newspaper's site. Interesting feature is that they have placed 24 kiosks called "JobView" in metro areas so job seekers can apply directly to positions listed. Career management columns authored by Amy Lindgren are available.

St. Petersburg Times

www.sptimes.com

(Publisher/Newspaper)
St. Petersburg Times
490 First Avenue, St. Petersburg, FL 33701
813-893-8554

Jobs? Yes
- Cost to post jobs: Fee
- Cost to see jobs: Free
- Specialty: All
- Industry: All
- Location: US/SE/FL/St. Petersburg

Resumes? No
- Cost to post resumes: N/A
- Cost to see resumes: N/A

Feature(s)? N/A

Career Advice? No

If you want to work in this part of Florida, the St. Petersburg Times has posted their help wanted ads online. The charge recruiters an extra $1 total for the privilege ($5 if it is a display ad).

St. Thomas Human Resource Centre

ein.ccia.st-thomas.hrdc-drhc.gc.ca/english.html

(Government)
HR Department Canada, Human Resources Development Canada
451 Talbot Street, St. Thomas, Ontario NSP 3V6
519-631-5470

Jobs? Yes
• Cost to post jobs: Free
• Cost to see jobs: Free
• Specialty: All
• Industry: All
• Location: Int'l/Canada

Resumes? No
• Cost to post resumes: N/A
• Cost to see resumes: N/A

Feature(s)? N/A

Career Advice? Yes

Direct contact information is now available for this Canadian run service. Employers wishing to post positions on this site need to contact their local Canadian Employment Center at 519-631-7760 or fax info to 519-631-3565. Their e-mail is:

Roshan@ein.ccia.st-thomas.on.ca.

Simple, easy and get's the job done.

StarChefs

www.starchefs.com

(Commercial)
Pat Greaney, Boiling Water, Inc.
270 Lafayette Street, Suite 205, New York, NY 10012
212-966-3775 Fax: 212-966-6644 e-mail: greaney@starchefs.com

Jobs? Yes
• Cost to post jobs: Free
• Cost to see jobs: Free
• Specialty: Restaurant/Chefs
• Industry: Hospitality
• Location: Int'l./US

Resumes? Yes
• Cost to post resumes: Free
• Cost to see resumes: Free

Feature(s)? N/A

Career Advice? Yes

StarChefs is for those who have the aspiration to be the next "Julia Child" The site posts opportunities by the score for restaurants all over the world. Sous Chefs, Executive Chefs, Pastry Chefs, even restaurant positions in sales and marketing can all be seen for free. All job listings are posted by date as are the resumes. Site uses it's search engine to find recipes rather then jobs or resumes. Priorities we guess. If you register they will place you on a mailing list and e-mail their latest culinary creations. Educational institutions have posted profiles about their culinary programs. The hospitality industry should be proud of this entry on the web.

Stern Alumni Outreach Career Resources Online

www.stern.nyu.edu/Alumni/career.html

(College/University)
Wendy Siegel, Stern School of Business
NYU, NY
e-mail: wsiegel@stern.nyu.edu

Jobs? Yes
• Cost to post jobs: Free
• Cost to see jobs: Free
• Specialty: All/Executive
• Industry: All
• Location: US

Resumes? No
• Cost to post resumes: N/A
• Cost to see resumes: N/A

Feature(s)? N/A

Career Advice? Yes

This Alumni site for the Stern NYU School of Business is an example of how what can be done. Employer's post jobs for free and dozens of links to executive recruiters, corporations and career information are maintained here. If other schools are looking for a model this is a good one to benchmark. We note that salaries for some of the positions posted were well into 6 figures.

StudentCenter

studentcenter.com

(Commercial)
Eve Yohalem, StudentCenter LLC
31 West 21st Street, Suite 1102, New York, NY 10010
212-929-7980 Fax: 212-255-6357 e-mail: info@studentcenter.com

Jobs? No
• Cost to post jobs: N/A
• Cost to see jobs: N/A
• Specialty: All/College
• Industry: All
• Location: US

Resumes? No
• Cost to post resumes: N/A
• Cost to see resumes: N/A

Feature(s)? JSK/Links, Career Mgm't.

Career Advice? Yes

Career advice is forte of the "Student Center" and it has a lot of it. Intended for college students and recent graduates, the site provides over 35,000 company links. Q&A regarding career decisions includes lot's of useful information. A cost of living calculator and extensive help preparing your resume are added attractions.

Summer Jobs

(College/University)
Bobbie Halfin, Fishnet New Media
180 State Road, Suite 2U, Bourne, MA 02532
508-888-3456 Fax: 508-888-3151 e-mail: bhalfin@adsmart.net

Jobs? Yes
• Cost to post jobs: Fee
• Cost to see jobs: Free
• Specialty: College
• Industry: All
• Location: Int'l/US

Resumes? No
• Cost to post resumes: N/A
• Cost to see resumes: N/A

Feature(s)? N/A

Career Advice? No

If you need Summer help this is the place to visit. Opportunities in the US or around the world are posted here for all to see with direct contact information. You can search by location, title or just browse through all the jobs.

The Sunday Paper

(Commercial)
Bulkin Enterprises, Inc.
56 Reyburn Drive, Henderson, NV 89014
702-837-3374 Fax: 702-837-3374 e-mail: info@sundaypaper.com

Jobs? Yes
• Cost to post jobs: Fee
• Cost to see jobs: Free
• Specialty: All
• Industry: All
• Location: US

Resumes? Yes
• Cost to post resumes: Free
• Cost to see resumes: Free

Feature(s)? N/A

Career Advice? No

When you were a kid, did you wake up early and run down the driveway to get the newspaper before anyone could see it? We always wanted to see the comics before anyone else could get their hands on them because we knew once our parents were up it was all over. Well, Sunday Paper is like our story. Only when we got to the driveway, it must have been Saturday because there was only 1 job listed- big disappointment. This site is designed like the classified in your local paper- selling everything from autos to websites. Nice concept but not worth the effort without the job postings. Maybe they should include a comics section.

SuperSite TechJobs

supersite.net/techjobsn2/docs/home.htm

(Commercial)
Keith Sharp, SuperSite.Net
10228 N. Stelling Road, Cupertino, CA 95014
408-343-0300 Fax: 408-252-3081 e-mail: oksharp@supersite.net

Jobs? Yes
- Cost to post jobs: Fee
- Cost to see jobs: Free
- Specialty: IT& NonExempt
- Industry: All
- Location: US

Resumes? No
- Cost to post resumes: N/A
- Cost to see resumes: N/A

Feature(s)? N/A

Career Advice? No

Technical positions are posted on this site from dozens of companies large and small. This is one of the few sites that lists "hourly positions" in large numbers that are specifically broken out into their own categories. Many packages to advertise positions at various rates are offered and it is best if you contact them directly for more info. Split screen makes it easy to find what you are looking for by title or corporation. You can travel from this site's home page (supersite.net/) to find other technical sites that are mirror copies of the SuperSite in more specific technical skill sets (see bottom of their home page).

Supermarket News

www.supermarketnews.com

(Publisher/Trade)
Fairchild Publishing
7 East 12th Street, New York, NY 10003
800-423-3314 Fax: 212-630-4634 e-mail: info@supermarketnews.com

Jobs? Yes
- Cost to post jobs: Fee
- Cost to see jobs: Free
- Specialty: All
- Industry: Retail
- Location: US

Resumes? No
- Cost to post resumes: N/A
- Cost to see resumes: N/A

Feature(s)? N/A

Career Advice? No

Supermarket News is a trade publication for the retail grocery marketplace. Employers pay for the print to have the opportunity to post on the web as well.

Syracuse OnLine

www.syracuse.com

(Publisher/Newspaper)
Stan Linhorst, Syracuse Herald Journal
Clinton Square, Syracuse, NY 13221
315-470-0032 Fax: 315-470-2050 e-mail: linhorst@mailbox.syr.edu

Jobs? Yes
- Cost to post jobs: Fee
- Cost to see jobs: Free
- Specialty: All
- Industry: All
- Location: US/NE/NY/Syracuse

Resumes? No
- Cost to post resumes: N/A
- Cost to see resumes: N/A

Feature(s)? N/A

Career Advice? No

Syracuse Online's classified ads are listed by broad subject titles which is very confusing. Without a search engine this site is difficult to use. Once you get through the maze, direct contact information is posted and jobs are in alpha order. You will be doing a lot of surfing at this site.

Tacoma News Tribune

www.tribnet.com/classads/

(Publisher/Newspaper)
Tacoma News Tribune
1950 S. State Street, Tacoma, WA 98405
509-459-5005 e-mail: bwatkins@p.tribnet.com

Jobs? Yes
- Cost to post jobs: Fee
- Cost to see jobs: Free
- Specialty: All
- Industry: All
- Location: US/NW/WA/Tacoma

Resumes? No
- Cost to post resumes: N/A
- Cost to see resumes: N/A

Feature(s)? N/A

Career Advice? No

Help-wanted classifieds are here to see. Positions are listed by sections: healthcare, part time, sales, high tech and other. Job seekers will find this site somewhat awkward trying to work with these limited choices.

Talent Alliance

(Non-Profit)
Jeannette Galvanek
P.O. Box 9239, Morristown, NJ 07960
888-967-5929 Fax: 888-517-4581 e-mail: info@talentalliance.org

Jobs? No
- Cost to post jobs: N/A
- Cost to see jobs: N/A
- Specialty: All
- Industry: All
- Location: US

Resumes? No
- Cost to post resumes: N/A
- Cost to see resumes: N/A

Feature(s)? Career Mgm't.

Career Advice? No

Ten major US companies (AT&T, DuPont, GTE, J&J, Lucent Technologies, Unisys, UPS, NCR, TRW and Union Pacific) form the core of a new concept called Talent Alliance that has enormous implications in it's goal to provide long-term employability to the consortium's employees and, at the same time, help companies with growth needs to quickly locate skilled workers. Jeannette Galvanek, a former VP of HR for AT&T is credited with spearheading this effort and obtaining renewable 3 year grants from the first 10 member companies. The Alliance will offer its member employees the following services:

* sophisticated job and applicant matching through an online database to support not only company outplacement efforts but to meet all employees career management goals.

* shared training resources and best practices.

* online and on-site career centers providing individual career management.

* educational forums, research and communication geared toward improving career management strategies. Several web-based organizations such as Intellimatch and I-Search have been tapped to support the Alliance. Reports that as many as 40 additional companies have asked to join the Alliance have not been confirmed. Best site for it's vision.

Talent Hunter

www.3dsite.com/ism/resumes/cgi-bin/talent-hunter.cgi

(Commercial/Agent)
Charles Anthony Viviani
e-mail: cav@ax.apc.org

Jobs? Yes
• Cost to post jobs: Free
• Cost to see jobs: Free
• Specialty: Graphic Arts
• Industry: All
• Location: US

Resumes? Yes
• Cost to post resumes: Free
• Cost to see resumes: Free

Feature(s)? Push to Employer

Career Advice? No

Once you register as a job seeker or as a corporation all searches are free. Talent Hunter's agent will match candidates to employer's job requirements. This site is for people in the graphics industry: 3-D, artists, modeling, special effects and interested in freelance or full time employment.

Talent Works: The Online Casting Source

www.talentworks.com

(Commercial)
Richard Brodsky, Talentworks
862 Sir Francis Drake Blvd., #255, San Anselmo, CA 94960
800-978-9911 Fax: 415-456-0588 e-mail: info@talentworks.com

Jobs? Yes
• Cost to post jobs: Free
• Cost to see jobs: Free
• Specialty: Entertainment
• Industry: Entertainment
• Location: US

Resumes? Yes
• Cost to post resumes: Fee
• Cost to see resumes: Free

Feature(s)? N/A

Career Advice? No

Acting sites still continue to amaze us. Imagine a search engine where you can ask for an accountant with a specific height and eye color. Only will work here. Direct contact information for the candidates is shown...along with their picture. Actors pay $50 and talent agencies pay $250 to show off their clients. You can post casting notices for free. You can try the site out for 10 days for free.

Technical Writers to the Rescue

www.mindspring.com/~panin/writers.htm

(Association)
Nina Panzica, Society for Technical Communications
e-mail: panin@mindspring.com

Jobs? No
- Cost to post jobs: N/A
- Cost to see jobs: N/A
- Specialty: Technical Writing
- Industry: All
- Location: Int'l./US

Resumes? Yes
- Cost to post resumes: Free
- Cost to see resumes: Free

Feature(s)? N/A

Career Advice? No

For short or long term technical writing visit Technical Writers to the Rescue. Resumes from all over the world are posted here for free by volunteers from the Society for Technical Communications.

TechWeb/TechCareers/TechHunter

techweb.cmp.com/

(Publisher/Trade)
Barbara Kerbel, CMP Publications
600 Community Drive, Manhasset, NY 11030
516-562-5218 Fax: 516-562-7830 e-mail: cmppr@techweb.com

Jobs? Yes
- Cost to post jobs: Fee
- Cost to see jobs: Free
- Specialty: IT
- Industry: High Technology
- Location: US

Resumes? Yes
- Cost to post resumes: Free
- Cost to see resumes: N/A

Feature(s)? Push to Applicant

Career Advice? Yes

TechWeb and E-Span have teamed up to create TechCareers where the job seeker can post a personal profile for free. The site pushes job openings to that match candidate skills. recruiters can post openings for 8 weeks for $95 each. Jobs posted here are also listed with other major online services and numerous bulletin boards. Salary surveys and career articles add value to this site. Why CMP doesn't require all it's publications to post here is way over our head.

Telecommuting Jobs

www.tjobs.com/index.html

(Commercial)
Sol Levine, Levine Communications
1001 Greenbay Road, Winnetka, IL 60093
847-835-2180 Fax: 847-835-2183 e-mail: ads@tjobs.com

Jobs?
- Cost to post jobs: Fee
- Cost to see jobs: Free
- Specialty: All/Telecommuting
- Industry: All
- Location: US

Resumes?
- Cost to post resumes: Free
- Cost to see resumes: Free

Feature(s)? N/A

Career Advice? No

If you are interested in jobs that can be done at home, this is the site that will give you some answers. Resumes can be posted for free. Jobs can be posted with costs ranging up to several hundred dollars depending on the category of the job you want placed. Site provides links to your information. Search engine makes this site easy to view. Includes a "notepad" feature.

Telecommuting, Telework & Alt. Officing

www.gilgordon.com

(Commercial)
Gil Gordon Associates
10 Donner Court, Monmouth Junction, NJ 08852
908-329-2266 Fax: 908-329-2703 e-mail: 74375.1667@compuserve.com

Jobs? No
- Cost to post jobs: N/A
- Cost to see jobs: N/A
- Specialty: Telecommuting
- Industry: All
- Location: Int'l/US

Resumes? No
- Cost to post resumes: N/A
- Cost to see resumes: N/A

Feature(s)? RT/Retention

Career Advice? Yes

If you want to learn about telecommuting from a world class expert, Gil Gordon's site is the place to visit. Take your time to browse the helpful articles and links to other experts in the field. Check out the tips on "real estate". The online suggestions you'll find here provide the insight you need to give your career at home a jump-start. Even more critical is the counsel that employers will find here - or by contacting Gil to ensure that their telecommuting program will really help to make their workforce more competitive. The content at this site was rated among the 10 best on the web for human resource professionals in 1997 by a well know HR trade publication. We agree. Ok, so we're also biased. It's our book.

Television & Radio News Research

www.missouri.edu/~jourvs/

(Career Management)
Vernon Stone, Missouri School of Journalism
U. of Missouri, 3805 W. Rollins Road, Columbia, MO 65203
573-882-9939 e-mail: jourvs@showme.missouri.edu

Jobs? No
- Cost to post jobs: N/A
- Cost to see jobs: N/A
- Specialty: Broadcast News/Journalism
- Industry: Broadcast Media
- Location: US

Resumes? No
- Cost to post resumes: N/A
- Cost to see resumes: N/A

Feature(s)? N/A

Career Advice? Yes

New articles are always being added to this unique source for career information on the radio & television broadcast news industry. Salary information is also available.

Top Jobs USA

www.topjobsusa.com

(Commercial)
Eric Marchant, TOPjobs
P.O. Box 1787, Provo, UT 84603
888-562-7872 Fax: 801-235-1964 e-mail: eric_marchant@topjobsusa.com

Jobs?
- Cost to post jobs: Fee
- Cost to see jobs: Free
- Specialty: All
- Industry: All
- Location: US

Resumes?
- Cost to post resumes: Free
- Cost to see resumes: Fee

Feature(s)? N/A

Career Advice? Yes

This site claims it has over 50,000 current job opportunities for Professionals, Managers and Technical Specialists. Hmmm. The emphasis here is on the western states but a Midwest presence is starting to build. It costs employers $65 per posting for 60 days. A resume database can be searched for an annual fee of $595. Other packages are available. A "Job Club" (weekly newsletter) is available for those seeking new occupations.

Top Jobs on the Net

www.topjobs.net

(Commercial)
Tove Sundqvist, The Corporate Net Ltd.
Sandpiper Quay, 30 Modwen Road, Salford, England M53EZ
440-161-8767600 Fax: 440-161-8767787 e-mail: tove.sundqvist@topjobs.co.uk

Jobs? Yes
• Cost to post jobs: Fee
• Cost to see jobs: Free
• Specialty: All/College
• Industry: All
• Location: Int'l/US

Resumes? No
• Cost to post resumes: N/A
• Cost to see resumes: N/A

Feature(s)? N/A

Career Advice? No

Top Jobs on the Net is a European based site that lists all types of jobs in England, France, Germany and other countries. It has numerous links to company recruitment pages and some of the job postings are in the language of the country they are posted in. Top Jobs has set up separate sites for Ireland, Poland, UK and the USA. Interesting aspect as of this site is the jobs for "top grads". Always fascinates us that Europe is very secretive about what their web site costs for advertising. Recommend you find out what it costs before you venture overseas on this cyber trip.

TownOnline

(Publisher/Newspaper)
Glenn Gutmacher, Community Newspaper Company
254 Second Avenue, Needham, MA 02194
617-433-8319 Fax: 617-433-7888 e-mail: jobsmart@cnc.com

Jobs? Yes
- Cost to post jobs: Fee
- Cost to see jobs: Free
- Specialty: All
- Industry: All
- Location: US/NE/MA

Resumes? Yes
- Cost to post resumes: Free
- Cost to see resumes: Fee

Feature(s)? Push to Applicant

Career Advice? Yes

New England local, weekly and daily papers (120) include a common publication "Working" that is now included in the newspaper (It used to be a stand alone insert when the site and publication were called JobSmart). This web version of the printed help-wanted section has a job agent to assist job seekers in their search. Set the criteria of the job you are seeking and the agent goes through the database to match against posted opportunities and then e-mail you the result. Owners have added a chat room and an "ask the career expert" Q&A section. Recruiters pay $75 to post a position and $250 to search the resume database. Both are for 4 week periods.

Training Net

www.trainingnet.com

(Commercial)
Amar Hhaliwal, TrainingNet Computer Services Limited
103-2609 Westview Drive, Ste 405, North Vancouver, BC V7N4N2
604-980-0643 Fax: 604-980-4448 e-mail: info@trainingnet.com

Jobs? Yes
- Cost to post jobs: Free
- Cost to see jobs: Free
- Specialty: Human Resources/T&D
- Industry: All
- Location: Int'l/US

Resumes? Yes
- Cost to post resumes: Free
- Cost to see resumes: Free

Feature(s)? N/A

Career Advice? Yes

Niche site that allows employers and job seekers free access to post jobs and resumes and see direct contact information. If training is your field, there is also an events calendar where you can click on your specialty and get advice about the latest conferences and seminars.

Training SuperSite Job Bank

www.trainingsupersite.com/jobset.htm

(Commercial)
Eric Snyder, Targeted Communication Management
64 Thare Cr., Nepean, Ontario, Canada K2J 2P6
613-823-0244 Fax: 613-745-8031 e-mail: egs@tcm.com

Jobs? Yes
- Cost to post jobs: Fee
- Cost to see jobs: Free
- Specialty: Human Resources/T&D, ER, HRIS
- Industry: All
- Location: Int'l/Canada/US

Resumes? Yes
- Cost to post resumes: Free
- Cost to see resumes: Free

Feature(s)? Push to Employer, Push to Applicant

Career Advice? Yes

The Training SuperSite Job Bank uses push technology and has a niche HR focus (training). An excellent value- ads cost $200/month. More than 3000 registered professionals receive regular notification of openings. Links to company web sites from each posting add value and this owner takes the time to post to newsgroups and especially to contact related listservs. Employers who register here can receive resumes from this site free via e-mail. Check out their bookstore.

Job, Resume & Career Management Sites on the World Wide Web
• The 1998 Directory •
- 320 -

trans-ACTION

(Publisher/Trade)
Chilton Company
Inside Sales, 4th Floor, 1 Chilton Way, Radnor, PA 19089
800-866-0206 Fax: 610-964-4663 e-mail: mmccadd@chilton.net

Jobs? Yes
- Cost to post jobs: Fee
- Cost to see jobs: Free
- Specialty: All
- Industry: All
- Location: US

Resumes? No
- Cost to post resumes: N/A
- Cost to see resumes: N/A

Feature(s)? N/A

Career Advice? No

Automotive and Trucking, Electronics, Optics & Ophthalmology, Industrial Equipment, Services, Food Equipment & Services, Assembly & Machinery, Metals & Metalworking magazines all have their job postings displayed on this site. Cumbersome, as you have to go to each individual category to see what is posted. Cost is $75 per month per insertion. Navigation on this site was difficult each time we visited.

Tsunami

(Commercial)
Russell Tewksbury, Market Works Corporation
e-mail: mktworks@goforit.com

Jobs? No
- Cost to post jobs: N/A
- Cost to see jobs: N/A
- Specialty: JSK/Links
- Industry: All
- Location: US

Resumes? No
- Cost to post resumes: N/A
- Cost to see resumes: N/A

Feature(s)? N/A

Career Advice? No

This Tsunami wave rolls in with about 20 links to major job sites. Graphics that are a little creepy when you first see them raise expectations but there is little more here. More foam than breakers.

TVJobs

www.tvjobs.com

(Commercial Resume Site)
Mark Holloway, Broadcast Employment Services
P.O.Box 4116, Oceanside, CA 92052
619-754-2115 Fax: 619-754-2115 e-mail: markch@tvjobs.com

Jobs? Yes
• Cost to post jobs: Fee
• Cost to see jobs: Free
• Specialty: Entertainment/Broadcasting
• Industry: Entertainment/Broadcast
• Location: US

Resumes? Yes
• Cost to post resumes: Fee
• Cost to see resumes: Free

Feature(s)? Push to Applicant

Career Advice? Yes

This site focuses on opportunities within the broadcast world. Resumes can be posted for 12 months for $75 and other packages are available. Job seekers see jobs posted and receive e-mail notification of new listings as well. Employers can post jobs for free (you do it online) and they are listed for 30 days. TV Jobs links to over 1,700 stations across the US. Also has recently added a Q&A section called "NetForum".

Twin Cities Job Page

www.fentonnet.com/jobs/html

(Commercial)
Michael Fenton, Fentonnet Inc.
3716 42nd Avenue South, Minneapolis, MN 55406
612-724-1845 e-mail: info@fentonnet.com

Jobs? Yes
• Cost to post jobs: Fee
• Cost to see jobs: Free
• Specialty: All
• Industry: All
• Location: US/MW/MN

Resumes? Yes
• Cost to post resumes: Free
• Cost to see resumes: Free

Feature(s)? N/A

Career Advice? No

A distinctive site for the Twin Cities area that allows the job seeker to post their resume and employers to view contact data for free. Resumes are not in any particular order so be prepared to let your fingers do the scrolling. Recruiters pay $50 to post a job.

US Air Force Employment Home Page

www.afpc.af.mil/dpc/afjob1.htm

(Government)
Don Pelfrey, US Government
800-688-9889 e-mail: pelfreyd@hq.afpc.af.mil

Jobs? Yes
• Cost to post jobs: N/A (See Notes)
• Cost to see jobs: Free
• Specialty: All
• Industry: Military
• Location: US

Resumes? Yes
• Cost to post resumes: Free
• Cost to see resumes: N/A (See Notes)

Feature(s)? N/A

Career Advice? Yes

If you want to fly, join the Air Force and see the world. You can send your resume via e-mail, while career information is also available on military and civilian job opportunities. Sorry recruiters, the Air Force is not going to share their resume database nor allow you to post jobs on their site.

US Job Network High Tech Job & Resume Bank

www.usjob.net

(Publisher/Trade)
Julie Deese, Jaye Communications
550 Interstate North Pkwy, Suite 150, Atlanta, GA 30339
770-984-9444 Fax: 770-612-0780 e-mail: julie.deese@usjob.net

Jobs? Yes
• Cost to post jobs: Fee
• Cost to see jobs: Free
• Specialty: IT
• Industry: All
• Location: US/SE

Resumes? Yes
• Cost to post resumes: Free
• Cost to see resumes: Fee

Feature(s)? N/A

Career Advice? No

Primarily a Southeast site, Job Network is expanding to the rest of the US market. Subscribers pay $295 per month to post unlimited positions and search the resume database.

USM Resources for G/L/B Students

macweb.acs.usm.maine.edu/csce/career_glb.html

(College/University)
Career Services & Coop. Education, Univ. of Southern Maine
100 Payson Smith Hall, P.O. Box 9300, ME
e-mail: bliss@usm.maine.edu

Jobs? No
- Cost to post jobs: N/A
- Cost to see jobs: N/A
- Specialty: College
- Industry: All
- Location: US

Resumes? No
- Cost to post resumes: N/A
- Cost to see resumes: N/A

Feature(s)? Diversity

Career Advice? Yes

Career counseling resources for gays, lesbians and bisexuals can be found here. Links to colleges universities links, and other networking resources are available.

Virtual Interviewing Assistant

www.ukans.edu/cwis/units/coms2/via/index.html

(College/University)
University of Kansas
Department of Comm. Studies

Jobs? No
- Cost to post jobs: N/A
- Cost to see jobs: N/A
- Specialty: All
- Industry: All
- Location: US

Resumes? No
- Cost to post resumes: N/A
- Cost to see resumes: N/A

Feature(s)? Career Mgm't.

Career Advice? Yes

Everything you always wanted to know about interviewing but were afraid to ask is here. Gets down to basics and the ones you never thought to ask. Check out the humor section. Anyone who has ever looked for a job will get a laugh here. Some of the links may be old but the bulk of the site is worth your visit.

Wall Street Journal Interactive Edition

(Publisher/Newspaper)
Sam Wheeler, Dow Jones & Company
New York, NY
214-640-7845 e-mail: cwc-sale@wsj.dowjones.com

Jobs? Yes
• Cost to post jobs: Fee
• Cost to see jobs: Free
• Specialty: All
• Industry: All
• Location: US

Resumes? No
• Cost to post resumes: N/A
• Cost to see resumes: N/A

Feature(s)? N/A

Career Advice? Yes

Corporations pay a fee to post jobs to the WSJ. Site has picked up on the "note pad" concept as you can use the search engine to select the positions that you have an interest in and hold them aside to act on at the end of your session. There were over 6,000 jobs posted on our last visit. Excellent career articles are different from the norm and make the WSJ site one you want to bookmark (some articles have an additional cost to view). Want ads are not posted from the newspaper.

Washington Post-Career Post

www.washingtonpost.com/wp-adv/classifieds/careerpost.search.htm

(Publisher/Newspaper)
Jamie Hammond, Washington Post
1150-15th Street N.W., Washington, DC 20071
202-334-6000 Fax: 202-334-5561 e-mail: hammondj@washpost.com

Jobs? Yes
- Cost to post jobs: Fee
- Cost to see jobs: Free
- Specialty: All
- Industry: All
- Location: US/E/DC

Resumes? No
- Cost to post resumes: N/A
- Cost to see resumes: N/A

Feature(s)? N/A

Career Advice? Yes

Job seekers can search two Sunday's worth of employment ads. Dick Bolles, author of "What Color is Your Parachute" dispenses career advice in a Q&A section. Search engine allows you to hunt by title of job, employer name, job location or key word. "Note Pad" format is used on this site (see WSJ review). The Post has a good handle on the use of technology with the classified sections of their papers. Emerging technology model in use by the Post allows companies to give the post access to their company site's jobs page and mirror it on the Post.

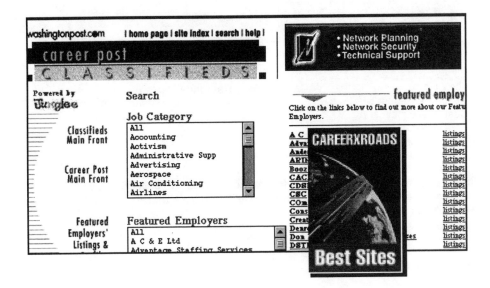

Web Developer's Virtual Library

www.stars.com/

(Commercial)
Alan Richmond, CyberWeb SoftWare
7002 Kingfisher Lane, Lanham, MD 20706
301-552-0272 e-mail: jobs@stars .com

Jobs? Yes
- Cost to post jobs: Free
- Cost to see jobs: Free
- Specialty: IT/Web
- Industry: All
- Location: Int'l./US

Resumes? Yes
- Cost to post resumes: Free
- Cost to see resumes: Free

Feature(s)? N/A

Career Advice? No

Web developers scouting the technical information at this site will also find jobs and resumes posted for free. Go to the Index after the home page to find the link to the jobs page. Jobs are listed in the Internet section and resumes are listed in the Gallery. Don't ask us why, we just find them. Jobs and resumes are from all over the world.

Web Dog's Job Hunt: The Best Jobs

Csueb.sfsu.edu/jobs.html

(College/University)
Jeff Schwartz, San Francisco State Career Center
e-mail: webdog@webdog.com

Jobs? No
- Cost to post jobs: N/A
- Cost to see jobs: N/A
- Specialty: College
- Industry: All
- Location: US

Resumes? No
- Cost to post resumes: N/A
- Cost to see resumes: N/A

Feature(s)? JSK/Links

Career Advice? No

Web Dog provides a long list of links for college students. We especially liked the new links to "distance learning" sites. A service of the California State University Employment Board. Faithfully maintained.

WebJobsUSA

(Commercial)
WEBJOBSUSA
295 Greenwich Street, Suite 149, New York, NY 10007
Fax: 212-344-2539 e-mail: jobs@webjobsusa.com

Jobs? Yes
- Cost to post jobs: Fee
- Cost to see jobs: Free
- Specialty: IT/New Media
- Industry: All
- Location: US/E/NY/NYC

Resumes? No
- Cost to post resumes: N/A
- Cost to see resumes: N/A

Feature(s)? N/A

Career Advice? No

Web Jobs USA specializes in administrative, design, marketing, production, research, sales, technical, training, and writing/editing of new media employment opportunities. $25 to post jobs. We believe this is primarily a NY site.

Weed Jobs

(Government)
Robert Campbell, Canadian Forest Service
P.O. Box 490, Sault Ste. Marie, Ontario, Canada P6A5M7
e-mail: bcampbel@nrn1.NRCan.gc.ca

Jobs? Yes
- Cost to post jobs: Free
- Cost to see jobs: Free
- Specialty: Science/Weeds & Dirt
- Industry: Agriculture
- Location: Int'l./Canada/US

Resumes? No
- Cost to post resumes: N/A
- Cost to see resumes: N/A

Feature(s)? N/A

Career Advice? No

Weed Jobs is sprouting positions for scientists, post doctoral and graduate students who are studying different areas of weeds and soil. Talk about a niche site! Some very large corporations have posted positions here. A service of Canadian Forest Service.

Westech's Virtual Job Fair

www.vjf.com

(Job Fair)
Bill Lennan, Westech
4701 Patrick Henry Drive #1901, Santa Clara, CA 95054
408-970-8800 Fax: 408-980-5103 e-mail: webmaster@vjf

Jobs? Yes
• Cost to post jobs: Fee
• Cost to see jobs: Free
• Specialty: IT
• Industry: All
• Location: US

Resumes? Yes
• Cost to post resumes: Free
• Cost to see resumes: Fee

Feature(s)? Search by State

Career Advice? No

Westech is one of the largest job fair promoters in the US. It also combines a huge print publication with each of it's events. Mainly a West coast operation, Westech was acquired by an Arizona publisher in 1997 and then bought an East coast job fair company (Target Career Fair) several months later. Job seekers can register their resume confidentially if they choose. Jobs are listed from corporations in many different states. This group will be the one to watch as the job fair market is reinvented during the next year or two.

Western New York Jobs

www.wnyjobs.com./#anchor263367

(Publisher/Newspaper)
WNY JOBS Weekly
36 Buffalo Street, Hamburg, NY 14075
716-648-5627 Fax: 716-648-5658 e-mail: wnyjobs@buffnet.net

Jobs? Yes
• Cost to post jobs: Fee
• Cost to see jobs: Free
• Specialty: All
• Industry: All
• Location: US/E/NY

Resumes? No
• Cost to post resumes: N/A
• Cost to see resumes: N/A

Feature(s)? N/A

Career Advice? No

Publisher of Western NY Jobs Weekly newspaper (Buffalo, Rochester, Niagara Falls and Jamestown, NY) lists classified positions on this website. Also provides list of links to area employers.

Wet Feet Press

www.wetfeet.com

(Commercial)
Wet Feet Press, Inc.
800-926-4502 Fax: 415-826-1750 e-mail: orders@wetfeet.com

Jobs? Yes
• Cost to post jobs: Fee
• Cost to see jobs: Free
• Specialty: All
• Industry: All
• Location: US/E/NY

Resumes? No
• Cost to post resumes: N/A
• Cost to see resumes: N/A

Feature(s)? Push to Applicant, Career Mgm't.

Career Advice? No

Career management information for a price with a long list of links to major corporations. Articles on working for venture capital firms, for the big six are examples of their work. Seems to give an in-depth analysis of some interesting topics, (you can only see a profile of the article) but for $25 a pop...

Who

www.perc.net/who.html

(Commercial)
Positive Employee Relations Council
e-mail: dkalish@perc.net

Jobs? No
• Cost to post jobs: N/A
• Cost to see jobs: N/A
• Specialty: Human Resources
• Industry: All
• Location: US

Resumes? No
• Cost to post resumes: N/A
• Cost to see resumes: N/A

Feature(s)? RKB Links

Career Advice? No

Who has links to numerous vendors for human resource products. Some interesting things here but that is all there is.

Windows NT Resource Center

(Commercial)
Dave Baker, Beverly Hills Software
8845 W. Olympic Blvd., Suite 200, Beverly Hills, CA 90211
310-358-8311 Fax: 310-358-0326 e-mail: webadsales@bhs.com

Jobs? Yes
- Cost to post jobs: Free
- Cost to see jobs: Free
- Specialty: IT/Windows NT Users
- Industry: All
- Location: US

Resumes? Yes
- Cost to post resumes: Free
- Cost to see resumes: Free

Feature(s)? N/A

Career Advice? No

Windows NT Resource Center is an active site for professionals with these skills. Resumes and jobs are posted for free for but you will need to register to gain access. Recruiters can search resumes by topic or by region. Split screen has been improved since our last visit and information is easily accessible.

Wisconsin Job Net

167.218.251.8/jobnet

(Government)
Marty Shannon, Dept. of Workforce Development
201 E. Washington, P.O. Box 7946, Madison, WI 53707-7946
608-266-0488 e-mail: shannm@mail.state.wi.us

Jobs? Yes
• Cost to post jobs: Free
• Cost to see jobs: Free
• Specialty: All
• Industry: All
• Location: US/MW/WI

Resumes? No
• Cost to post resumes: N/A
• Cost to see resumes: N/A

Feature(s)? N/A

Career Advice? Yes

The Badger state does an excellent job of providing information for the job seeker. Site is well thought out and this is one of the few state employment services that provides direct employer contact information. It also will advise you if the opening is located on a public transportation route. Map of the state allows you to click on the region where you are searching for employment. A search engine allows you to look for job titles or names of employers. Dozens of links to other organizations who can assist job seekers with finding employment. Site is a model that should be used by other government agencies.

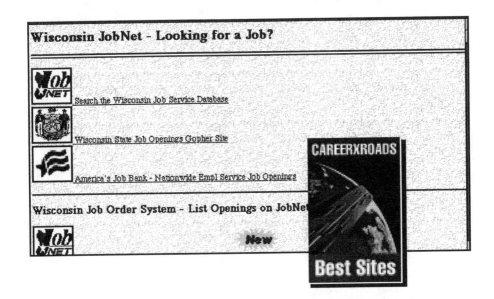

Women in Computer Science & Engineering

www.mit.edu:8001/people/sorokin/women/index.html

(Association/Diversity)
MIT
e-mail: sorokin@mit.edu

Jobs? Yes
- Cost to post jobs: Free
- Cost to see jobs: Free
- Specialty: IT/Engineering
- Industry: All
- Location: US

Resumes? No
- Cost to post resumes: N/A
- Cost to see resumes: N/A

Feature(s)? Diversity

Career Advice? Yes

Interesting list of links for women in computer science and engineering fields. Lots of informational links to non-job related content for women. A few jobs are shown.

Women in Higher Education

www.itis.com/wihe/

(Publisher/Trade)
Mary Zenke, Wenniger Company
1934 Monroe Street, Madison, Wisconsin 53711
608-251-3232 Fax: 608-284-0601 e-mail: women@wihe.com

Jobs? Yes
- Cost to post jobs: Fee
- Cost to see jobs: Free
- Specialty: Teaching
- Industry: Higher Education
- Location: US

Resumes? No
- Cost to post resumes: N/A
- Cost to see resumes: N/A

Feature(s)? N/A

Career Advice? Yes

You can reach 12,000 women who work or have aspirations for the field of education. Recruiters will pay $360 and up to be in their monthly publication with the web site thrown in. Positions are grouped by title from president, vp, dean, faculty and "other" opportunities.

Women in Technology & Industry-WITI

www.witi.com

(Association)
David Leighton, Int'l Network of Women in Technology
4641 Burnet Ave., Sherman Oaks, CA 91403
818-990-6705 Fax: 818-906-3299 e-mail: dave@witi.com

Jobs?
- Cost to post jobs: Fee
- Cost to see jobs: Free
- Specialty: All/Executive
- Industry: All
- Location: Int'l/US

Resumes?
- Cost to post resumes: N/A
- Cost to see resumes: N/A

Feature(s)? Push to Applicant, Diversity

Career Advice? Yes

Women in International Technology & Industry is a non-profit organization founded in 1989 and continues to be one of the top sites on the web. This organization is dedicated to increasing the number of women in executive roles, helping women become more financially independent, technology-literate and to encourage young women to choose careers in science and technology. With it's search engine you can view numerous topics from career management to leadership assistance. Many top FORTUNE 500 corporations have posted profiles and linked their positions to this site. You can subscribe to their classified job center where the site will e-mail you it's latest job postings. Managerial level and above positions should be posted here as this site has gained enormous visibility in the last year and we believe it will continue to do so in the future.

Women's Connection Online

(Association)
e-mail: sdefife@ibm.net

Jobs? No
- Cost to post jobs: N/A
- Cost to see jobs: N/A
- Specialty: All
- Industry: All
- Location: US

Resumes? No
- Cost to post resumes: N/A
- Cost to see resumes: N/A

Feature(s)? Diversity

Career Advice? Yes

Women's Connection Online has created a center for individuals to obtain career information and discuss any topic they choose. A chatroom is available with an online newsletter. A membership directory will available soon. Networking could not be easier and, if you are female and cybersavvy, bookmark and visit often.

Work Avenue

(Publisher/Newspaper)
Jamie Flaws, Star Tribune
42 Portland Avenue, Minneapolis, MN 55488
612-673-9012

Jobs? Yes
- Cost to post jobs: Fee
- Cost to see jobs: Free
- Specialty: All
- Industry: All
- Location: US/MW/MN

Resumes? Yes
- Cost to post resumes: Free
- Cost to see resumes: Fee

Feature(s)? N/A

Career Advice? Yes

You might think you're at the classifieds of a major paper. Nah, although the Minneapolis Star Tribune is one of the partners of this regional job and resume site, you won't find thousands of jobs listed here (There were fewer than 400 positions listed in early May-1997). The cost is right on the money though. Just $35 to post a job - but there is a catch. WorkAvenue uses it's technology to match an employers posted position with existing resumes and make them available to the recruiter for only $100 each. Fortunately, you only pay for the ones you choose. We understand this model is undergoing re-engineering. Maybe somebody noticed that they are competing with their own print product.

Work OnLine Network Systems

www.wons.com

(Commercial)
Wons K. Lee
38-2608 Whiteley, North Vancouver, BC, Canada V7J2R6
604-985-6746 Fax: 604-985-1623 e-mail: feedback@wons.com

Jobs? Yes
- Cost to post jobs: Free
- Cost to see jobs: Free
- Specialty: All
- Industry: All
- Location: US/Canada

Resumes?
- Cost to post resumes: N/A
- Cost to see resumes: N/A

Feature(s)? Push to Applicant

Career Advice? No

WONS is free to post openings or see the niche jobs that are available from here for US and Canada locations. WONS has the ability to send you an e-mail and advise you when openings occur that may be of interest when you register. Fascinating.

Workforce Online

www.workforceonline.com

(Publisher/Trade)

Jobs? Yes
- Cost to post jobs: Fee
- Cost to see jobs: Free
- Specialty: Human Resources
- Industry: All
- Location: US

Resumes? No
- Cost to post resumes: Free
- Cost to see resumes: Fee

Feature(s)? Push to Applicant

Career Advice? Yes

Workforce Online appears to be a partnership with E-Span and the Monster Board as both allow you to post positions... but we are not sure where they will be posted. Site has been set up for HR Professionals. The HR tip of the day, a Research Center and a legal Q&A make this a site you will want to visit. Recruiters pay $150 to post on one side of the house and $95 on the E-Span side. Job seekers (600 jobs posted) can have positions e-mailed directly to them once they register and put their resume online. Will your resume then be in the Monster's belly? You should check.

Workplace

galaxy.einet.net/galaxy/Community/Workplace.html

(Commercial)
TradeWave Corporation
e-mail: galaxy@tradewave.com

Jobs? No
• Cost to post jobs: N/A
• Cost to see jobs: N/A
• Specialty: All
• Industry: All
• Location: US

Resumes? No
• Cost to post resumes: N/A
• Cost to see resumes: N/A

Feature(s)? JSK/Links

Career Advice? No

Workplace provides links to dozens of sites, but the most interesting are the links to university and college job listings. Many employers are posting to school websites trying to attract alumni. This site is trying to capitalize on this service and should be commended for it.

World Hire

www.world.hire.com

(Commercial)
Hank Stringer, World Hire
6101 Balcones Drive, Suite 201, Austin, TX 78731
800-953-4473 Fax: 512-418-8851 e-mail: sales@world.hire.com

Jobs? Yes
• Cost to post jobs: Fee
• Cost to see jobs: Free
• Specialty: All
• Industry: All
• Location: US

Resumes? Yes
• Cost to post resumes: Free
• Cost to see resumes: Fee

Feature(s)? Virtual Job Fair

Career Advice? Yes

World hire provides an interesting concept as it allows employers to go online for virtual recruiting job fairs. The site advertises a date and the time and the employer communicates in real time with prospective candidates via e-mail. Employers can post unlimited positions for 3 months for $2,500 which includes searching their resume database. Job seekers can post a secure profile and when an employer has an interest, they will receive a direct e-mail. Site is also in the software business for intranets and e-mail access of resumes for corporations.

World Wide Job Seekers

www.cban.com/resume/

(Commercial)
Andrew Stanley-Jones
e-mail: webmaster@cban.com

Jobs?
- Cost to post jobs: N/A
- Cost to see jobs: N/A
- Specialty: Finance
- Industry: All
- Location: US

Resumes?
- Cost to post resumes: Free
- Cost to see resumes: Free

Feature(s)? N/A

Career Advice? No

World Wide Job Seekers is a resume database specializing in the financial and accounting areas. Price is right. Candidates listed are from entry level to CFO.

Yahoo Classifieds

classifieds.yahoo.com/employment.html

(Commercial)
Yahoo
408-731-3300

Jobs? Yes
- Cost to post jobs: Free
- Cost to see jobs: Free
- Specialty: All
- Industry: All
- Location: Int'l/US

Resumes? No
- Cost to post resumes: N/A
- Cost to see resumes: N/A

Feature(s)? Search by State

Career Advice? No

Yahoo is the site that everyone is watching in the job and recruitment marketplace. Employers post jobs for free. From here, Yahoo can distribute company openings to 24 major cities. One of the few sites where you know the stats on the traffic at the site is not all hype. It does take longer than it should to drill down to the job level and employers posting an opening will not find it user friendly. Still, Yahoo is definitely worth an experiment.

Youth@Work

www.youthatwork.org/

(Non-Profit)
Larry Pitchford, NOVA Private Industry Council
408-522-9845 Fax: 408-522-9850 e-mail: youth@novapic.org

Jobs? Yes
- Cost to post jobs: Fee
- Cost to see jobs: Free
- Specialty: College
- Industry: All
- Location: US

Resumes? No
- Cost to post resumes: N/A
- Cost to see resumes: N/A

Feature(s)? N/A

Career Advice? No

Youth@Work's primary objective is to link job-seeking youths and hiring managers throughout Santa Clara and San Mateo Counties in California. With simple buttons that state "Hire Me" or "Work for Me" this site almost has its act together. There are over 900 jobs posted in all categories from temporary to full time openings. Search engine works well but all jobs are coded and you have to contact a Youth@Work Office by telephone to obtain additional information. We thought this would be a sure winner but they just do not get the power of the web.

BEST OF THE BEST

The sites below are a diverse lot. They include large career hubs and small niche sites. What they have in common is a blend of insight and timing which has allowed each to stand out in their own way. Content, navigation, marketing strategy and other factors described earlier contributed to our selection of these sites as the best of the best we've seen. There are at least as many new sites with "BOB" potential.

4Work
    www.4work.com
AboutWork
    www.aboutwork.com
American Journ. Review Online
    www.newslink.org/joblink.html
America's Employers
    www.americasemployers.com
America's Job Bank
    www.ajb.dni.us
America's Talent Bank
    www.atb.org
Asia-Net
    www.asia-net.com
Branch Out
    www.branchout.com
CareerBuilder
    www.careerbuilder.com
CareerMagazine
    www.careermag.com
CareerMosaic
    www.careermosaic.com
CareerPath
    www.careerpath.com
CareerSite
    www.careersite.com
CollegeCentral Network
    www..collegecentral.com
CoolWorks
    www.coolworks.com/showme/
DICE
    www.dice.com
E•Span
    www.espan.com
Hard@Work
    www.hardatwork.com
HeadHunter .NET
    www.HeadHunter.NET/

Heart
    www.career.com
I-Search
    www.isearch.com
IntelliMatch
    www.intellimatch.com
Internet Job Locator
    www.joblocator.com
JobDirect
    www.jobdirect.com
JobNet.com
    www.jobnet.com
JobWeb
    www.jobweb.org/
Mercury Center Web
    www.sjmercury.com
MonsterBoard
    www.monster.com
NationJob Network
    www.nationjob.com
Net Temps
    www.net-temps.com
Online Career Center
    www.occ.com
SHRM HR Jobs
    www.shrm.org
Talent Alliance
    www.talentalliance.com
Town Online
    www.townonline.com/working
Washington Post-Career Post
    www.washingtonpost.com/wp-adv/
    classifieds/career
Wisconsin Job Net
    167.218.251.8/jobnet
Women in Technology & Industry-WITI
    www.witi.com

Many of today's sites are offering career management and job hunting tips. Here are the sites we think have the most to offer. You be the judge on what works for you.

AAA Resume Service
www.infi.net/~resume
About Work
www.aboutwork.com
Acorn Career Counseling
www.acornresume.com
American Physical Therapy Assoc.
//.apta.edoc.com
Brave New World
www.newwork.com
Career Action Center
www.careeraction.org/CACpublic/intro
Career Counseling Lite
www.execpc.com/~cclite/
Career Crafting
www.careercraft.com
Career Doctor
www.career-doctor.com
Career Lab
www.careerlab.com
Career Mosaic
www.careermosaic.com
Career Talk
www.careertalk.com
Career Toolbox
www.careertoolbox.com
College Connection
www.careermosaic.com/cm/cc/cc1.html
Entry Level Job Seeker Assistant
//.members.aol.com/Dylander/jobhome
Finding and Getting a Job
//.edie.cprost.sfu.ca/~gophers/find
Getting Past Go: A Survival Guide for College
www.lattanze.loyola.edu/:80/mongen/home

Global Job Net
//.riceinfo.rice.edu/projects/careers
Heart
www.career.com
Internet Career Interest Assesment
www-personal.ksu.edu/~dangle/icia/
Job Security
www.jobsecurity.com
Job Web
www.jobweb.org/
Learning@Living
www.living-icic.com
My Future
www.myfuture.com
National Business Employment Weekly
www.nbew.com
The National (Int'l) Home Workers Assoc.
www.homeworkers.com
Online Career Center
www.occ.com
Parksville/Qualicum Career Center
//.qb.island.net/~careers/
Peterson's Education Center
www.petersons.com
Resumania On-line
www.umn.edu/ohr/ecep/resume
Student Center
//.studentcenter.com
Talent Alliance
www.talentalliance.com
Virtual Interviewing Assistant
www.ukans.edu/cwis/units/coms2/via/index

COLLEGE

College seniors looking to get a fast start in their career are exploring the sites that emphasize entry level professional opportunites. The sites below are all vying for the college marketplace. Employers who research the career planning web pages of their targeted colleges will have an additional competitive edge if they negotiate directly for banners and links.

4.0 Resumes and Job Listings
www.4pt0.com/index.html
Ad Guide
www.adguide.com/
Allcampus Internet
www.allcampus.com
Best Bets for Summer Abroad
www.cie.uci.edu/~cie/staff/index
BridgePath Employment Services
www.bridgepath.com
College Central Network
www.collegecentral.com
College Connection
www.careermosaic.com/cm/cc/cc1
College Grad Job Hunter
www.collegegrad.com
College Net
www.collegenet.com
College News Online
www.collegenews.com
Cool Works
www.coolworks.com/showme/
Cultural Human Resource Council
www.culturenet.ca/chrc/ehpchrc
Entry Level Job Seeker Assistant
//.members.aol.com/Dylander/jobhome
Getting A Job
www.americanexpress.com/student/
Getting Past Go: A Survival Guide for College
www.lattanze.loyola.edu/:80/mongen/home
Global Job Net
riceinfo.rice.edu/projects/careers
Great Summer Jobs
www.greatsummerjobs.com

Hire Wire
www.hirewire.com
Job Direct
www.jobdirect.com
Job Source Careers for College Grads
www.jobsource.com/
JOB TRAK
www.jobtrak.com
Job Web
www.jobweb.org/
Main Quad
www.mainquad.com
MBA Central
www.mbacentral.com
MBA Employment Connection Assoc.
www.mbanetwork.com/meca
My Future
www.myfuture.com
Online Directory of Internships in Youth Dev.
www.nassembly.org
Peterson's Education Center
www.petersons.com
Quest Match
www.decisivequest.com
Student Center
studentcenter.com
Summer Jobs
www.summerjobs.com
Top Jobs on the Net
www.topjobs.net
USM Resources for G/L/B Students
//.macweb.acs.usm.maine.edu/csce/career_glb
Web Dog's Job Hunt:The Best Jobs
www.itec.sfsu.edu/students/projects/jschwartz
Youth@Work
www.youthatwork.org/

Diversity sites involved in the employment process are meking themselves felt on the net. The sites below are all involved.

Africa Online Jobs
www.AfricaOnline.com/AfricaOnl
Afro-Americ@: The Job Vault
www.afroam.org/information/vau
Arizona Careers Online
diversecity.com/jobs.html
Asian Career Web
www.rici.com/acw
Asia-Net
www.asia-net.com
Association for Women in Computing
www.halcyon.com/awc/
The Black Collegian Online
www.blackcollegian.com
Black Data Processing Assoc. Online
www.bdpa.org
Black E.O.E Journal
www.usa-ca.com/blk_eoe_jrnl
Career Center for Workforce Diversity
www.eop.com
Career China
www.globalvillager.com/village
Career Magazine
www.careermag.com
Career Mosaic
www.careermosaic.com
Careers On-Line
www.disserv.stu.umn.edu/COL/index
CLNET
//.latino.sscnet.ucla.edu/
Diversity Careers Online
www.diversitycareers.com
E Span
www.espan.com
El Nueuvo Herald Digital
www.elherald.com

Forty Plus (Northern Calif.)
//.web.sirius.com/~40plus/#contact
Frasernet
www.frasernet.com
Hispanic Network Magazine
//.members.aol.com/hnmagazine/index
Interesting Web Sites
//.go4win.com
Job Accommodation Network (JAN)
www.jan.wvu.edu/english/homeus.htm
Job Search Strategies
www.vjf.com/pub/docs/jobsearch.html
Job Web
www.jobweb.org/
Latino Web
www.catalog.com/favision/latnoweb
Minorities Job Bank
www.minorities-jb.com
National Diversity Journalism Job Bank
www.newsjobs.com
National Society of Black Engineers
www.nsbe.com
Saludos Web
www.saludos.com
SC WIST Work Pathfinder
www.harbour.sfu.ca/scwist/pathfinder/index\
USM Resources for G/L/B Students
macweb.acs.usm.maine.edu/csce/career_glb
Women in Computer Science & Eng.
www.mit.edu:8001/people/sorokin/women/index
Women in Technology & Industry-WITI
www.witi.com
Women's Connection Online
www.womenconnect.com

Collected below are niche sites specializing in one discipline or industry. You'll be amazed at who is really out on the net.

SPECIALTY

-Advertising/Graphic Arts-
Adweek Online
Oasys Network
Talent Hunter
Creative Freelancers Online

-Airline Pilots-
Aviation Employee Placement Service
Corporate Aviation Resume Exchange

-Broadcast News/Journalism-
Television & Radio News Research

-Driver/Trucking-
Layover
Loading Zone

-Engineering-
Engineering Job Source
Engineering Jobs
Society of Women Engineers
National Society of Black Engineers
  -Engineering/Aerospace-
Space Jobs
  -Engineering/Agricultural-
American Soc. of Agricultural Eng.
  -Engineering/Civil/Design-
Engineering News Record
  -Engineering/Design-
Pro/E Job Network
  -Engineering/Electrical/Electronic-
IEEE
Electronic News OnLine
  -Engineering/Instrumentation & Control-
ISA Classifieds
  -Engineering/Packaging-
Food and Drug Packaging Online
  -Engineering/PE-
National Society of Professional Eng
  -Engineering/Power-
Electric Power NewsLink

-Environmental-
American Water Works Association
Environmental Careers World
  -Environmental/Internship-
The Environmental Careers Organization
  -Environmental/Water-
Employment Opportunities in Water Resources

-Executive-
Imcor Provides Top-Level Executive
Execubank
Stern Alumni Outreach Career Resources
NACUBO
Wall Street Journal Interactive Edition
Women in Technology & Industry-WITI
Netshare

-Finance-
World Wide Job Seekers
  -Finance/Accounting-
Accounting Net
American Assoc. of Fin & Accounting
Quest Match
  -Finance/Banking-
ExecuBank
  -Finance/Business
100 Careers in Wall Street
Wall Street Journal
Careers in Management Consulting
Business Job Listing
  -Finance/Executive-
Fin Career Global Financial Careers
  -Finance/Wall Street-
Bloomberg Online

-Finishing-
Finishing.com

-Health Care-
Future Med
Health Careers Online
Health Opps
Healthcare Careers
Med Hunters

Hospital Web
  -Health Care/Allied Health-
Allied Health Opportunities Directory
  -Health Care/MD-
EmployMed
Emergency Medicine Practice Opportunity
Med Connect
Medical Jobs
Doctor Link
Physician Recruit Net
Physicians Employment
New England Journal of Medicine
  -Health Care/MD/Emergency Room-
Ed Physician
  -Health Care/Nursing/OR-
Perioperative Online Employment Opps
  -Health Care/Physical Therapy-
American Physical Therapy Assoc.
  -Health Care/Physician/Research-
Academic Physician & Scientist

  -Hospitality-
Penton Publishing's Career Link

  -Household/Caretaker-
Au Pair in Europe

  -Human Resources-
HR World
HRCOMM
IPMA HR Job Pool
PHRC Job Opps
SHRM HR Jobs
Workforce Online
  -Human Resources/Benefits-
IFEBP Online
Benefits Link
  -Human Resources/HRIS-
HRIM Mall
International HRIM
  -Human Resources/T&D-
Training Net
  -Human Resources/T&D, ER, HRIS-
Training SuperSite Job Bank

  -Insurance-
Insurance Career Center

  -IT-
ACM
Association for Women in Computing
Black Data Processing Assoc. Online
Career Command Center
Career Exchange
Career NET (Career/NET)
Software Contractors' Guild
Chicago Software Newspaper
Atlanta ComputerJobs Store
Computer World's IT Careers
Contract Employment Connection
Contract Employment NACCB
Contract Employment Weekly
DICE
NC World Magazine
Future Tech Careers
HeadHunter .NET
Hot Jobs
Ingram Recruiting Solutions
Job Lynx
Job Navigator
Job Serve: IT Vacancies in the UK
Jobs Jobs Jobs
Multimedia Jobs (UI-Design Jobs)
NAACB Job Board and Resume Bank
America's Online Help Wanted
Omicron Personal Career Center
Pro Net Search
Recruit '97
Silicon Valley Technical Employ. Agencies
TechWeb/TechCareers/TechHunter
US Job Network Hi-Tech Job & Resume Bank
Westech's Virtual Job Fair
  -IT/Academic-
ACM's Sigmod's Database Job Openings
  -IT/Client Server-
Infoworld
  -IT/Engineering-
Electronic Engineering Times
Women in Computer Science & Eng.
Quest Match

-IT/Geographic Systems-
GeoWeb for GIS/GPS/RS
-IT/Graphics/Communications-
ICS NY Job Listings
-IT/Internet-
Internet.com
-IT/JAVA-
Java World
-IT/Macintosh-
Macintosh Employment Registry
-IT/Multimedia-
MMWire Online
BAMTA
New Media Assoc. of NJ
-IT/Multimedia/Graphic Arts-
DesignSphere Online
-IT/Network/IS Management-
Network World Fusion
-IT/New Media-
Web Jobs USA
-IT/RS 6000-
RS/6000 Employment Page
-IT/University-
Computer Science Jobs in Academia
-IT/Web-
100 Careers in Cyberspace
-IT/Web-
Cyberspace Jobs
-IT/Web-
Web Developer's Virtual Library
-IT/Windows NT Users-
Windows NT Resource Center
-IT/WWW/Communications-
Association of Online Professionals
-IT & NonExempt-
Super Site

-Journalism-
American Journalism Review Online
California Job Bank
Journalism-Related Jobs
National Diversity Journalism Job Bank

-Law-
Law Employment Center

Seamless Website, The
-Law/Paralegal-
National Paralegal Reporter

-Leasing-
Equipment Leasing Association Online

-Marketing-
Direct Marketing World Job Center
Marketing Classifieds

-Mortuary-
Funeral Net

-Public Health-
Career Espresso/Emory University

-Purchasing-
Purchasing NAPM

-QA/QC-
American Society for Quality

-Radio-
Radio Frame

-Real Estate-
Real Bank
-Real Estate Agent-
Real Jobs

-Restaurant/Chefs-
Star Chefs
Escoffier On Line

-Science
Cell Press Online
SC WIST Work Pathfinder
Science Global Career Network
-Science/Agriculture-
Agricultural Job Listings
-Science/Agriculture-
ATI-Net
-Science/Astronomy-
American Astronomical Society

-Science/Biology-
Bio Online: Life on the 'Net
BioSpace Career Center
SciWeb - The Life Science Home Page
-Science/Biomedical-
Med Search
-Science/Biomedical/Genetics-
Biomedical Positions
-Science/BioTech-
Nature Biotechnology
-Science/Chemistry-
Academic Chem. Employ. Clearinghouse
American Chemical Society Job Bank
PolySort
-Science/Chemistry/Pharmaceutical-
Medzilla
-Science/Crystallography-
Crystallography Worldwide
-Science/Mathematics-
e Math
-Science/Mathematics/Teaching-
NCTM Jobs Online
-Science/Medical Devices-
Medical Device Link
-Science/Medicine-
Nature-Medicine
-Science/Optical Physics-
SPIE's Employment Center
-Science/Pharmaceuticals-
Pharmaceuticals Jobs Today
-Science/Physics-
AIP Physics Careers Bulletin Board
-Science/Physics-
Plasma Laboratory Wis
-Science/Weeds & Dirt-
Weed Jobs

-Sports-
Online Sports Career Center
-Sports Coaching/Football-
Coach's Nationwide Job Board
-Sports/Outdoors/College-
Cool Works
-Education/Administration-

-Teaching/Education/Admin-
Academic Employment Network
Chronicle of Higher Education
Educator's Network EDNET
Job Search Academic Links
Jobs in Higher Education
National Educators Employment Review
Education Job Marketplace
O Hayo Sensei
Project Connect
Women in Higher Education
-Teaching/Academic Research-
Academic Position Network
-Teaching/Administration-
Academe This Week
-Teaching/Education/Executive-
NACUBO

-Technical Writing-
Technical Writers to the Rescue

-Telecommuting-
Telecommuting, Telework & Alt. Officing
Telecommuting Jobs

INDUSTRY/Supplemental

-Construction-
Building Industry Exchange
Engineering News Record
National Society of Professional Eng.

-Education/Teaching/Univ. Research-
Academic Employment Network
Academic Position Network
Biomedical Positions
College Net
NCTM Jobs Online
e Math
Job Search Academic Links
Jobs in Higher Education
NACUBO
Education Job Marketplace

O Hayo Sensei
Plasma Laboratory Wis
Project Connect
Women in Higher Education
  -Education/HS & College-
Coach's Nationwide Job Board
  -Education/K-12-
Educator's Network EDNET
  -Education/University-
Academe This Week
Academic Chemistry Employment Clearing-
  house
ACM's Sigmod's Database Job Openings
American Astronomical Society
Chronicle of Higher Education
Computer Science Jobs in Academia
Crystallography Worldwide

  -Entertainment/Acting-
Airwaves Media Web
Auditions Online
Creative Freelancers Online
Casting Net
Hollywood Web
Job X Change Coolest Jobs on the Planet
Airwaves Media Web
Antenna's Internet Broadcast Jobs
Radio Frame
Show Biz Jobs
Talent Works: The Online Casting Source
TV Jobs

  -Food/Bakery-
Bakery Net

  -Funeral-
Funeral Net

  -Government-
Abag Globe
Federal Job Announcement Search
Federal Jobs Digest

IPMA HR Job Pool

  -Hospitality-
Escoffier On Line - Employment Re-
  sources
  -Hospitality-
Hospitality Net
  -Hospitality-
Star Chefs
  -Insurance-
Insurance Career Center
  -Journalism-
Journalism-Related Jobs
  -Legal-
Law Employment Center
  -Legal-
National Paralegal Reporter
  -Manufacturing-
Finishing.com
  -Manufacturing-
Food and Drug Packaging Online
  -Maritime-
International Seafarers Exchange
  -Military-
Navy
  -Military-
US Air Force Employment Home Page
  -Music-
Music Pages
  -Non-Profit-
Community Career Center
  -Non-Profit-
Good Works
  -Non-Profit-
Impact Online
  -Non-Profit-
Online Directory of Internships in Youth
  Dev.
  -Non-Profit-
The Nonprofit/Fundraising Jobnet
  -Publications-
California Job Bank
  -Publishing-

American Journalism Review Online

-Publishing-
National Diversity Journalism Job Bank

-Real Estate-
Real Bank
 -Real Estate-
Real Jobs

 -Recreation-
Great Summer Jobs
 -Recreation/Hospitality-
Cool Works

 -Retail-
Supermarket News
 -Retail/Recreation-
Online Sports Career Center

 -Rubber and Plastics-
PolySort

 -Science-
Science Global Career Network

 -Transportation; Int'l Bus.-
Global Careers

 -Trucking-
Layover
Loading Zone

 -Utility/Power-
Electric Power NewsLink

 -Water-
American Water Works Association
Employ. Opps in Water Resources

JOBS

All the jobs for free and for a fee. These databases have as few as 1 and as many as 500,000 openings listed. No, we didn't include the newsgroups here- see the related article in the section of articles for recruiters and jobseekers.

Post Jobs for FREE

4.0 Resumes and Job Listings
Abag Globe
Academic Chem. Employment Clearinghouse
ACM's Sigmod's Database Job Openings
Africa Online Jobs
Agricultural Job Listings
Airline Employment Ass't. Corps
Airwaves Media Web
American Journalism Review Online
American Water Works Association
America's Job Bank
Antenna's Internet Broadcast Jobs
Association of Online Professionals
ATI-Net
Auditions Online
Aviation Employee Placement Service
Bakery Net
BAMTA
Best Bets for Summer Abroad
Biomedical Positions
Boldface Jobs
Building Industry Exchange
Business Job Listing
Career File
Career NET (Career/NET)
Careers On-Line
CLNET
Computer Science Jobs in Academia
Creative Freelancers Online
Crystallography Worldwide
DesignSphere Online
Direct Marketing World Job Center
Doctor Link
Drake Beam Morin
Eastern & European JobBank
Ed Physician
Employment Opp. in Water Resources
Engineering Jobs
The Environmental Careers Organization
Escoffier On Line - Employ. Resources

Execubank
Exec-U-Net
Finishing.com
Funeral Net
Get Me A Job
HeadHunter .NET
Hospitality Net
HR World
HRIM Mall
ICS NY Job Listings
Impact Online
Info Louisiana
Int'l. Human Resource Information
Job Search Academic Links
Job Vault
Jobs in Higher Education
Journalism-Related Jobs
Latino Web
Multimedia Jobs (UI-Design Jobs)
National Diversity Journalism Job Bank
National Educators Employment Review
Needle In Cyberstack
Netshare
New Media Assoc. of NJ
NJ Job Search
Online Directory of Internships in Youth
Pharmaceuticals Jobs Today
PHRC Job Opps
Plasma Laboratory Wis
Potpourri Shoppers
Project Connect
Purchasing NAPM
Real Jobs
Recruitex Technologies
Right Management Consultants, Inc.
RS/6000 Employment Page
SEACnet Southeastern Atlantic Coast Care
Seamless Website, The
Siam Net
Society of Women Engineers

Star Chefs
St. Thomas Human Resource Centre
Talent Hunter
Training Net
Web Developer's Virtual Library
Weed Jobs
Windows NT Resource Center
Wisconsin Job Net
Women in Computer Science & Engineering
Yahoo Classifieds

Post Jobs for a FEE

100 Careers in Cyberspace
100 Careers in Wall Street
4 Work
Academe This Week
Academic Employment Network
Academic Physician & Scientist
Academic Position Network
Accounting Net
ACM
Ad Guide
Ad One Classified Network
Ad Search
Adia
Adweek Online
Afro-Americ@: The Job Vault
Agri Careers
AIP Physics Careers Bulletin Board
Allied Health Opportunities Directory
American Assoc. of Fin & Accounting
American Astronomical Society
American Chemical Society Job Bank
America's Employers
America's Online Help Wanted
America's TV Job Network
Americn Society for Quality
Anchorage Daily News
Appointments Section
Arizona Careers Online
Asian Career Web

Asia-Net
Atlanta ComputerJobs Store
Augusta Chronicle
Benefits Link
Best Jobs U.S.A.
Bilingual-Jobs
Bio Online: Life on the 'Net
BioSpace Career Center
The Black Collegian Online
Bloomberg Online
Boston Globe
Boston Herald Job Find
Boston Job Bank
Branch Out
BridgePath Employment Services
California Career and Employment Center
California Job Bank
Career America
Career Board
Career Builder
Career Center for Workforce Diversity
Career China
Career City
Career Command Center
Career Doctor
Career Exchange
Career Exposure
Career Finder
Career Internetworking
Career Link USA
Career Magazine
Career Mart
Career Mosaic
Career Opportunities in Singapore
Career Path
Career Shop
Career Site
Career Spot, The
Career Web
Carolina Career Center
Cell Press Online
Chase Pro
Chattanooga Publishing
Chicago Software Newspaper

JOBS

Chicago Sun Times
Chicago Tribune
Christian Jobs Online
Chronicle of Higher Education
Cincinatti Employment Classifieds
College Central Network
College Connection
College Grad Job Hunter
College News Online
Colorado Jobs Online
Columbus Dispatch
Community Career Center
Computer World's IT Careers
Contract Employment Connection
Contract Employment NACCB
Contract Employment Weekly
Cool Works
Dallas Morning News
Denver Post
DICE
Digital City/South Florida
Diversity Careers Online
e-Math
E•Span
Eagleview
Education Job Marketplace
Educator's Network EDNET
El Nueuvo Herald Digital
Electric Power NewsLink
Electronic Engineering Times
Electronic News OnLine
Emergency Medicine Practice Opp.
Employers Applicant Bank
EmployMed
Employment Channel
Employment Post
Engine Room
Engineering Job Source
Engineering News Record
Environmental Careers World
EPage Greater NYC Classifieds
Equipment Leasing Association Online
ExecuBank
Fin Career Global Financial Careers
Food and Drug Packaging Online

Frasernet
Future Access Employment Guide
Future Business Centre On-Line
Future Resource Systems
Future Tech Careers
The Gate
Get a Job!
Global Careers
Great Summer Jobs
Hartford Courant
HEALTH BANK USA
Health Care Jobs
Health Opps
Healthcare Careers
Heart
Help Wanted
Help Wanted USA
Hong Kong Jobs
Hong Kong Standard
Hot Jobs
Houston Chronicle Interactive
HRCOMM
IEEE
IFEBP Online
Imcor Provides Top-Level Executives
Ingram Recruiting Solutions
InJersey
Insurance Career Center
IntelliMatch
International Pharmajobs
Internet Job Locator
IPMA HR Job Pool
ISA Classifieds
Jaeger's Interactive Career Center
Java World
Job Assistant.com
Job Bank USA
Job Center
Job Direct
Job Navigator
Job Net.com & Online Opportunities
Job Search
Job Serve: IT Vacancies in the UK
Job Source Careers for College Grads
JOB TRAK

Job Web
JobXChange Coolest Jobs on the Planet
Jobs Jobs Jobs
JWT Specialized Communications
Kansas City Star
Knoxville News-Sentinel Online
Law Employment Center
Layover
Lendman's Recruiting Resources
Gateway
Loading Zone
Los Angeles Times
Macintosh Employment Registry
Malaysia Online
Manpower
Marketing Classifieds
MBA Central
MBA Employ. Connection Assoc.
Med Connect
Med Hunters
Med Search
Medical Device Link
Medical Jobs
Medzilla
Mercury Center Web
Metroworld
Milwaukee Journal Sentinel
Minneapolis Star Tribune
Minorities Job Bank
Mississippi Careers Online
MMWire Online
The Monster Board
NAACB Job Board & Resume Bank
NACUBO
Nando Times
National Paralegal Reporter
National Society of Black Engineers
National Soc. of Professional Eng.
The National Home Workers Assoc.
NationJob Network
Nature Biotechnology
Nature-Medicine
NC World Magazine
NCTM Jobs Online
Net Jobs Information Services

Net Temps
Network World Fusion
New England Journal of Medicine
New Haven Register Online
New Jersey Online
New York Times
NJ JOBS
The Nonprofit/Fundraising Jobnet
Norfolk Virginian-Pilot Online
O Hayo Sensei
Online Career Center
Online Sports Career Center
Orlando Sentinel
Passport Access
Penton Publishing's Career Link
Perioperative Online Employ. Opps.
Peterson's Education Center
Physician Recruit Net
Physicians Employment
Pioneer Press
Planet Jobs
PolySort
Princeton 1Info (US 1)
Pro Net Search
Pro/E Job Network
Quest Match
Raleigh Classifieds On-line
Real Bank
Recruit Net
Recruiters Online Network
Resumes on the Web
Roanoke Times Online
Rocky Mountain News
Sacramento Bee
Saludos Web
San Francisco Chronicle
Science Global Career Network
SciWeb - The Life Science Home Page
Seattle Times
Shawn's Internet Resume Center
Show Biz Jobs
SHRM HR Jobs
Singapore On Line
Southern Jobs - Job Digest
Space Jobs

JOBS

SPIE's Employment Center
St. Paul Pioneer Planet
St. Petersburg Times
Summer Jobs
Sunday Paper
Super Site
Supermarket News
Syracuse Online
Tacoma News Tribune
TechWeb/TechCareers/TechHunter
Telecommuting Jobs
Top Jobs on the Net
Top Jobs USA
Town Online

Training SuperSite Job Bank
trans-ACTION
TV Jobs
Twin Cities Job Page
US Job Network Hi-Tech Job & Res. Bank
Wall Street Journal Interactive Edition
Washington Post-Career Post
Westech's Virtual Job Fair
Western New York Jobs
Women in Higher Education
Women in Technology & Industry-WITI
Work Avenue
Workforce Online
World Hire
Youth@Work

Job seekers and recruiters interested in developing their own "best sites" list can link to tens of thousands of additional sites from here.

Allcampus Internet
www.allcampus.com
American Assoc. of Fin & Accounting
www.aafa.com/
American Soc. of Agricultural Eng.
asae.org/jobs
Black Data Processing Assoc. Online
www.bdpa.org
Bullseye Job Shop
interoz.com/usr/gcbristow
Can Work Net
www.hrdc.ingenia.com/cwn/engli
Career Espresso/Emory University
www.sph.emory.edu/studentservices
Career Resource Center
www.careers.org
Career Toolbox
www.careertoolbox.com
Career Transitions
www.bfservs.com:80/bfserv.html
Careers & Jobs
www.starthere.com/jobs
Computer Science Jobs in Academia
www.cs.brandeis.edu:
80/~zippy/academic-cs-jobs
Connect to Jobs
www.cabrillo.cc.ca.us/connect/index
Cyberspace Jobs
www.best.com:80/~lianne/
The Definitive Internet Career Guide
phoenix.placement.oakland.edu/career/Guide
Future Med
ourworld.compuserve.com/homepages/
futuremed/main.
Gordon Group Home Page
www.owt.com/jobsinfo/jobsinfo.htm
Hospital Web
neuro-www.mgh.harvard.edu/
hospitalweb.nclk
Inter Links
www.nova.edu/Inter-Links/employment
Interesting Web Sites
go4win.com
Internet Job Surfer
www.rpi.edu/dept/cdc/jobsurfer/jobw

Job Hunt: On-Line Job Meta-List
www.job-hunt.org
Job Lynx
//.joblynx.com
Job Resources by US Region
www.wm.edu/csrv/career/stualum/
jregion.html#top
Job Search Academic Links
www.bgssu.edu/departments/english/
GSC_MLA/JobSearc
Job Search Strategies
www.vjf.com/pub/docs/jobsearch.html
Links on the Web
www.cob.ohio-state.edu/other/
other.html#jobs
One Net
w3.one.net/~denek/Employ/emp496
Purdue's Job List
www.ups.purdue.edu/student/jobsites
Quintessential Career & Job Hunting Guide
www.stetson.edu/~rhansen/careers.html
Radio Frame
www.mindspring.com/~coleman/radioframe
Recruiting-Links.com
www.recruiting-links.com/
Red Guide to Temporary Agencies
www.best.com/~ezy/redguide/intro.html
The Riley Guide
www.dbm.com/jobguide
RPI Career Resource Home Page
www.rpi.edu/dept/cdc/homepage.html
SenseMedia Job Board
sensemedia.net/getajob/
Silicon Valley Tech. Employment Agencies
www.sease.com/jobs.html
Student Center
//.studentcenter.com
St. Louis Area Companies on the Net
www.st-louis.mo.us/st-louis/companies
Web Dog's Job Hunt:The Best Jobs
www.itec.sfsu.edu/students/projects/jschwartz/
Workplace
galaxy.einet.net/galaxy/Comunity/Workplace

LOCATION

Actually, the job and resume sites NOT listed in this section have openings throughout the US. These sites focus on the geographic areas noted below. To find the best sites in your area, go to a Search Engine like HotBot and type in "City Name" and "Jobs".

INTERNATIONAL

-Int'l.-
Au Pair in Europe
Best Bets for Summer Abroad

-Int'l./Africa-
Africa Online Jobs

-Int'l./Asia/Europe-
International Pharmajobs

-Int'l./Australia-
Cowley Job Centre

-Int'l./Canada-
Can Work Net
Canadian Job Source
Agri Careers
Parksville/Qualicum Career Center
SC WIST Work Pathfinder
St. Thomas Human Resource Centre
Net Jobs Information Services

-Int'l./Canada & US-
Ad One Classified Network
Career Exchange
Get Me A Job
Gordon Group Home Page
Learning@Living
Med Hunters
Pro Net Search
Career Internetworking
Recruitex Technologies
Training SuperSite Job Bank
Weed Jobs
Work OnLine Network Systems

-Int'l./China-
Career China

-Int'l./Europe, Asia-
Bilingual-Jobs

-Int'l./Hong Kong-
Hong Kong Jobs
Hong Kong Standard

-Int'l./Malaysia/Singapore-
Malaysia Online

-Int'l./Singapore-
Career Opportunities in Singapore
Singapore On Line

-Int'l./South Africa-
Job Navigator

-Int'l./Thailand-
Siam Net

-Int'l./UK-
Appointments Section
Engine Room
Job Serve: IT Vacancies in the UK
Execubank
Recruit Net

-Int'l. & US-
ACM's Sigmod's Database Job Openings
Adia
The Monster Board
Asian Career Web
Asia-Net
BioSpace Career Center
Career File
CAREERXROADS
Escoffier On Line
Coach's Nationwide Job Board
Career Mosaic
Career Web

Cell Press Online
Crystallography Worldwide
Engineering News Record
NC World Magazine
Finding A Job
Future Med
Nature-Medicine
Nature Biotechnology
Future Business Centre On-Line
Global Careers
Global Job Net
Global Job Services
Heart
Hoovers
Hospitality Net
Imcor Provides Top-Level Executives
Impact Online
Infoworld
Internet.com
ISA Classifieds
Job Center
Job Security
Jobs in Higher Education
Multimedia Jobs (UI-Design Jobs)
Bloomberg Online
Biomedical Positions
Education Job Marketplace
Future Resource Systems
Star Chefs
O Hayo Sensei
Pharmaceuticals Jobs Today
Physician Recruit Net
Plasma Laboratory Wis
Eastern & European JobBank
Fin Career Global Financial Careers
Pro/E Job Network
Real Jobs
The Riley Guide
Science Global Career Network
Summer Jobs
Technical Writers to the Rescue
Telecommuting, Telework & Alt. Officing
Top Jobs on the Net
Training Net

Web Developer's Virtual Library
Women in Technology & Industry-WITI
Yahoo Classifieds
Manpower
Netshare

ALL STATES
-Sites with Capability to Search by State-

4 Work
Academic Employment Network
Ad One Classified Network
America's Job Bank
America's Talent Bank
Career Magazine
Career Mosaic
Career Path
Coach's Nationwide Job Board
E•Span
Ed Physician
Education Job Marketplace
EmployMed
Healthcare Careers
Heart
Hospital Web
HRCOMM
Job Resources by US Region
Job Web
Jobs in Higher Education
Manpower
Monster Board
National Educators Employment Review
National Paralegal Reporter
National Society of Professional Eng.
Online Career Center
Online Directory of Internships in Youth Dev.
Perioperative Online Employment Opp.
Physicians Employment
Pro/E Job Network
Saludos Web
Westech's Virtual Job Fair
Yahoo Classifieds

LOCATION

EAST COAST

-US/E/CT-
New Haven Register Online
-US/E/CT/Hartford-
Hartford Courant

-US/E/DC-
Washington Post-Career Post

-US/E/MA-
Town Online
-US/E/MA/Boston-
Boston Globe
Boston Herald Job Find
Boston Job Bank

-US/E/NJ-
InJersey
Princeton 1Info (US 1)
New Jersey Online
New Media Assoc. of NJ
NJ Job Search
NJ JOBS

-US/E/NY-
ICS NY Job Listings
Law Employment Center
Western New York Jobs
-US/E/NY/NYC-
100 Careers in Wall Street
Employment Channel
ExecuBank
Red Guide to Temporary Agencies-
Web Jobs USA
New York Times
-US/E/NY/Syracuse-
Syracuse Online

-US/E/PA-
Future Tech Careers
Job Net.com & Online Opportunities

Job Vault
Metroworld
-US/E/PA/Phil.-
Planet Jobs
-US/E/PA(NJ)-
America's TV Job Network

SOUTH EAST

-US/SE-
Medical Jobs
SE Atlantic Coast Career Network
US Job Network High Tech Job
    & Resume Bank

-US/SE/FL-
Digital City/South Florida
-US/SE/FL/Ft. Lauderdale-
Career Spot, The
-US/SE/FL/Miami-
El Nueuvo Herald Digital
-US/SE/FL/Orlando-
Orlando Sentinel
-US/SE/FL/St. Petersburg-
St. Petersburg Times

-US/SE/GA-
Georgia Job Bank
-US/SE/GA/Atlanta-
Atlanta ComputerJobs Store
-US/SE/GA/Augusta-
Augusta Chronicle

-US/SE/NC-
Carolina Career Center
-US/E/NC/Raleigh-
Nando Times
Raleigh Classifieds On-line

-US/E/VA/Norfolk-
Norfolk Virginian-Pilot Online
-US/E/VA/Roanoke-
Roanoke Times Online

MIDWEST

-US/MW-
American Soc. of Agricultural Eng.
Careers in Management Consulting
Engineering Job Source
NationJob Network

-US/MW/IL/Chicago-
Career Finder
Chicago Software Newspaper
Chicago Sun Times
Chicago Tribune-
Pioneer Press

-US/MW/KS-
Kansas Careers

-US/MW/MN-
Careers On-Line
Work Avenue
-US/MW/MN/Minneapolis-
Minneapolis Star Tribune
Twin Cities Job Page
-US/MW/MN/St. Paul-
St. Paul Pioneer Planet

-US/MW/MO/KC-
Kansas City Star
-US/MW/MO/St. Louis-
St. Louis Area Companies on the Net

-US/MW/OH-
Career Board
-US/MW/OH/Cincinatti-
Cincinatti Employment Classifieds
-US/MW/OH/Columbus-
Columbus Dispatch

-US/MW/WI-
Wisconsin Job Net
-US/MW/WI/Milwaukee-
Milwaukee Journal Sentinel

SOUTH

-US/S-
Southern Jobs - Job Digest
-US/S/LA-
Info Louisiana
-US/S/MS-
Mississippi Careers Online
-US/S/TN/Chatanooga-
Chattanooga Publishing
-US/S/TN/Knoxville-
Knoxville News-Sentinel Online

SOUTH WEST

-US/SW/AR-
Arizona Careers Online

-US/SW/TX/Dallas-
Dallas Morning News
-US/SW/TX/Houston-
Houston Chronicle Interactive

NORTH WEST

-US/NW/AL/Anchorage-
Anchorage Daily News

-US/NW/WA-
Doctor Link
-US/NW/WA/Seattle-
Seattle Times
-US/NW/WA/Tacoma-
Tacoma News Tribune

WEST

-US/W/CA-
Agricultural Job Listings
Auditions Online

BAMTA
California Job BankJob Search
CLNET
Connect to Jobs
Educator's Network EDNET
Forty Plus (Northern Calif.)
Job Search Academic Links
Job Smart California Job Search Guide
Latino Web
California Career and Employment Center
Career Action Center
Potpourri Shoppers
Purchasing NAPM
Saludos Web
Seamless Website, The

-US/W/CA/LA-
Los Angeles Times

-US/W/CA/Sacramento-
Sacramento Bee

-US/W/CA/San Francisco-
Abag Globe
The Gate
Jobs Jobs Jobs
San Francisco Chronicle
Silicon Valley Tech. Employ. Agencies

-US/W/CA/San Jose-
Mercury Center Web

-US/W/CO-
Colorado Jobs Online

-US/W/CO/Denver-
Denver Post
Rocky Mountain News

Almost every daily newspaper has its classified on the web. Trade and association publications are racing to join this free-for-all. 1998 will be a very important year for print classified. Can they combine the strengths of both mediums to enhance the value to job seekers and companies alike? Stay tuned. These sites contain some of the largest classified sections or the means to find them.

NEWSPAPERS

	OWNER
Ad One Classified Network www.adone.com	AdOne Classified Network, Inc.
Afro-Americ@: The Job Vault www.afroam.org/information/vau	Afro-American Newspapers
Anchorage Daily News www.adn.com/classifieds/jobs.h	Anchorage News
Augusta Chronicle www.augustachronicle.com/class	Augusta Chronicle
Boston Globe www.boston.com	Boston Globe
Boston Herald Job Find www.jobfind.com	Boston Herald
Brave New World www.newwork.com	New York News
Career Finder www.chicago.tribune.com	Chicago Tribune
Career Path www.careerpath.com	CareerPath
Career Spot, The www.careerspot.com	Ft. Lauderdale Sun Sentinel
Chattanooga Publishing www.chatpub.com	Chattanooga Free-Press
Chicago Sun Times www.suntimes.com	Chicago Sun Times
Chicago Tribune www.chicago.tribune.com/career	Chicago Tribune
Cincinatti Employment Classifieds careerfinder.gocinci.net	Cincinati Enquirer/Post
College News Online www.collegenews.com	Central Newspaper, Inc.
Columbus Dispatch www.dispatch.com	The Columbus Dispatch
Dallas Morning News www.dallasnews.com	Dallas Morning News
Denver Post www.denverpost.com	Denver Post
Digital City/South Florida southflorida.digitalcity.com	Ft. Lauderdale Sun-Sentinel
El Nueuvo Herald Digital	Miami Herald

www.elherald.com
The Gate   San Francisco Chronicle/Examiner
   www.sfgate.com/classifieds/
Hartford Courant   Hartford Courant
   www.courant.com
Hong Kong Standard   Hong Kong Standard Newspapers Ltd.
   jobmarket.hkstandard.com/online/job/hksjob
Houston Chronicle Interactive   Houston Chronicle
   www.chron.com
InJersey   Asbury Park Press
   www.injersey.com
Kansas City Star   Kansas City Star
   www.kccareers.com/
Knoxville News-Sentinel Online   Knoxville News-Sentinel
   www.knoxnews.com/classifieds/
Los Angeles Times   Los Angeles Times
   www.latimes.com
Mercury Center Web   San Jose Mercury News
   www.sjmercury.com
Metroworld   Montgomery Newspapers
   metroworld.com
Milwaukee Journal Sentinel   Milwaukee Journal
   www.onwis.com
Minneapolis Star Tribune   Minneapolis Star Tribune
   www.startribune.com
Nando Times   Raleigh News & Observer
   www.nando.net
National Diversity Journalism Job Bank   Florida Times-Union
   www.newsjobs.com
New Haven Register Online   New Haven Register
   www.ctcentral.com
New Jersey Online   Newark Star Ledger
   www.nj.com
New York Times   New York Times
   www.nytimes.com
Norfolk Virginian-Pilot Online   Norfolk Virginian-Pilot
   www.infi.net/pilot
O Hayo Sensei   1032 Irving Street
   www.oasysnet.com/home.html
Orlando Sentinel   Orlando Sentinel Online
   www.orlandosentinel.com
Pioneer Press   Pioneer Press
   www.pioneerlocal.com
Planet Jobs   Philadelphia Inquirer
   www.phillynews.com/programs/ads/SUNHLP
Potpourri Shoppers   Harte-Hanks Communications

www.netview.com/pp/employ/
Princeton 1Info (US 1)   US 1 Newspapers
 www.princetoninfo.com
Raleigh Classifieds On-line   Raleigh News & Observer
 www.news-observer.com/classads
Recruit Net   The Guardian Media Group
 recruitnet.guardian.co.uk/
Roanoke Times Online   Roanoke Times & World News
 www.roanoke.com
Rocky Mountain News   Rocky Mountain News
 www.denver-rmn.com
Sacramento Bee   Sacramento Bee
 www.sacbee.com/classads
San Francisco Chronicle Classified/Gateway San Francisco Chronicle
 www.sfgate.com/classifieds/
Seattle Times   Seattle Times
 www.seatimes.com/classified/
St. Paul Pioneer Planet   St. Paul Pioneer Press
 www.pioneerplanet.com/classifieds/
St. Petersburg Times   St. Petersburg Times
 www.sptimes.com
Syracuse Online   Syracuse Herald Journal
 www.syracuse.com
Tacoma News Tribune   Tacoma News Tribune
 www.tribnet.com/classads/
Town Online   Community Newspaper Company
 www.townonline.com/working
Wall Street Journal Interactive Edition Dow Jones & Company
 careers.wsj.com
Washington Post-Career Post Washington Post
 www.washingtonpost.com/wp-adv/classifieds/career
Western New York Jobs   WNY JOBS Weekly
 www.wnyjobs.com./#anchor263367
Work Avenue   Minneapolis Star Tribune
 www.startribune.com/workavenue

TRADE & PROFESSIONAL PUBLICATIONS

Academe This Week   The Chronicle of Higher Education
 www.chronicle.com
Adweek Online   BPI Communications Inc.
 www.adweek.com
Agri Careers
 www.agricareers.com
Allied Health Opportunities Directory Great Valley Publishing Company

www.gvpub.com

The Black Collegian Online   Black Collegiate Service, Inc.
www.blackcollegian.com

Black E.O.E Journal   Olive Tree Publishing
www.usa-ca.com/blk_eoe_jrnl

Bloomberg Online   Bloomberg Financial Markets
www.bloomberg.com/fun/jobs.html

Career Center for Workforce Diversity   EOP, Inc.
www.eop.com

Cell Press Online   Cell Press
www.cellpress.com

Chicago Software Newspaper   Chicago Software Newspaper
www.chisoft.com

Chronicle of Higher Education   Chronicle of Higher Ed
www.chronicle.com

Computer World's IT Careers   Computerworld
www.computerworld.com

Contract Employment Weekly   C.E.Publications
www.ceweekly.com

Diversity Careers Online   Diversity/Careers in Eng. & IT
www.diversitycareers.com

Electric Power NewsLink   McGraw-Hill/Power
www.powermag.com

Electronic Engineering Times   CMP Media Group
techweb.cmp.com/eet/823/

Electronic News OnLine   Electronic News
www.sumnet.com/enews

Engineering News Record   The McGraw-Hill Companies
www.enr.com

Federal Jobs Digest   FJD Hotline
www.jobsfed.com

Food and Drug Packaging Online   Food & Drug Packaging
www.fdp.com

Future Tech Careers   Montgomery Newspapers
www.advancehtc.com

Hispanic Network Magazine   Olive Tree Publications
members.aol.com/hnmagazine/index

Infoworld   CMP
www.infoworld.com

Internet.com   Mecklermedia
www.iworld.com

Java World   Web Publishing Inc.
www.javaworld.com

Law Employment Center   New York Law Publishing Company
www.lawjobs.com/

Medical Device Link   Canon Communications, Inc.

www.devicelink.com

Minorities Job Bank   Black Collegian Online
www.minorities-jb.com

MMWire Online   Phillips Business Information
www.mmwire.com

National Business Employment Weekly Dow Jones & Company, Inc.
www.nbew.com

National Educators Employment Review
www.teacherjobs.com/

NC World Magazine   SuperSite.Net
supersite.net/NCWorldJobBank

Network World Fusion   Network World
www.nwfusion.com

New England Journal of Medicine   New England Journal of Medicine
www.nejm.org/

Penton Publishing's Career Link   Penton Classifieds
www.penton.com

Nature Biotechnology   Nature America
www.biotech.nature.com

Nature-Medicine   Nature America
www.medicine.nature.com

Nurses   Association of Operating Room Nurses
www.aorn.org

Physician Recruit Net   Transcontinental Publishing
www.physiciannet.com/index.html

Saludos Web   Saludos Hispanos
www.saludos.com

Science Global Career Network   Science Magazine
www.sciencemag.org

Supermarket News   Fairchild Publishing
www.supermarketnews.com

TechWeb/TechCareers/TechHunter CMP Publications
techweb.cmp.com/

trans-ACTION   Chilton Company
www.trans-action.com

US Job Network High Tech Job & Resume Bank Jaye Communications
www.usjob.net

Women in Higher Education   Wenniger Company
www.itis.com/wihe/

Workforce Online   Workforce Magazine
www.workforceonline.com

PUSH

The debate over the value of "push" wouldn't last one minute if you ask the job seeker: "Would you like to register your interest and skillls here at the site and then have us inform you via e-mail whenever an opportunity is posted?". The sites below "get it" and, they've all got it.

4 Work
www.4work.com
Ad One Classified Network
www.adone.com
American Water Works Association
www.awwa.org
Asian Career Web
www.rici.com/acw
Asia-Net
www.asia-net.com
Association of Online Professionals
www.aop.org
Benefits Link
www.benefitslink.com/
Bilingual-Jobs
www.bilingual-jobs.com
BridgePath Employment Services
www.bridgepath.com
Canadian Job Source
www.irus.rri.uwo.ca/~jlaw/nati
Career Builder
www.careerbuilder.com
Career Mart
www.careermart.com
Career Site
www.careersite.com
Career Web
www.cweb.com
CAREERXROADS
www.careerxroads.com
Chase Pro
www.chasepro.com
Chicago Sun Times
www.suntimes.com
Computer World's IT Careers
www.computerworld.com
e-Math
www.ams.org/committee/profession/employ

Eagleview
www.eagleview.com
Employers Applicant Bank
eab.datastar.net/eab.html
Employment Channel
www.employ.com
Engine Room
www.iweb.co.uk/iwsearch.html#map
Engineering Job Source
www.wwnet.com/~engineer/
ExecuBank
www.execubank.com
Funeral Net
www.funeralnet.com/classifieds/index
The Gate
www.sfgate.com/classifieds/
GeoWeb for GIS/GPS/RS
www.ggrweb.com
Hard@Work
www.hardatwork.com
HeadHunter .NET
www.HeadHunter.NET/
HRIM Mall
www.hrimmall.com
IEEE
www.ieee.org
Ingram Recruiting Solutions
www.netaxs.com/people/ying1/
IntelliMatch
www.intellimatch.com
Internet Job Locator
www.joblocator.com
Job Bank USA
www.jobbankusa.com
Job Center
www.jobcenter.com/
Job Direct (JobDirect)
www.jobdirect.com

Job Serve: IT Vacancies in the UK
www.jobserve.com

Knoxville News-Sentinel Online
www.knoxnews.com/classifieds/

Learning@Living
www.living-icic.com

Macintosh Employment Registry
www.mactalent.com

Malaysia Online
www.mol.com.

MBA Central
www.mbacentral.com

Mercury Center Web
www.sjmercury.com

The Monster Board
www.monster.com

NationJob Network
www.nationjob.com

Netshare
www.netshare.com

Pharmaceuticals Jobs Today
pharma.mond.org/jobs.html

Pro Net Search
bisinc.com/pronet/ccc

Pro/E Job Network
www.pejn.com

Pyramus Online
www.pbgi.com/resucom/search.htm

Quest Match
www.decisivequest.com

Recruit Net

recruitnet.guardian.co.uk/

Rehab Options
www.rehaboptions.com

San Francisco Chronicle
www.sfgate.com/classifieds/

SHRM HR Jobs
www.shrm.org

Skill Bank
lapis.com/skillbank/index.htm

Skill Scape
www.skillscape.com

Society of Women Engineers
www.swe.org

Space Jobs
www.spacejobs.om

Talent Hunter
www.3dsite.com/ism/resumes/cgi-bin/talent-hunter

TechWeb/TechCareers/TechHunter
techweb.cmp.com/

Town Online
www.townonline.com/working

Training SuperSite Job Bank
www.trainingsupersite.com/jobset.htm

TV Jobs
www.tvjobs.com

Women in Technology & Industry-WITI
www.witi.com

Work OnLine Network Systems
www.wons.com

Workforce Online
www.workforceonline.com

RESUMES

All the resumes for free and for a fee. Be careful what you wish for...

POST RESUMES FOR FREE

4 Work
4.0 Resumes and Job Listings
Accounting Net
Africa Online Jobs
Agri Careers
Airwaves Media Web
American Journalism Review Online
America's Online Help Wanted
America's Talent Bank
Appointments Section
Asian Career Web
Asia-Net
Atlanta ComputerJobs Store
Bakery Net
Best Jobs U.S.A.
Bio Online: Life on the 'Net
Biomedical Positions
The Black Collegian Online
Black E.O.E Journal
Bloomberg Online
Boldface Jobs
Boston Herald Job Find
BridgePath Employment Services
Building Industry Exchange
Career Board
Career City
Career Command Center
Career Doctor
Career Exchange
Career File
Career Magazine
Career Mart
Career Mosaic
Career NET
Career Opportunities in Singapore
Career Path
Career Shop
Career Site
Career Web
Careers On-Line
Cell Press Online

Chase Pro
Christian Jobs Online
College Central Network
College Connection
Colorado Jobs Online
Computer World's IT Careers
Contract Employment Connection
Contract Employment NACCB
Contract Employment Weekly
Corporate Aviation Resume Exchange
Creative Freelancers Online
DesignSphere Online
DICE
Direct Marketing World Job Center
Diversity Careers Online
Doctor Link
Drake Beam Morin
e Math
E•Span
Eagleview
Eastern & European JobBank
Employers Applicant Bank
Employment Channel
Engine Room
Engineering Jobs
Entry Level Job Seeker Assistant
Escoffier On Line
Frasernet
Funeral Net
Future Access Employment Guide
Future Business Centre On-Line
Future Resource Systems
Georgia Job Bank
Get Me A Job
Global Careers
HeadHunter .NET
Health Opps
Heart
Help Wanted
Hollywood Web
Hong Kong Jobs
Hong Kong Standard
Hospitality Net

RESUMES

Hot Jobs
HR World
Imcor Provides Top-Level Executives
Ingram Recruiting Solutions
Insurance Career Center
IntelliMatch
International Pharmajobs
Internet Job Locator
Job Assistant.com
Job Direct (JobDirect)
Job Navigator
Job Net.com & Online Opportunities
Job Serve: IT Vacancies in the UK
Job Source Careers for College Grads
JOB TRAK (JOBTRAK)
Job Vault
JWT Specialized Communications
Kansas City Star
Kelly Services
Lee Hecht Harrison
Lendman's Recruiting Resources Gateway
Main Quad
Malaysia Online
Marketing Classifieds
MBA Central
MBA Employment Connection Assoc.
Med Connect
Med Hunters
Med Search
Medzilla
Mercury Center Web
Minorities Job Bank
MMWire Online
The Monster Board
NAACB Job Board and Resume Bank
National Educators Employment Review
NationJob Network
Navy
Net Temps
NYC Headhunter's Mall
O Hayo Sensei
Oasys Network
Omicron Personal Career Center
Online Career Center
Passport Access
Pharmaceuticals Jobs Today

PHRC Job Opps
Princeton 1Info (US 1)
Pro Net Search
Pro/E Job Network
Quest Match
Real Jobs
Recruit '97
Recruiters Online Network
Recruitex Technologies
Rehab Options
Resume-Link
RS/6000 Employment Page
Saludos Web
SciWeb - The Life Science Home Page
Seamless Website, The
Siam Net
Skill Bank
Skill Scape
Southern Jobs - Job Digest
Space Jobs
SPIE's Employment Center
Star Chefs
Sunday Paper
Talent Hunter
Technical Writers to the Rescue
TechWeb/TechCareers/TechHunter
Telecommuting Jobs
Top Jobs USA
Town Online
Training Net
Training SuperSite Job Bank
Twin Cities Job Page
US Air Force Employment Home Page
US Job Network High Tech Job & Resume Bank
Web Developer's Virtual Library
Westech's Virtual Job Fair
Windows NT Resource Center
Work Avenue
Workforce Online
World Hire
World Wide Job Seekers

POST RESUMES FOR A FEE

100 Careers in Wall Street
Airline Employment Ass't. Corps
American Chemical Society Job Bank
America's Employers
America's TV Job Network
Arizona Careers Online
Au Pair in Europe
Aviation Employee Placement Service
Bilingual-Jobs
California Career and Employment Center
Career America
Career China
Career Link USA
Carolina Career Center
Community Career Center
Education Job Marketplace
Employnet
Execubank
ExecuBank
Forty Plus (Northern Calif.)
GeoWeb for GIS/GPS/RS
HEALTH BANK USA
Help Wanted USA
International Seafarers Exchange
ISA Classifieds
Job Bank USA
Job Center
Job Lynx
Job Search
Layover
Loading Zone
Macintosh Employment Registry
Mississippi Careers Online
The National (Int'l) Home Workers Assoc.
Net Jobs Information Services
Netshare
NJ JOBS
Perioperative Online Employment Opps
Pyramus Online
Real Bank
Resumatch, Inc.
Resume Exchange
Resumes on the Web

Right Management Consultants, Inc.
Shawn's Internet Resume Center
Show Biz Jobs
Software Contractors' Guild
Talent Works: The Online Casting Source
TV Jobs

SEE RESUMES FOR FREE

100 Careers in Wall Street
4.0 Resumes and Job Listings
Accounting Net
Africa Online Jobs
Agri Careers
Airline Employment Ass't. Corps
Airwaves Media Web
American Chemical Society Job Bank
American Journalism Review Online
America's Talent Bank
America's TV Job Network
Arizona Careers Online
Aviation Employee Placement Service
Bakery Net
Biomedical Positions
Bloomberg Online
Boldface Jobs
Building Industry Exchange
California Career and Employ. Center
Career America
Career Link USA
Career Magazine
Career Mosaic
Career NET (Career/NET)
Careers On-Line
Cell Press Online
College Connection
Colorado Jobs Online
Corporate Aviation Resume Exchange
Creative Freelancers Online
DesignSphere Online
Direct Marketing World Job Center
Doctor Link
Drake Beam Morin
e Math
Eastern & European JobBank

Education Job Marketplace
Employers Applicant Bank
Employnet
Engineering Jobs
Entry Level Job Seeker Assistant
Escoffier On Line
Execubank
ExecuBank
Forty Plus (Northern Calif.)
Future Access Employment Guide
GeoWeb for GIS/GPS/RS
Get Me A Job
Global Careers
HeadHunter .NET
HEALTH BANK USA
Health Opps
Help Wanted USA
Hollywood Web
Hospitality Net
HR World
International Seafarers Exchange
Internet Job Locator
ISA Classifieds
Job Assistant.com
Job Center
Job Vault
Lee Hecht Harrison
Macintosh Employment Registry
MBA Employment Connection Assoc.
Mississippi Careers Online
MMWire Online
National Educators Employment Review
National (Int'l) Home Workers Assoc.
Net Jobs Information Services
NJ JOBS
O Hayo Sensei
Omicron Personal Career Center
Pharmaceuticals Jobs Today
PHRC Job Opps
Princeton 1Info (US 1)
Pyramus Online
Real Bank
Real Jobs
Recruitex Technologies
Resumatch, Inc.
Resume Exchange
Resumes on the Web
Right Management Consultants, Inc.

RS/6000 Employment Page
Saludos Web
SciWeb - The Life Science Home Page
SEACnet
Seamless Website, The
Shawn's Internet Resume Center
Siam Net
Skill Bank
Skill Scape
Software Contractors' Guild
Southern Jobs - Job Digest
SPIE's Employment Center
Star Chefs
Sunday Paper
Talent Hunter
Talent Works: The Online Casting Source
Technical Writers to the Rescue
Telecommuting Jobs
Training Net
Training SuperSite Job Bank
TV Jobs
Twin Cities Job Page
Web Developer's Virtual Library
Windows NT Resource Center
World Wide Job Seekers

SEE RESUMES FOR A FEE

4 Work
America's Employers
America's Online Help Wanted
Appointments Section
Asian Career Web
Asia-Net
Atlanta ComputerJobs Store
Best Jobs U.S.A.
Bilingual-Jobs
Bio Online: Life on the 'Net
The Black Collegian Online
Black E.O.E Journal
Boston Herald Job Find
BridgePath Employment Services
Career Board
Career China
Career City
Career Command Center
Career Doctor

RESUMES

Career Exchange
Career File
Career Mart
Career Path
Career Shop
Career Site
Career Web
Carolina Career Center
Chase Pro
Christian Jobs Online
College Central Network
Community Career Center
Contract Employment Connection
Contract Employment NACCB
Contract Employment Weekly
DICE
Diversity Careers Online
E Span
Eagleview
Employment Channel
Engine Room
Frasernet
Funeral Net
Future Business Centre On-Line
Future Resource Systems
Georgia Job Bank
Heart
Help Wanted
Hong Kong Jobs
Hong Kong Standard
Hot Jobs
Imcor Provides Top-Level Executives
Insurance Career Center
IntelliMatch
International Pharmajobs
Job Bank USA
Job Direct
Job Lynx
Job Net.com & Online Opportunities
Job Search
Job Serve: IT Vacancies in the UK
Job Source Careers for College Grads
JOB TRAK
Layover
Lendman's Recruiting Resources Gateway
Loading Zone

Main Quad
Malaysia Online
Marketing Classifieds
MBA Central
Med Connect
Med Hunters
Med Search
Medzilla
Minorities Job Bank
The Monster Board
NAACB Job Board and Resume Bank
Net Temps
Netshare
NYC Headhunter's Mall
Oasys Network
Online Career Center
Passport Access
Perioperative Online Employment Opps.
Pro Net Search
Quest Match
Recruit '97
Recruiters Online Network
Rehab Options
Resume-Link
Show Biz Jobs
Top Jobs USA
Town Online
US Job Network High Tech Job & Resume Bank
Westech's Virtual Job Fair
Work Avenue
Workforce Online
World Hire